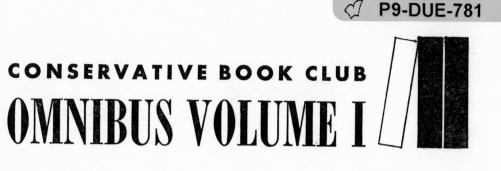

# CONSERVATIVE BOOK CLUB
# OMNIBUS VOLUME I

THE BIG MAN
*Henry J. Taylor*

HOW TO WIN AN ELECTION
*Stephen C. Shadegg*

SCREWTAPE PROPOSES A TOAST
*C. S. Lewis*

THE CONVENIENT STATE
*Garry Wills*

CONSERVATIVE BOOK CLUB
542 Main Street
New Rochelle, New York

MANUFACTURED IN THE UNITED STATES OF AMERICA

# THE BIG MAN

*Books by Henry J. Taylor*

**NONFICTION**

*Germany's Economy of Coercion*
*Time Runs Out*
*Men in Motion*
*Men and Power*
*An American Speaks His Mind*

**NOVEL**

*The Big Man*

# THE BIG MAN

by Henry J. Taylor

TO *Herbert R. Mayes*

With the exception of the historical personages referred to, the characters in *The Big Man* are entirely the product of the author's imagination and have no relation to any person in real life.

# 1

"I THINK YOU get a great deal more pleasure in understanding people than in condemning them," Sally Bryce told Philip Winston Allen when she went to see him about Frank Killory, holding out her hand with a frank and charming smile—a finely shaped, weightless hand.

He saw her hair in high coiffure—the blue-black hair of Mediterranean women; moist, brown, wide-set eyes and cherry-red lips. Her complexion was golden brown from the sun and the only make-up she was wearing was lipstick. Even in a moment that was so important to her, Sally flew her initial conversation impromptu, *ad libitum*, by the seat of her pants.

She had a musical laugh, infectious and sometimes even triumphant, Allen noted. Her voice was low for a woman of such vitality. But it had an unmistakable ring of authority—he also noted—when Sally wished to ring it, just as did the squeeze of her hand in a man's hand when she wished to draw him to a chair.

"Do sit down," Sally would say, her wrist working in its imperceptible way, an exquisitely mild sort of judo, her face utterly passive in contradiction to her nature and her eyes the eyes of a shy shepherd girl who is as timid as her goats.

This first impact would always stick in Allen's mind.

Women, as did Allen, figured prominently in Frank Killory's life. He had on his side the beauty and strength of intelligence, love and a sense of humor, and these are the weapons of the angels. He also had a certain very engaging gravity, although he was an out-giving man, and a very active and ambitious out-giving man at that.

Maybe it is the I in us that causes much of the trouble; but the I in us is also the cause of our painting, our music, or poetry, our politics. And so what?

In any case, Philip Winston Allen was the man who began the whole thing for Frank Killory, and this was the place where, six years before, he had begun it (history, mark your "X"): in the law offices of Allen, Van Biber, Caxton & Shaw.

The three floors of offices were as full of specialists as a baseball crowd is of peanuts, but this was the partners' floor, the comfortable office of the senior partner.

It was far above the noises in the streets; a bright high-ceilinged room. The library end had bookshelves to the ceiling, tables piled with books as they generally are by a man who likes to read, a large fireplace with a heavily carved mantel, good lights beside deep leather chairs.

There were no pictures on the paneled walls, except one near the mantel with deep green, dark blue and garnet red from Gauguin's palette and a companion of this, on the other side of the mantel, by Picasso in one of his rare moods of happiness. Both had been given Allen by the Republic of France.

The desk was unique, for it had once been the Kaiser's big Berlin desk, made of timbers from Nelson's *Victory*. It was a gift to Allen from the British Admiralty, instead of the fee he refused, as a token of respect and thanks for having done his part well as chairman of the British wartime Purchasing Commission in the United States.

He was a big man; Philip Winston Allen stood well over six feet—six feet three, to be exact—and he was built like Zybysko, the wrestler from Poland.

His face was as tough as an old copper kettle and just about as battered. His massive head bristled with white hair, the eyebrows of a patriarch; his shoulders were as formidable as the great stone lions of Babylon. His back was a carrier's back under a beautifully tailored coat, his arms heavy, and you could see that his strength was still prodigious. There was nothing ponderous about him, however, the way he moved, the way he spoke, or the way he laughed. There was youth and zest in his blue eyes and only the deep wrinkles and the mass of white hair on his head marked him as a man well into his sixties. Fame had come early. But he had gone straight ahead along the way he had discovered for himself and created his own life of ever-increasing depth and usefulness.

He had had many occasions to walk with kings, and no illusions about the great and powerful remained in him as he viewed the snapshot forecasts and eloquent trivia, the ambiguities and adolescent judgments often calcified as history. Our troubled world? Allen would ask: Has there ever been any other kind? Moreover, what is history? A fiction that prevailed over the facts.

A large French clock that might have come from Versailles ticked on a tall stand. Someone was humming softly in the distance. This was Mary-Louise Bracken, Allen's secretary, busy in her adjoining room, and the humming stopped when she greeted William S. Shaw at the door. It was a fine morning. There was the pleasant early-morning feeling of a hot day, and Allen was enjoying it.

"Are you free, Phil?" this partner asked.

"Certainly," he answered as Shaw came in with a slow, easy stride and sat down beside the desk; open-faced as an old-fashioned American apple pie.

Shaw leaned forward and put his hands on the edge of the desk, brushing some ashes into a cupped palm and dropping them into the basket beside Allen's chair. Philip sensed that something important was coming from his colleague, for he knew the look in the eye, but he could not have been more surprised by the turn of events if both his legs had vanished upward into the air.

"Well," Shaw said, "we lost the case."

"We did what!"

"We lost the case."

Philip Winston Allen lifted his massive head and looked over the top of some papers in his hand. Alfred Caxton once said: "There's a rainbow in Philip someplace." There seemed to be. For he had an Italianate touch, graceful and consoling, an inborn courtliness, an instinctive courtesy, a gallantry, that shown from him like a lamp: "the last of the old school," as contemporaries say of a few in all generations. He was, of course, a natural for the statement, perhaps more cliché than proverb: "They don't make them like that any more." But he was mad now. Crushing his cigar in a large silver tray, he let out an aigrette of ill-smelling smoke.

"Mary-Louise," he bellowed through the open door, "bring me the file on that case out in Illinois; United Motors versus that local dealer and his wife." Then he turned to Shaw and his exasperation exploded like the last breath of Vulcan. "My God," he said, "they didn't have a single point of law, not one, on their side. Nothing! Naked! Didn't you tell old Potter, too, that these people offered to settle out of court a dozen times?"

"Twice."

"All right, twice. A man who could lose that case could lose anything, Bill." Shaw knew Allen would settle down and listen, but not now. "Here we go traipsing out there because every point supported us. I insisted to old man Potter that his company would never find a better chance to get a favorable judgment on its franchise. Now you tell me we lost the case! Bill, that's ridiculous. How could we; what happened to you?"

Allen knew a good and solid answer was coming. Behind an able man there are always other able men. This able man had shared with Alfred Caxton the leadership of the firm under Allen for nearly thirty years.

"Well, Phil," Shaw replied, "I'll tell you exactly what happened. But I wish you had been there, that's all. I wish the whole firm had been there"—a smile crossing his face at the idea of what a scene that would have been; the thirty-eight partners lined up on the hard wooden bench in the Braidwood, Illinois, courtroom.

"The judge all but told the jury to toss the Harpers' side of the case out the window," Shaw grimaced. "Why, the whole business should have been over twenty minutes after the jury had the case."

Mary-Louise brought in the bulky file and placed it on Allen's desk. "Put that away," Shaw said, "it hasn't anything to do with the case. The only thing that has to do with the case is a man named Killory—Frank Killory."

"Who?"

"This lawyer out there in Braidwood. A lawyer, Phil—but, heaven knows, he didn't bring any law into this case. He just got up there, put his heart in it, and began to talk. He has an easy way with him, until he gets going. Then he's on his way. He falls into a broad grin, too, when something humorous crosses his mind; and out there they listen to this man."

Allen grunted, looking steadily at Shaw, but he did not interrupt him.

"Killory started talking in a sort of confidential manner about how the Harpers, man and wife, had started their United Motors dealership back in the Depression when nobody else in Braidwood was starting anything. 'You remember,' he said, and if there was a head in the courtroom that didn't nod I didn't see it. He said that they had courage to do this. Phil, he was right about that.

"He said this man and wife took the risk on money they borrowed from the Braidwood bank, and the president of the bank—a tall, thin man with a bald head named Mayo—was sitting in the front row, nodding his bald head and looking as anxious and worried about the trouble the Harpers were in with us as if they had been his own flesh and blood.

"Braidwood is a coal-mining town and was especially—terribly—hard hit in those Depression years. Well, Killory named a dozen people, or more, that the Harpers helped who absolutely had to have transportation but were unemployed and flat on their backs. The Harpers gave them a car for nothing down; if they couldn't manage to do better than that. No notes. No nothing. The Harpers just asked their word that they'd pay when they could during those hard times. It left them with a lot of pride in being trusted. Young Killory pointed out that the Harpers themselves were surviving on a shoestring and this added risk took lots of nerve and confidence—'and human understanding, as well as kindness, too,' Killory added."

The puckered wrinkles on Allen's craggy face showed that his patience was going. Shaw said, "Now don't get restless, Phil, I'm coming to the point."

"I hope so, or at least to the case we lost."

"If these people the Harpers helped weren't in that courtroom, some neighbor was there who knew all this was true—and typical of the way the Harpers ran the business after the Depression, too. Moreover, I can tell you, for it's a fact, that Killory hadn't asked a single one of them to come to that court.

"Next, Killory showed that if United's franchise required the Harpers to sell only United's products, the Harpers' customers either had to buy these or not deal with the Harpers."

Allen moved to the library end of the room. What he was hearing didn't sound like Shaw. "But that's the purpose of a franchise, and should be," Allen protested, with all the left-over exasperation that was in him. "That's the whole thing, naturally."

"I know. You know. United knows, and the judge knows," Shaw agreed, "but, Phil, you should have seen the jury."

"Well, well, so the jury went down like the walls of Jericho at the sound of the first attacking trumpet. And what were you doing all this time?"

Serenity in that face? "If I should die tomorrow the world would owe me nothing," Allen often said. "The Lord has been good to me; my family, my friends, my profession, my country has been good to me. What more could any living soul on earth ask?" But the fighter was there, too. Oh, yes; and a very famous fighter, indeed. Allen wanted to know—and bluntly: what was his partner doing all that time while Killory ran away with their case?

Shaw had a husky voice, low and not unpleasant. Allen heard him say, as if he were talking to himself: "It was a very odd experience—very odd."

Shaw reached in his pocket and pulled out a paper. He straightened his glasses and looked up at the giant in the chair, musing. "Phil," he said, "here's a section of the court record I had typed for you. Braidwood, you know, is only about a hundred miles from Springfield, or a little more. That's Lincoln country out there; Lincoln country with a capital L. Here's how Killory started this case. Listen, Phil, but don't fly off the handle and get the idea Killory was using Abraham Lincoln as a crutch, as I'm sure you will, because, really, he wasn't." Shaw began to read:

" 'All but a few in this courtroom have stood where Abraham Lincoln is buried. I stood there again only yesterday. See him towering over you in bronze: the shapely, expressive hands turned inward, curved; the haggard, deep-set eyes in this bony face; the head tilted as though attending and yet not wanting to hear through the blurred vision of his anguish.

" 'You remember Lincoln walked about twenty miles through the wilderness to borrow an English grammar and an American history. He couldn't get other books to read so he read and reread the laws of the state, with half the pages missing.

" 'At this moment he was starting in life; just as there are today men and women in early stages of their journey seeking to make their own way through life, independently and on their own, as did Mr. and Mrs. Arthur Harper.' "

"Oh my, oh my," protested Allen, "Bill!"

"Quiet now, my friend, quiet," Shaw urged, holding up his hand and reading on.

" 'Wrote Lincoln in his first Annual Message to Congress, delivered in the year 1861: "The penniless beginner who labors for a while saves a surplus with which to buy tools and land for himself." ' Then Killory looked skyward for an instant and added, with great firmness, 'or a dealership,' and continued, ' "then labors on his own account another while and at length hires another beginner to help him. This is the just and generous and prosperous system which opens the way to all, gives hope to all and consequently energy and progress and improvement to all!"

" 'Ladies and gentlemen, this is the Harpers, this is the system of which they are a very, very important part, this is the system that was so strained by the awful Depression, which was beyond their control even as it was beyond your control or mine. If we do not save the Harpers, we cannot long save the system.' "

"Phil," said Shaw, laying down the crumpled memorandum, "that's enough reading!" As if a signal had been passed between them, both men seemed to relax and a smile came over Shaw's face as Allen drummed on the edge of the chair.

"Not using Lincoln as a prop, eh, in a small-town courtroom?" Allen exclaimed. "My dear friend, you are out of your mind."

"You know, Phil, Killory even sold me. I thought to myself, 'What's the law in this answer?' I couldn't find it because it wasn't there in anything young Killory said. He didn't go against the law; he just didn't deal with it. But I got so fascinated by what he was saying, and his obvious sincerity in every word, that I began to think that because what he said was not wrong, it must be right.

"As for the jury, why, they just melted. We lost them like a schoolroom loses kids to a fire across the street. And when we lost them, we lost the case. Phil, I wish you had been there, that's all. At the end, he sounded like a combination of Patrick Henry and Billy Sunday, but with a lot more Patrick in it than Billy. Killory is a very serious fellow."

Allen bit the end from a cigar with a hard crunch and blew the piece into the fireplace. He looked at his partner, frankly puzzled and curious, as if all this were strangely out of character for Shaw, the best trial lawyer in Allen, Van Biber, Caxton & Shaw to plead the firm's cases persuasively in court. "Bill," he said, "dear Bill, you should be ashamed of yourself talking like this about moonbeams. Why, you've seen things like this pulled all your life in court, and what on—"

"Not like this, Phil, oh, no. First, it wasn't pulled. A smart play to the grandstand wouldn't have worked in Braidwood. Moreover, the Lincoln citation would have exploded any grandstand play. Why, in that country, everything having to do with Abe Lincoln has been used a thousand times and is worn as a thin dime. Any idea that Killory was falling back on old Abe as a prop would have blown it up so fast you could hear the rafters split. What's more, it wouldn't have worked on me, of course."

"I'm not so sure," Allen chuckled, "but maybe so. Maybe you're right. Even a stopped clock must be right once a day."

Here was Shaw with a mind as airy and solid as the architecture of a modern bank, telling his senior partner a heresy. Allen knew, of course, that this partner was a hard man to fool, very hard, out in Lincoln country or any place, and certainly no man to be trifled with in a law court. He also saw that Shaw himself looked a little puzzled by his own explanation.

"Killory seemed to be tapping something inside these people. But not the underdog feeling, Phil, not really that, entirely."

"Oh, Bill—"

"No, Killory did not play on that, which is the impression I'd expect you or anyone to have. He didn't play on that any more than he made a crutch of Lincoln."

"Didn't set up United Motors as a giant crushing the little Harpers? Maybe I'm deaf."

"No, he really didn't, Phil. But in some way, and outside the law, Killory did seem, so help me, to be on the side of justice."

Allen walked over to the windows that looked across the bustle and toot-toot of the New York harbor at the Battery docks and to the faint line of the Jersey coast under an immense skullcap of clouds lowering on it. He stood tapping the broad sill with impatience.

"Justice?" Allen rumbled. "Why, damn it, there's no breach of justice involved. This suit was based on the equitable terms of a mutually beneficial franchise which we want to be valuable to dealers everywhere. You can't have franchises and have anarchy in dealer relationships at the same time. Justice?"

Shaw relaxed beside the broad, leather-topped table. But the giant was pacing in frustration. He did not like to lose a case outside the law. Nor had he ever seen Shaw so placid in the face of outrageous defeat. Twice he made the rounds of the room.

Shaw lit his pipe in globs of fire from a long, old-fashioned match. "This was something special, Phil," he said. Shaw had come to know things about people just from watching them. Like a specialist in diagnosis, he was able to see and interpret signs and symptoms hidden from others. And Allen knew that Shaw was seldom wrong.

"There was a good cross section on the jury, including four women. On the last day, they all but jumped out of the jury box before Killory finished to show him how they intended to vote. They were going to vote for him."

"A staged play by our opponent," Allen growled, without conviction. He was at the windows, looking down on the harbor and the nightmare of the crisscross streets. Ah, he thought, as he had thought so many times looking down at the ships, the misery of harbors by the names they conjure up when you are not going any place. The rising heat set him to thinking of his place in Maine and the knowledge that within a few weeks, he would spend a month in fresh, cool air, scented by pines, beside the rocks and sea.

Mary-Louise came in, neat, crisp, efficient. She had some letters and Allen motioned her to put them on the desk. "Mr. Shaw," he said, "is telling me something about people jumping out of jury boxes. You should stay and hear this, Mary-Louise." She smiled at the two partners and left.

Shaw answered: "I started by saying I wish you had been there. I'll end with that, too. Killory was natural, that's all. Those people listened. They liked his voice. They liked him. And those listeners wanted to help him as much as, or more than, they wanted to help the Harpers. That's the thing."

"A good lawyer?"

"Yes."

"What's he like?"

"Well, he's a very decent, simple man, I'd say. He seems somewhat distracted at times; preoccupied, in an odd sort of way. When he's like this his wife says he's in his 'birdwatcher mood'—looking around and nodding—distracted, but thinking all the time. Still in his thirties. Married as soon as he got back from the war. A Chicago girl who came down to the proms at the University of Illinois; two children, both girls. He lives a very nice life around Braidwood. He has no partners—practices alone—works hard and does well for himself. Represents the area's United Mine Workers of America union, and two bread-and-butter accounts besides others, I gather—the Excelsior Shoe Company there and an insurance company in Chicago, Mid-Continental Life."

"That's Donald Morton's company."

"Yes. Killory has done their central Illinois legal work for years. He and his wife were very hospitable to me. She's very sweet. I had dinner with them and the two daughters—his wife just loves that house and garden, very nice house—the first night I came to town."

Allen smiled, sitting down beside the table and taking a cigar from the humidor. "Well," he said, "there's a lot to be said for a life in a place like that; a great deal. People like this get a good look at the outdoors every day and never get too far from the soil. These are the people who move the country, you know, Bill. If we all lived like that, or could live like that, so many patients in our nation's hospitals wouldn't be mental cases."

Shaw laughed as Philip went on. "I remember one time a relative of mine in Circleville, Ohio, said to me: 'You poor Yankees in New York are to be pitied for many things, but for nothing so much as your distance from Circleville.' And by God, the old lady meant it. I feel a little like that, too, at the moment."

"You sound like a country boy."

"Well, my people were country people. And your Mr. Killory is a country boy, isn't he? And what happened to New York's William S. Shaw—emerging this morning as the finest flop this profession has seen in many a blue moon."

"My friend, you put it mildly."

"Killory sounds to me like a politician."

"Well, he isn't. This man isn't interested in politics."

"That's good. But sort of strange for a lawyer in a small town. 'Most of them are conspirators and all of them are politicians' you once said, Bill," he observed.

He might have added that personal politics bored him. And also that his own political impartiality pleased nobody. He attached importance to questions such as the survival of the free nation, concepts of human liberty and dignity, and the demands all Americans are entitled to make on their elected leaders for selflessness, talent, courage.

Under either political party he was always worried about the country; a fighter perpetually dissatisfied with his great country compared to what it could be and full to the brim with fiery contempt for anyone who misled the people. He was always striking out angrily at sham and pretense and avariciousness, and always with great love and compassion for the true American underneath. He kept on going at this, and nobody ever captured his bullet-torn battle flag or silenced his drums.

Shaw continued, blazing another long match on his burned-out pipe: "Anyway, I do know Killory never ran for anything. He told me so himself.

"He's asked to make quite a few speeches, and he made a speech on Woodrow Wilson not long ago, dedicating the new Braidwood High School, I'm told. But this was strictly a civic affair. No, he's not a politician and he's not in politics."

"How did he happen to go way back to Woodrow Wilson, for heaven's sake?"

"Well, I gather that Killory talked about Wilson's intellectualism and the personal tragedy in him."

Allen pricked up his ears. On his timber desk was an informal, autographed picture of Woodrow Wilson, in a small leather frame. Far in the past, when in the White House, Wilson had inscribed it to Allen: "A man to ride the river with," as the westerns used to say.

"You'd imagine a man talking about Wilson after all these years," he answered, "would go over like a lead balloon in Illinois."

"Anyway, Killory did it."

Allen chuckled again as he asked: "What will I say to old Potter at United Motors? You know, Bill, after all, we lost a case. And I still think any man who lost that case could lose a bass drum in a telephone booth. No, we took United into it and we shouldn't have lost it. We certainly did not go to court to listen to what the law didn't have, I don't think."

Shaw raised his eyebrows and slowly dragged on his pipe. He looked down and blew a stream of gray smoke to the floor.

"I'll see Mr. Potter tomorrow," he answered. "We can turn it around on the appeal surely. But that's the score right now. I'm sorry."

As Shaw left, Allen turned in his chair. The sunlight fell on him; the mass of white hair, his blue eyes, the battered, kindly, competent face.

He glanced, as he did so often, at the only other picture on the broad desk. It was a large, formal photograph of his wife. Her hair was in a pompadour, in the style of the early century, and she was wearing a lovely white lace dress with long sleeves and a large skirt that fell in folds and made a beautiful, graceful train behind her. Straight, calm, a closed fan held loosely in one hand, the other resting in her lap, her face an exquisite study in gentility, but with a touch of impish humor in her eyes: Marion Allen.

They loved each other dearly and shared the constant grief of being childless. This was the cross these two had to bear and, while they were resigned to it, the yearning struck at the deepest core of Phillip's nature as cruelly as it did at hers.

"Marion," he had said to her years ago, "the real Atlas is a woman carrying the earth on her shoulders. We men make the history and fix up the story in our own way, but women have always been the bearers of the heaviest burdens, and the most unthanked.

"Why, dear, let the average man be a woman for only a month or so. The experience would teach us to complain a lot less about women.

"Heavens above, for every man in a thousand who will risk his life in a cause, I'll show you a thousand mothers who will risk their lives for their child; just as you would have, Marion.

"Oh, my dear, dear Marion—how suited you are! My heart aches sometimes so hard that I think it will break because, my darling, you missed this; and together we have missed it in your life."

Goethe writes: "Every woman excludes, by her nature, every other woman. Man requires a man's world; he would create another man if there were none. A woman could live an eternity without wishing to produce another woman." Doubtless Goethe was sincere, but at least in this case he was also wrong. Were Allen to create anybody, it would have been Marion.

She had died ten years ago. Her illness must have been silently preparing itself for a long time but to him it seemed incredibly sudden. The end came in a long vigil, like Faulkner's clock in *Soldiers' Pay*, that ticked out: Life, death; life, death. Allen had recovered slowly from the blow. How can one abandon without despair a hand which one has covered with kisses and which one longs to keep forever close to one's heart?

Philip never spoke of it, but perhaps the aching void of his childlessness accounted for the fact that promising young people attracted him with special intensity. "The future is in their hands. Whose else?" And in addressing a Yale Commencement he had been observed laying down his manuscript and heard to say, in an aside, "Oh, young men, you young men. What wouldn't I give to be your age again, to start all over?"

He was forever and jubilantly on the lookout for companionable youth among his friends and neighbors, eager to advance any hope, any dream, or to share any disappointment.

Each year the firm tendered an office dinner to those who had entered its ranks. Years ago his late partner Clarence Van Biber had opened the first of these reception affairs with a toast. Philip never failed to stand in Van Biber's stead and repeat it.

"Good young gentlemen, you are older now," he would say. "Allow us who are your seniors, please, to welcome you to your seniority." Then he would begin, this great giant of a man, glass high, chin up, gallant, his voice a beautiful melody of encouragement and understanding:

"Let us fill a cup and drink with love to that most noble, ridiculous, laughable, sublime figure in all our lives—the Young Man Who Was. Let us drink to his dreams, for they were rainbow-colored; to his appetites, for they were strong; to his blunders, for they were huge; to his pains, for they were sharp; to his time, for it was brief; and to his end, for it was to be—to become one of us."

Time? How little we know when a moment, being measured far away, is affecting us.

The tall clock ticked off each swing of its pendulum. Yes, how silently, how silently it all occurred. For after Shaw left this consequential office the clock was ticking in a very important pause. During it, Allen made a resolution that changed the course of Frank Killory's life.

While nothing disturbed the windless surface of Frank's Braidwood existence, one corner of the book of fate was stabbing him. That was what happened. Thus a legend is born.

Allen glanced at the calendar. He threw a tiny switch on the intercom phone.

Shaw answered. "Yes, Phil."

"I'll be in Chicago next week, the Implements Company meeting," Allen said. "Let's see, let's see—on Wednesday. Telephone your friend Killory and ask him if he can drop up to Chicago and meet me at the Chicago Club at ten o'clock."

# 2

THE FOOTBALL FLEW across Wall Street. Harvard's all-time great, Charley Brickley, had drop-kicked it from the sidewalk to Yale's Jack Gates, standing on the balcony of the New York Stock Exchange.

The White House had released the news. President Wilson's message was on the wires of the nation: "My Fellow Countrymen: The Armistice was signed this morning. Everything for which America fought has been accomplished. It will now be our fortunate duty to assist by example, by sober friendly counsel, and by material aid in the establishment of just democracy throughout the world."

Janet met Frank in New York. She watched him swing up Fifth Avenue in the greatest outpouring of pride and affection that mighty America had ever brought to the ears of homecoming sons. She could not see Frank in those ranks of marching men, the great khaki phalanx, swords flashing at salute in the hands of the officers, the bayonet-spiked rifles as straight as arrows in the sharp lines they made above the close-packed khaki forms, arms swinging to the cadence of the brass bands, heads up, chins up, left-right, left-right; the banners flying and each shoulder lit with the beautiful patch of America's Rainbow Division.

They swung through the tall arch in Washington Square. Brigadier General Douglas MacArthur led the division home as he had led it overseas; a handsome man riding a fine white horse that pranced under the curb of the general's firm hand and tossed his mane in the proud shakings of a beautiful head.

MacArthur saluted often, his gloved fingers to the visor of his cap; a soldier reporting to the people on a task that had been done. Billowy oceans of cheers swept the crowd, and the windows of the Avenue came alive with the shouts of the city, and a nation, beside itself with joy and relief and the poignant glory of these men marching in silence behind the American flag. No, Janet could not see him in the ranks; but she knew he was there.

Frank was home, thank God.

They walked in Central Park that night. An early snow had fallen. In the thick glen below the sparkling panorama of Central Park South, the tall buildings were a fairyland of hospitality and light. The shimmering reflections fell on the leaves of the snow-touched trees like twinkling fireflies and cast the light in a gorgeous filter where they walked. And moonlight, too, glittering on the leaves of the trees, lit them as if millions of silver fish were swimming and pulsating in the dark waters of the night.

The war had come and gone and youth was ready for the future. "What do you want to do, Frank?" Janet asked. "I want to go back to the office in the Forrest Building and be a good lawyer," he said, as simple as that; and as if it were impossible that some change could come in his life through these months away in a world at war. "I want to get married tomorrow. Then I want to start as soon as we can in Braidwood." History, the war, had taken no hand in Frank's destiny.

They were married the next day at City Hall.

The marrying room looked as heartless as a well-swept execution yard. Except for a small alcove window of painted glass and the electric cheapness of a sign that said "Chapel," the great City of New York provided neither color nor comfort of any kind, although the official magistrate in the civil ceremony was, of himself, a kindly man and read the bare ritual with as much feeling and care as he could.

The ceremony took less than five minutes and Janet included the optional word *obey*. Then there was the signing of the records, with the feeling of finality that goes with this, and the clerk handed them a copy to carry back to Illinois. All had been done that needed to be done to give them each other.

Janet wanted it this way. Her mother's efforts to prevail on her to be married in the local church or their comfortable home in Chicago—or, more accurately, in the suburb of Oak Park—had come to nothing. "It's not like Janet to be so headstrong," she had said to her husband since the word arrived that Frank was starting home. "She seems determined to marry Frank the very day he gets back. If this means some God-awful port where his transport docks that's the way it's to be. But I should think Frank might know us and Janet's friends and neighbors a little better, and feel more at home in our house, if they were married here. John, I don't understand it. I've never seen Janet so stubborn."

Her husband made hardly a reply to this motherly view. His outlook was as simple as the letter O. Janet was solving the matter in her own way, he pointed out, as she solved most things, and, after all, a sensible girl like Janet did have her own life to lead. It's a good thing for two young people to start out married in their own way. Lots of trouble came from parents interfering. Just leave Janet and Frank alone. They will be all right, you wait and see. A very perceiving man, her father, under his shell.

Frank, in turn, could give his view only from the agonizing anonymity of "Army Post Office: Somewhere in France"; but he was obviously happy about Janet's plan. "You see, Mother," Janet said, radiant. Moreover, Frank had convinced his Aunt Margaret in Braidwood, his only relative, that it was much better like this than for her to attempt a trip to Chicago.

"Everything is just right," Frank had written Janet from his ghostly locale, "and, anyway, darling, that 'everything' just means you." Dear Frank, dear, dear Frank.

It is never advisable to make judgments about other people's love affairs, but their marriage seemed an accepted fact from nearly the beginning. They both accepted the naturalness and sincerity of their attachment from the first time they met at Urbana. Their engagement on Frank's graduation from the law school was but a step. And from then on Janet carried her ring high on her hand, only waiting and praying for the war months to pass and bring this one man in the world safely home.

Both were singularly free of turmoil; what their courtship missed in excitement and suspense it made up for in the delights of quiet confidence and comfort, one with the other. They shared the legacy of life in a small community. Although Janet grew up on the outskirts of a great city, her life had been primarily a suburban life in Oak Park, in the pattern of Frank's life in Braidwood.

If this bucolic circumstance seemed dull and unpromising to cosmopolites or others, it seemed suitable and desirable to them. That life would be good to them was a matter of faith rather than of proof. Frank had grown to manhood on an assumption that he must—and would—make something of his life. Janet grew up on the assumption that in fate's lottery there was to be a right husband for her and for the children they would have. She no more questioned this than she doubted the serenity and love of her own parents and their exchange of devotion with her.

The recital of this is easy. But her Frank had been born during a storm, which placed in his cradle an image of his destiny. And, like an Arab's date tree, his trunk had scarcely sprung from the rock before it was battered in the wind.

The wind was the death of both his parents. The tragedy came too early for him to remember and so close to his infancy that his Aunt Margaret Killory, who brought up this boy, was all he had ever known of family and parentship.

She was a fine woman, extraordinary in many respects, whose life was in the Braidwood library where she was the librarian and in the boy whose life she made her own. Margaret never married and young Frank became her universe. She added up all the disappointments of her existence and he was the recompense for the total.

She loved to take him on her knee, and turn his face to the light and talk to him and play with him, so that she could look at his eyes and see the joy in them. She saw something in his face that was more than beauty as his childhood developed; a light, a spirit perhaps, that made his chin and lips and eyes and brow something both strong and tender, something one wanted to love and protect. And she found in him her first and overwhelming discovery of happiness.

Margaret's scholarship in the little town was a bright island floating in the morning mist, like a gift from the sea. But a quiet humility ran through her intellectualism and she spoke without a hint of spinsterish precision. Moreover, a gentle exhilaration flowed to the townspeople from her, as well as sympathy and understanding, for her heart was as big as Pagliacci's drum and she had the tranquillity that comes out of deep faith. Dry season, full season, her disposition remained unchanged. All who came to the library found Aunt Margaret—

everyone called her that—a constant antitoxin in the daily round of petty disconcertions.

It was a God-fearing home, this little union of the maiden aunt and the young boy, and Aunt Margaret carried their lives forward with courage and dignity.

Her prayer each night, kneeling with the child, was simple and it was her own: "May God give us health, courage, strength, worth, the ability to help, the will to work, the gift of foresight, keenness of mind, kindness of heart, faith, hope and charity. Amen."

The blessing that she said at each meal contained not one word about devils and disaster. It was a plea to the Almighty that all of us might be properly grateful for the benefits that had reached us; for life and health and the power to do good. And there was a special plea for the boy.

Margaret had a wicker chair where she rocked on the rag carpet and plied her needles, and told him marvelous tales that had come to her from her grandparents about the Illinois wilderness, and the melancholy howl of the big timber wolves, and how the boars could easily and quickly rout any wolf or pack of wolves, for the Illinois boars were vicious and terrible creatures. And when she came to the scary parts she reached out to hold his hand to help tide him over.

On special days there would be roasted piglet from Mr. Mayo's farm with a shiny red apple in its mouth, and large cakes of maple sugar—and finally the time when the hickory nuts were cracked and eaten. One Christmas she laid before him a fragile china cup marked in gold and blue lettering—TO A GOOD BOY—and it was long Frank's most treasured possession.

Dr. Gunther usually escorted Aunt Margaret to church, although Mr. and Mrs. Mayo often joined them, for Mrs. Mayo was Margaret's dearest friend in the community. Margaret alone or this little assembly would lead the boy into the pew and sit him there, shining from soap, the cowlick in the back of his hair standing straight up in defiance of Margaret's brushes and combs, his suit crisply starched and ironed, his copper-toed boots abandoned for the day.

The years passed this way in an unfaltering procession of Sundays until Frank was old enough to be in the choir. Then he made the journey from the Ridge Street house by himself, of course, and his little voice, reaching for the high note, songbook in hand, eyes staring at the page, made the sight Margaret relished more than any.

"He cannot sing," Dr. Gunther would tell her, laughing. "Margaret, he simply cannot sing. But, my heavens, he tries!"

"Well, he does sing quite well, I think," she answered. "But, after all, he really doesn't go there to sing. He goes there to be near to God, please remember."

She never ceased to excoriate to him a lack of Christianity, with Christianity's emphasis on the Golden Rule, and cited Samuel Butler's description of the bigoted little Battersby congregation that "would have been equally horrified at hearing the Christian religion doubted, and at seeing it practiced."

The Big Four Coal Company, with two deep shafts at Braidwood and two other mines at nearby Eileen and Coal City, had experimented with a breeding group of pure-blood Shetland ponies, crossing them with ordinary jack mules to produce tough, wiry little Shetland mules for the tight, small entries and for digging rooms far back in the mines. The experiment was not a success, but this was also banker Mayo's company and he gave Frank one of the breeding group's Shetland ponies.

"Now this dear little pony is yours, my boy," the tall man beamed, "take good care of it." Good care of it! Frank lived no waking hours when his eyes were not on Dinah and his heart inside that shaggy coat.

Dinah lived in a small barn Aunt Margaret built behind the Ridge Street house, but in the hot summers Frank fed her her oats and sweet hay on the back porch or sometimes down the stairs in the cool cellar. And then, in the cowboy chaps, broad hat and tiny beaded vest Dr. Gunther had given him, the boy and the pony would roam the Braidwood meadows. There he could chase the surprised sheep or shoot at hawks with his slingshot, and nothing in the most wonderful, far-off city in the whole world could compare with the thrills of these hours, surely; or with the surge of adventure in his heart.

The busy area of the Big Four's Braidwood mines was also a part of Frank's playground. There was no limit to the interesting things to do around the tipples with the cages carrying their small coal-filled pit-cars up suddenly out of the black depths one by one. Then the clang-clang of the signal bells as each pit-car broke to the surface—bursting the unloading crews and railroad switch engines into new activity. Coal dust was in Frank's veins. He loved that happy playground.

But one awful November day tragedy struck. When a pit-car loaded with hay for the mules' stables underground reached the bottom of the shaft, nearly three hundred feet below the surface, the carbide flame on the cap of a miner pulling the car from the cage brushed into the hay.

Suddenly fire engulfed the shaft and burned in roaring billows up its oil-drenched, wooded lining. The frantic miner lunged at the signal line and gave two fast jerks—"Lift." The engineman in the tipple above, operating the immense wire-rope hoist drum, threw his lever. But the burning pit-car, half off the cage, half in the mine's entryway, jammed the cage like an iron wedge by the lifting and snapped the hoist cable. The mine was on fire, the great, racing tongue of fire and smoke, feeding on the coal walls, seared back through the entries and cross-cuts. Two hundred and fifty-nine miners were entombed. The horrible Cherry Mine disaster crackled across the news wires of the nation.

The immense stirring, the days and nights of terrible, macabre vigil, the shrieking hysteria of loved ones at the head of the shaft, the town invaded by helpers but in utter agony—all this Aunt Margaret tried to shield Frank from as best she could. But it was as useless as to try to shield the boy entirely from the mass funerals where the widows' tortured veils beat against their hair and faces. For the first time in his life, he was transported—dazed and uncomprehending—into the knowledge that this little world of his also contained grief;

an awful, sickening, tragic awakening as mysterious as it was bewildering to him. Childhood suffered its first trauma—unforgettably. The total recall of this never left Frank, and for some time Aunt Margaret found it hard to keep his heart afloat. (What, oh what, could lurk in a happy, happy playground!)

Both the grammar school near Masonic Hall and the weatherbeaten Braidwood High School found Frank a good, alert student. The teaching he adored, but what remained with him most on his way to the state university came from the gradual embrace of his aunt's mind.

"Renaissance Florence was smaller than Springfield," she explained. "Chicago today is three times the size of the hub of the world when it was imperial Rome. The Athens of Pericles was never larger than Peoria. With all its glamour and greatness, the ancient world at its most luxurious hour was still dirt-poor. And even today, half the human race goes to bed hungry every night.

"Our America," she taught him, her fingers busy with her knitting needles, "is a creation of Europeans who did not like in Europe the injustice, the intolerance, the inequity. And they did not like the poverty—the poverty of those who inherit not only a poor soil but a poor spirit, and who had in so many cases a hopeless, apathetic inability to find their way out of the rut. How blessed you are, Frank, merely to be young in such a land as this!"

Or Margaret at another time would launch into heroes. "Failure is shared by many," she insisted, "success must be carried alone. But the only men whom time honors are those who have been willing to fight for other men. The rest aren't real, Frank. The millions of bewildered students, like you, who have had to read the *Iliad* and the *Odyssey* know Homer's heroes always somehow cracked the knuckles of those around them. He tells of some hero who made it his business to always excel others and stand higher than other people. What an incompassionate, disagreeable person he must have been! Homer's heroes generally came to a bad end, as undoubtedly did this gentleman, sooner or later.

"There may be no peace in the world for anybody, including ourselves. But I do know a man must be true to himself." She told him to guard that as he went through life. Frank came to know all about this, but it took him a long time to find out, for this is not the kind of thing that is taught at schools and universities. (Oh, dear Aunt Margaret, you tried!)

Orphan that he was, this man who married Janet had a very good upbringing, and all of Braidwood knew it. So did Frank, in the way a man does. And so did Janet. Can you unlive the life that produces a man like this?

Aunt Margaret had always been convinced that Frank's best future would be in a profession; to be a doctor, lawyer or engineer, a training that could give specific application to whatever abilities he had.

They had all but decided Frank would be a doctor. But long discussions with Dr. Gunther convinced them that, at bottom, this idea was really born more of their affection for him than anything. Mr. Mayo wanted Frank to prepare to come into the bank "and work with my son as another son," as he so faithfully put it.

No, Frank would be a lawyer. Even in this early and major decision, the decision itself and the recognition of its wisdom came nearly as a matter of course to Frank. You would never think he had given a passing thought to anything else. As he was to later in his love for Janet, and in nearly every important turn of his life, he swung to this as naturally as a retriever does to water.

As for Aunt Margaret's feelings: " 'On three things stands the world,' said Simon the Just, 'on law, on worship and on charity.' "

By continuing on at the University of Illinois to study law he could cut short his academic years and also include some pre-law courses. His aunt felt this represented too "single" an education. She wanted him to break off after he had finished college in Illinois and go to one of the big law schools in the East, or west to Leland Stanford. The thought lay like a heavy stone in her heart, for she knew this meant losing him soon. But it was a thought for Frank, and she spoke of it eagerly.

"It's just not practical, Aunt Margaret," he insisted. "It would take me at least a year longer over-all if I made the transfer, I think; it's more expensive, and they can teach me more law at Urbana than I'm going to be able to swallow anyway. And, for heaven's sake, I don't want to leave you." Tears filled her eyes and she came around his chair, with love, and kissed him. "Oh, Frank, I love you so," she said, and then had to leave the room, her face protected by her handkerchief.

Before graduation he had two offers to go into law offices after he passed the bar examinations; one in old Mr. Billings' Braidwood firm, the other from a lawyer already established in Springfield. But Frank decided to go it alone and opened his office in the Forrest Building next door to Masonic Hall.

He was supremely happy in this start. His aunt was happy and grateful for his happiness, the promise she saw in him, and his unrepressed adoration of her. But she found it harder now to teach him much more.

Sam Welsh came to work for him a few months after Frank returned from the war. He was a sparse little man with almost no shoulders, long in the waist but short in the leg, and as pale as he was big-hearted. There is a town in Illinois called Fury, and Frank never ceased to wonder that Sam had come from there.

This helper was a ceaseless digger for details. Moreover, he soon had a dogged faithfulness to Frank. Sam's apotheosis of him yielded its principal reward to them both during Frank's periods of discouragement. These came seldom but were intense, and when Frank felt the full kiss of discouragment his response was unvarying: he fell into iron silence for an indefinite time.

Actually, Sam welcomed these periods. They were an opportunity to apply his faithful feelings and Pickwickian benevolence. On one occasion, at least, Sam prepared in advance for an opportunity. Under Aunt Margaret's guidance at the library he located the text of a letter—rumor having reached him that it existed. It was written by a very discouraged man at the age of forty. Sooner than Sam supposed he had an opportunity to spring it for the support of Frank Killory.

Jack Collins, Frank's opponent in a preposterous case, the most lowly regarded lawyer in Will County, sued the Mid-Continental Life Insurance Company for an unjustified payment of a large cash award. The claim was utterly without merit, as was also Collins' argument. His client, equally unworthy, nevertheless had the faith of a pauper and sat there smugly contemplating the huge bank balance and voluptuous revels Collins could provide him.

No matter how the disaster be explained, the fact remains that somehow Collins' fuzzy contentions caught Frank as if in a gear and propelled him into a major legal stupidity that cost Mid-Continental ten thousand dollars.

Mr. Donald Morton, Mid-Continental's president, expressed himself promptly. His letter to Frank began with polite outrage, and then expanded.

Sam's sense of drama had its day. Exactly at the moment Frank laid down Mr. Morton's harpoon, Sam stood before him, straight and ready.

"I want you to hear another letter," he said, and zestfully put himself to work reading it to the silent man. "If what I feel were equally distributed to the whole human family,'" Sam intoned, "'there would not be one cheerful face on earth. Whether I shall ever be better than I am, I cannot tell. I fear I shall not. To remain as I am is impossible. I must die to be better, it appears to me.'

"Frank," he sighed, "why am I reading you a letter written by a discouraged forty-year-old failure? No future, eh? No future for a man many years older than you are this very minute? Well, Frank, let me tell you that this self-acknowledged failure made quite a reputation for himself during the rest of the time life allowed him. His name was Abraham Lincoln."

Sam paused, a bit flustered, for not a wisp of response or even a grunt had enlivened the elegiac scene. "Frank," he said, "Frank . . . you're a big man . . . a big man." The good, simple Sam had finally come out with it. It revealed a conviction so many, many others were one day to share.

It is difficult to say when Frank first became conscious that, somehow, leadership flickered in him. Although he did not analyze—and certainly did not glamorize—the reasons, he recognized the fact quite early. He accepted his magnetism as if this were merely the way things worked in life for some people and not for others. In truth, it worked for Frank largely because he saw people as they saw themselves; he had a gift of perception which enabled him to pierce the defense of others, to find and ally himself with the harried creature underneath.

This was a real talent; and it was to become a main talent.

For Janet the first problem in Braidwood had been their home. She decided on a run-down clapboard house no one wanted, one that Jim McCarthy, the real estate agent down the hall from Frank's office, could hardly give away. "That house couldn't be sold to a blind Eskimo," Jim had confided to his wife, who promptly confided the remark to Janet. It was gloomy and full of dull brown wood walls that let in little light through their small, broken windows and seemed as depressing and forsaken as a sunken ship. The location, however, was excellent.

It stood on a lovely wooded hillside. A small stream cascaded down through what could be a beautiful garden. The trees were magnificent—tulip poplars, cedars and great oaks—and there was an abundance of planting that needed only to be pruned. Once you forgot the house, there was a possible paradise on the eight acres, with the view and everything, and Janet had one idea after another about what could be done to give even this house great charm.

"Go ahead, honey," Frank said, to the utter astonishment of McCarthy. "It's ours."

The house leapt alive at her touch and soon, with the basic reconstruction and the changes under way, "what Janet has done to the old Ellis house" became the wonder and awe of the Braidwood ladies who came to see how anything so pleasing could be made of the place.

To Frank and Janet's joy, the financial side of this problem had been workable—as if by a miracle—from the very week that Frank returned to Braidwood from France.

He had walked into his office to find a stranger sitting in the chair beside his desk.

"Well, hello," he said in obvious surprise and, sticking out his hand, "Glad to see you."

The man lifted a big brief case off his lap and stood up, smiling and a bit flushed as if he felt he were intruding. He was young, fattish and blond, with a bright yellow corduroy vest that nearly matched his hair.

"Welcome back, Mr. Killory," he said, in a rather husky voice, "I'm Jacob Morton. I travel Illinois and Indiana and Iowa for the Legal Department of my father's firm, the Mid-Continental Life Insurance Company of Chicago."

"Oh, yes, Mr. Morton. Glad to see you, sit down. I didn't know you were here. Nice to have you come in."

"Mr. Killory, our company wants to join in welcoming you home."

"Thanks, and best wishes. They're good folks up there, I'm sure."

"You see, Mr. Killory, we were all saddened last month to lose Billings as Mid-Continental Life's counsel for this area. He was the first local attorney my father ever appointed. Even though Mr. Billings could do very little for us in these late years, his stroke was a shock."

"He was failing even before I left, but I only heard from my wife when I got to New York that Mr. Billings suffered a stroke. I'm sorry."

"We want to appoint you our area counsel in his place, Mr. Killory. There's quite a backlog of work Mr. Billings couldn't take care of. When you get that cleaned up, however, we think the worst will be behind you. We would like very much to have you undertake this representation, Mr. Killory. *The American Bar* register indicates you have no conflicting account—"

"No, I've no conflicting account, Mr. Morton. In fact, I'm just hoping I still have the accounts I had when I went away."

"Oh, you have them all right, Mr. Killory, you have them. We were interested to see that you represent the United Mine Workers of America locally."

"Well, John Mitchell, who founded that union back at the turn of the century, was born here in Braidwood. In those days only ten thousand out of the three hundred thousand miners in the bituminous fields were members of his union. John Mitchell built it up from here and when John L. Lewis inherited the union it had around eight hundred thousand members. A great man, Mitchell."

"You knew him?"

"No, but my aunt knew him well. She has told me how those were tough days, as tough as any in the history of our country, and the coal mines were tough places. Mitchell had black hair and a swarthy face that made many mistake him for an Italian. Mitchell was Irish. And when quitting time came, and the mine whistle blew, Mitchell would get up on the tipple and gather the miners around him. It was in the days of the trusts—the companies were too big and powerful then, and the men didn't have a chance. There's little law work to be done here in Braidwood now for the union, and even less in the way of fees. But I've always been close to those people and they've always treated me fine."

"Mr. Killory, do I understand you will undertake our representation? You'll be on a permanent basis as the area counsel, of course, and we believe your monthly retainer will be entirely satisfactory. We would be very happy to have you with us, Mr. Killory."

"And I'd be very happy—*very* happy—to be with you, Mr. Morton. Just how any lawyer coming back home could have a better greeting than that, I don't know. I'm delighted, and I want to thank you and everybody in your home office who had anything to do with this. I'm delighted, Mr. Morton."

Young Morton stood up to leave. "I think your wife's father, Mr. Rice, in Chicago, and my father are friends," he said.

"Oh, are they?"

"Yes, Mr. Rice has been talking a lot to my father about you. Father has a lot of respect for Mr. Rice's opinion. Father says he's indebted to Mr. Rice for the idea that this business should come to you."

"Well, thank you. I'm much obliged to Mr. Rice, too. Come back soon, Mr. Morton, come back soon. We'll do the best we can for you in this area. Goodbye, Mr. Morton, come back and see us soon."

The alterations were made on the house as soon as spring came, and Frank and Janet moved in exactly six months after they stood in the barren room in City Hall.

"It's our first half-year anniversary, dear," Janet exclaimed.

"I count every day as our anniversary, honey, and I always will," Frank replied. This had the true ring and instantly brought the whole train of ideas which, in Janet's mind, were connected with him. It was a lyric moment, as so many were with Frank, and on the way to the stock show at Braidwood's Fair Grounds Janet moved over close to him in the car.

"I've been thinking about what you said about every day being our anniversary, darling," she mused. "Why, Frank, that's beautiful." Her eyes were closed and she was smiling.

Janet did not understand him completely, in a deeper sense, but she wanted to. He did not understand her completely, because he was distracted. Art is a process of rediscovery, whether the source is music, theatre, painting or literature. So was Janet's love for this man. A parallel has been offered: An artist can take a fifty-cent piece of canvas, paint a picture on it, and make it worth thousands of dollars. That is art. Love can take an ordinary life, wash it, put its spirit into it, and make it a blessing to a woman who is entranced. That was Janet.

Little Janet—difficult little Jan—was born four years later, and Margaret followed two years afterward. There had been hardly a crisis in the family until Margaret was born. Then Janet suffered a terrible ordeal in having the baby.

Neither Janet nor Frank was at all prepared for this and neither was Dr. Gunther. No prenatal indications gave any such warning, and what had been the developing life of this family from the moment in the New York chapel was threatened, in almost the twinkling of an eye, by the rushing prospect of stark, grim tragedy.

It happened in the dead-still, unlit part of the morning; the time when old people die, the time when hospital corridors are empty, echoing places of pain.

It is generally said that babies bring with them all the love they need, but this baby brought with her the closest possible flicker of death to Janet; merciless, unmistakable.

To Frank, Janet's parents and Aunt Margaret it was blank, tangled terror; to Dr. Gunther, utter incredulity.

Then Janet rested weak and white, on the bed. The pain was all gone but she was deeply spent and felt infinitely frail. Her forehead and all her body were wet with agony. But she no longer thought of that. She had heard her baby's first cry. She lay there limply.

The mainsprings of her cheerfulness and enthusiasm did not desert her, although the convalescence was long and not at all steady. Frank could not believe, and Janet did not know, that she had been so hurt and that she would struggle against disabilities from which Dr. Gunther felt she could never fully recover. The mark was lasting.

The seashore, it seemed, would do wonders for Janet, so Frank arranged their longer vacations that way. When he could take only short holidays from the Forrest Building, they generally drove with the children to French Lick Springs, Indiana, or down through the Ozarks; for Frank loved the mountains. "I think you have mountainitis," said Janet once, as they came to the foothills.

But when he was able to take a real vacation—and they found they could afford this about every other year—Frank took Janet to Bimini, in the Bahamas. They left the children with Aunt Margaret—"these are the happiest weeks of my whole year," she always said, beaming—and off they went alone.

The island's climate was healthy but hot, and even the early spring sun drove every breathing thing under cover, and stationed the fishermen under canopies on their small boats.

The island was a speck in the bluish immensity of the Gulf Stream but it was unique in the whole Atlantic as the place where giant blue marlin could be found. Janet blossomed in the warm salty air, and each time they came there through the years it represented the rekindling of the romance that they had somehow lost along the way but which was always in her heart as it was still in Frank's.

Sometimes, although not until their second trip, the waves were lit by the famous phosphorescent light produced by myriads of insects whose love-making, electrified by storms, twinkled on the surface of the sea in a universal wedding. The shadow of Bimini, tiny, dark and motionless, rested in the middle of a moving plain of diamonds. It was a far cry from the Braidwood courtroom that had become Frank's life.

The sleepy little British rock consisted of only one wandering street, a few native shacks, a decrepit store, the small radio shack on the sandy hill, and Mrs. Duncombe's two-story clapboard hotel, The Compleat Angler; or, more elaborately on its stationery, The Compleat Angler, King's Highway, Bimini, B.W.I.

"When a marlin hits," Frank explained back home, "you are struck by an adventure. A real adventure. It's worth waiting for in the boat day after day, and worth paying for—it's very expensive, though, with the charter and the special boat, special fishing captain, and all—to have a blue marlin on your line; flying through the air and then diving into the ocean like an express train into a tunnel, and then up again, breaking to the surface perhaps a half-mile away, to leap and twist and twist—and never knowing whether you can bring him aboard or not in a fight that can easily run two hours or more."

Janet was ever so much stronger as a result of these visits and they were happy as bees in a bank of flowers when there. Frank had his first blue marlin—a 462-pound one—mounted as if leaping, and hung it on his office wall.

His impulse—in fact, his drive—toward a wider, more dynamic life had not asserted itself, and Janet had no such drive. However, one year they had just come home from their sea paradise when an event occurred that was to bear them on the shoulders of Frank's growing reputation. This next big event had a splendid outcome, but it was also cast against a backdrop of suffering and sorrow.

Violent, bloody strikes and fatal riots erupted at the Herrin coal fields in Williamson County in the bottom peninsula of the state, some two hundred and fifty miles below Braidwood. The tragedy engulfed all southern Illinois and Frank was called to Herrin to arbitrate.

His decisions were to be accepted by the United Mine Workers union, his client, and by the Illinois Coal Operators Association as well: the binding decisions of one arbitrator who also represented one of the sides. This had never happened before in the labor-management wars. "A great mark of trust," all said, and they were right.

It was clear throughout each session that Frank remained concerned with the fundamental issue of justice, and the distractions from this he merely shrugged off. He made a little hole here, a little hole there, a little hole some-place else. But by concentrating on one main point at a time he brought the opponents together and proved equally useful to both sides.

"Frank's selflessness," exclaimed Mr. Mayo, "his ability to convince both ▸itter sides that he wasn't looking for anything out of this for himself, including ▸ublicity and glory, is the key to his fine success at bloody Herrin."

The day the miners re-entered the mines and went back to work, Frank eturned to Braidwood. There was a message of thanks waiting for him from he Governor of Illinois, Glenn H. Patterson.

During this period Mrs. Rice stayed in Braidwood and Janet's father came ▸ften. There was no more than the usual strain of well-meaning parents in the ▸ome, and the only thing which got under Frank's skin was his father-in-law's ▸losely restrained enthusiasm about everything; about life, about the world, ▸nd, in fact, about the affairs that passed in the family in an ordinary day, ▸enerally hidden behind a mask of grave, candid inquiry. But everything was ▸lways clear with Father Rice. You never needed to ask about him: is this the ▸ull depth of his thoughts, or a false bottom? You always knew exactly where ▸ou stood with Father Rice.

Frank occasionally called him, jokingly, "Mephistopheles, the learned de-▸non of despairs," but this was not quite fair. Neither Janet nor her mother ▸hought it amusing, although Father Rice did not seem to care.

But one evening shortly after Frank received the telegram of congratula-▸ions from Governor Patterson he told Janet, quite gratuitously and to her great ▸urprise: "I often think Father Rice would have gone much further in life if he ▸ad had more enthusiasm, optimism, and sense of dedication and drive."

Dismay flooded her face. She was deeply shocked. "Why, dear," she said, ▸n a low, slightly trembling voice, "that doesn't sound like you. Father go ▸urther! My father, I think, has done very well with his life, indeed. So does ▸Mother. Frank, that is a very odd thing for you to say." She laid down a ▸nagazine, puzzled and angry.

"Oh, now, honey. You know what I mean. You would really think a man as ▸intelligent as Father Rice would make more of a mark—up there in Chicago, ▸and all."

"Frank! My father's temperament is just a little different than yours. We ▸can't all have the same drive, you know. But if that sounds like I'm apologizing ▸for Father, believe me, I am not. No dearer man ever lived than my father. ▸He's always given Mother and me a very good life—a very good life." She ▸knew she was going to cry, but she continued. "I think it's much more a ▸question of what's in the heart, which is, after all, exactly what the Bible says, ▸isn't it? Maybe success is nothing tangible, but rather a state of mind that ▸makes you reasonably content within the frame where life has placed you." She ▸lifted her head and faced him squarely, saying, "I sometimes think you may be ▸putting too much emphasis on 'bread alone.'"

"That's easy to say in the comfort and security of this house, and every-▸thing," Frank replied, plainly nettled.

"I don't mean hunger, Frank, and you know it," Janet exclaimed, passion-▸ately. "I just believe 'bread alone,' the way I think of it, ignores a lot of other ▸things which are important, very important, to people. They certainly are to ▸you and me, and we want them to be to our children."

"Why, I don't think that's fair at all, Janet," he protested. "You know what I mean, even if I didn't say it just right. For heaven's sake, I wasn't choosing my words carefully."

"I think you always choose them carefully, Frank," Janet said, slowly looking at him with unforgettable eyes where cold anger and hot tears mingled.

# 3

SALLY BRYCE was a lean, long-legged, handsome girl. She had a bend to her body like a strong cowhide whip, and when she crossed her legs and lifted her tight skirt, bells rang in any parlor, tramcar, gallery or bar. It was the whole of Sally that seemed so provocative; the way she lifted her arms, her hands cupped on her chest, and stretched like a bronzed and yawning cat, or paced in the streets as a fine animal paces on the early morning bridle paths of the Bois de Boulogne.

To look at Filippo Lippi's great "Madonna" in the Louvre, you would never think the model is probably frying in hell at this moment. Lippi, too, for that matter. Nor could you tell much more from Sally's face.

She was a dark brunette, smooth-haired in high fashion, but her memorable face belied most of her moods and much of her life. For it was limpid and reflective, although perhaps the impassiveness itself may have enhanced the look of invitation and acquiescence that seemed to rest in her wide-set eyes. There was something in them, a continually changing expression, a certain softness, which suggested a bland personality that simply was not there.

But, stretching, pacing, or anything else, while hating or loving, and at all waking hours (Sally came awake quickly), there was a mind at work. It had some of the agility and drive of her French grandmother's, although there was a masculine tang to it that she prized and cultivated. Many said that in this good and energetic brain Sally was visualizing everything ahead like the moves in a chess game. But even at her young age there were few who said they did not find her fascinating, alert and somehow possessed an assorted set of convictions that redeemed her.

Sudden emotions of joy or dismay came on this high-strung woman like wavebursts. But Sally had a storage place for her anxieties, her feelings, and

verything that spun in her mind. She could sleep. She had a remarkable call
n the gift of sleep. In fact, when Sally was upset about anything, miracle of
miracles, she could enter the guiltless world of sleep, slipping into it as easily as
. deer or a child.

She was waking now, however, and turning to the coffee that had just
)een placed beside her bed. The corners of her mouth quivered and her chest
elt tight. One hand was fingering her rumpled hair. The other hand was
·lasped under the soft circle of her breast. Drowsy, alone, naked. There was a
all dressing mirror near her bed and in it the face was frank, and almost
nnocent, young and clever and charming. Memory stirred, the suspicious,
entative assembling of wispy images and a bringing of some order into them.
Chen Sally lay flat on her back, her eyes closed. Was she trying to keep back
he tears?

She propped herself on her large pillow and sipped her coffee quietly.
"Stupid," she murmured out loud. "Just plain damn stupid." She sat up slowly,
her face wrenched into a scowl, her voice a little tart and peevish.

"Hurry if you will, Marie," she said in French to the maid who was
)acking her set of Vuitton traveling cases in the center of the room. "My train
eaves at one o'clock."

The maid gave her a cheerful glance and her hands flew from closets into
he luggage.

The apartment where she lived in the rue Capucine overlooked one of
hose gardens where the earth comes into its own in the heart of Paris, on the
:dge of cliffs and beaches of stone. The sun was beating on the windows.
Summer noises came in from the street. The lifted shutters and open curtains
brought the strong light square on Sally's nude body as she squirmed out of the
sheets and stood on the floor. Sally stretched, and threw her shoulders back in
a full-throated yawn.

She moved toward the bathroom. "Run my tub," she told Marie, "and hot,
hot, hot." In her hurry to comply the maid tipped over a small table by the
chaise and sang out the French curse *Merde!* Sally laughed. Her whole expression changed when she laughed. The impassiveness vanished, animation
took its place, and men felt her laugh was the kind of music you must hear in
heaven. She would wiggle her tigerish little nose, her eyelids half-closed, and
become—for the moment—the very symbol of provocativeness.

Some felt a withering coldness underneath this, however, like the soil of
Labrador which has gay little flowers on the surface and a foot down is
frozen. Others attempted to snatch amorous opportunity out of what they saw
with their eyes as they appraised Sally's animalism and watched it increase
under their gaze. In fact, only the previous night an interesting young Belgian
made the frequent mistake. Six feet three, dark and glittering, he looked like a
sword. Visiting Paris, he had met Sally at a friend's dinner and later taken her
to Maxim's. It was there that his amorous eyesight failed him.

Darting out of the arms of this captor in a corner near the bar, she had
seized her handbag and fetched the eager man a resounding crack over the

head. The bag must have been full of nails, for he went down swimming an
came up with fragments of shattered crockery in his hair. He gave her a
incoherent apology and a Hamlet smile and imagined that that was that. Th
mistaken hoper even hesitated to escort her home.

Yet within thirty minutes, back at Sally's apartment, her mood change
and she lay with him on her sofa; her body limp and strangely graceful, n
unlike Michelangelo's Adam awaiting the life-giving touch. He took off he
clothes and then, with a decisive gesture, tossed away his own. The interestin
Belgian had left her bed hardly an hour before the maid opened the curtains o
this summer day.

The loveliest city of them all smiled and bowed under the leaves of th
chestnut trees and of the Eiffel spire and the two great square towers of Notr
Dame, holding back the sky. But it was unbearably hot, dreadfully hot, an
Sally was unbearably annoyed, as well, by a promise she had given the man i
her bed that she would be his for the remaining week of his stay in Pari
Stupid.

The door had not been closed more than a minute on the back of hi
tapered shoulders before Sally was on the telephone to the hall porter at th
Ritz. The simple solution would be to leave town. By that evening she woul
be in the cool air of Mont Blanc with its white signpost so high above th
clouds. She arranged a railroad ticket and seat to Chamonix. My God, sh
thought, returning to bed, it will feel good to be in the mountains.

The aristocracy has three ages: the age of superiority, of privilege, and o
vanity; once it has left the first behind, it degenerates in the second and expire
in the third. Sally's parents, America-based, remained in the first. Sally was i
the second; the product of a broken home.

Her name was Sarah but it somehow had liquefied in infancy into Sally
She came from a rich mother whose philosophy reached deep into some sourc
of contented despair and a father who treated life like a huge, rich slice o
Turkish delight. The impact on Sally's childhood was a recipe for dismay, if n
panic. And then when they were divorced, these parents competed with eac
other in pampering her. Their efforts were a perpetual making of bricks with
out straw—and were always exerted at a distance. She was more an echo tha
a sound in either of their hearts.

Invaded early by a sense of foreboding, she began by seeing ill omens i
everything, and usually they came true. Moreover, the bad things that nearl
happened were as vivid to her, in a way, as what actually did happen, an
certainly no easier to forget. In Sally, nothing ever went completely away.

Paris was the world she loved, full of color and sound and smell that fee
her lustily and let her triumph over the pitfall, the black pit of possible loneli
ness.

In her sybaritic circle there, and especially for one who lived alone, loneli
ness was not a potential condition. It was felt to be a sin; it threatened like a
evil ghost dragging a chain and spraying a warning fire through the fingers o
its black hands and from its infernal eyes. Her friends among the fashionabl

xquisites made a career of defeating it at all costs; yet most of them were
rced again and again to that recurrent, awful moment when they whispered
 themselves: "Where do I go next?" "Who will be there?" "Who will come
ith me?"

Few had ever known quiet companionship or simple love. The curse of
neliness, the prospective wall of loneliness that could slowly close them in,
as the leukemia to be feared. Defenses against it must be staked out in all
irections—names and addresses stored away, gossip gleaned about new places
 go—like bets spread across a roulette layout.

For this protection the brain had to go faster and faster. A woman in the
attle could have little rest from it. And, generally, this threat that came like
in pelting on the roof, had been over these fashionable exquisites as long as
ey could remember.

Sally struggled not to be one of them, but she did know the possibilities of
e black pit, even so young. Diffidence characterized her early life. Little of
e excitement others felt in surroundings or events stirred her interest or
pproval. The drawback to the growing girl was that things lost their savor.

But she fought against this with surprising wisdom as she grew older—a
dulous, solitary fight. Self-pity, of course, wouldn't do at all—it wasn't Pa-
sian (and in her xenophobic Gallic heart she was a born Parisian).

Chiefly, she read, read, read; she studied and learned. Sally enjoyed this.
Ioreover, from her Lausanne schooldays onward, she was a glutton for the ink
f newspapers; a bonanza for neighboring late-night kiosks. The itch of the
atural-born newspaper reader was impregnated in her.

She was attracted by informed people and could, when she wished, extract
ore information from even an unwilling source in half an hour than even the
ost expert district attorney could in a day. Their minds snapped apart like
nunks of a jigsaw puzzle. She could achieve this in a drawing room, in bed or
foot, or sitting cross-legged on some bewildered Oriental's little rope mat. In
ort, people talked to Sally when she wanted them to talk and she seldom
rgot what they said. And as for the phonies, it was second nature for her to
e able to see through the curling smoke-trails that covered their duplicity, or
iscover the small flaw in their balloon.

Boredom, in turn, would fetch Sally's long fingers nervously to her throat
r show in the quiet, involuntary drumming of her delicate nails on an arm-
hair or tablecloth, or an impatient prodding of the speaker by the push of
nd—" "and—" "and—" However, she was seldom bored. She simply van-
hed.

Dripping inside the folds of her giant towel, the sun sparkling on the beads
f water, Sally polished herself dry after her bath while Marie finished the
acking, glowing in a hard rub-down of her long legs, her flat belly, the
oulders and back that had been tense but were now relaxed.

She looked at some letters that had come and tossed them in her desk
ther than skim through them, pressed for time. It never occurred to Sally to
ke them with her. She glanced under the wicker lid of the lunch basket

prepared for the train trip and pulled herself into the skirt and blouse of som
country clothes. She finally satisfied herself as to her accessories, the things i
her handbag, and her supply of cigarettes. She snapped one bag closed, the
pulled a bright bandana back out of another and wrapped it tight around he
head to hold her hair.

Flowers in this apartment were as indispensable a part of Sally's life as a
itself and somehow she had acquired a superstition, a fixation, that a singl
rose—cut short for her to wear—was a talisman of safety and good luck whe
she traveled. Sally clipped one from the vase as she hurried toward the door.

Then she gave Marie one of her direct looks, fleeting, accompanied by
small warning to the black-uniformed maid that no one was to be told wher
she had gone, although Marie, in fact, did not know where she was going.

Now Sally was off to the station, careening through the traffic in her ta
like a beautiful dove from Noah's Ark signaling to everyone that all trouble wa
over.

Porters were scarce on the dust-blown platform, but suddenly on
emerged from nowhere and jostled her and her luggage through the ranks of
company of blue-bonneted Alpine Chasseurs to a seat far forward in the trai
Two elderly women, country people, and a squat Frenchman with a sparl
sputtering pipe, his yellow teeth glowing in his white beard, were in the com
partment the porter chose. The two women exchanged cool, murmured gree
ings with her and then all four lapsed into silence. In a few minutes a shri
whistle on the platform and a banging of doors announced that they were off.

A final lurch and the train poured away into a viaduct tunnel, the broa
window tight shut against the billowing smoke and stinging cinders. Sall
opened the top buttons of her blouse and settled down to survive the suffc
cation and the bronchial breathing of the bearded man.

There was a heavy brown mist lying in tufts and billows on the country
side. Finally, they were in vineyards near the Côte-d'Or, traveling along th
chalky hills on the bank of the Saône in the broad and fertile Burgundian plai
There was a thunderclap as the heat broke and a storm burst, the torrer
bringing its relief just as the sun was about to fall.

Frank's Braidwood client, the Excelsior Shoe Company, had hurriedl
sent him to negotiate with the French leather cartel at Dijon for the protectic
of its suede imports. All was finished, and well finished, but the documen
were being circulated through the government and several days would elaps
before these papers would be returned to Dijon to be signed.

Frank came aboard at Dijon. As the two women and the squat Frenchma
wedged out through the door, he pushed his traveling bag in front of him an
tossed it up on the overhead rack. Then he sat down on the broad seat facin
Sally, whose legs were straight out and feet were on the cushion, wedging h
comfortably in her place beside the window.

It would be nice to be able to recount that some electric spark passe
between these two. It simply did not happen. Frank saw the face, the legs, th

ose, the open blouse, he saw the girl; but Destiny was mute. Sally saw the
ace, she saw the hands rustling a newspaper, and she saw the rest of the man.
Oh, Shades, oh, Destiny—*Mektoub:* it is written—or whatever the word may
e for Fate in any language. Whoever says he foresees the future is usually
lind!)

The cast of Sally's mind was analytical and interpretative—people, be-
avior, motive—but strangers had long been discounted. People who talk to
ou on trains can be awful bores.

"Good evening, madam," he said. "This rain certainly helps." Yes, the first
vords he ever spoke to Sally Bryce were as banal as that.

"Yes, it does," Sally answered, wondering as she often did how American
nen always instinctively assumed that she was another American and not
'rench when there was not an American stitch on her body and she had had
o chance to open her mouth. The thought didn't displease her, merely puzzled
er, and here it was again.

The train rushed on through the pelting rain and the little clang-clang at
he road crossings came more and more seldom as they roared south toward the
wiss frontier. The train would stay on the French side and climb through the
avoyan Alps to Annecy. There, a few miles from the border of Italy, and
Chamonix passengers would change to the mountain train.

Sally was sitting still, a soft and absent look on her face. She drank some
nilk and ate part of the cold duck left in the basket. She offered what was left
o Frank. "Will you have some?" she asked, bending forward in a jack-knife
osition over her outstretched legs and passing the basket toward him, her very
retty breasts easily revealed.

Life has its ups and downs, but he had seldom received such a pleasant
urprise. A cool customer, Frank had thought to himself, and she will sit here
ating everything in that damn basket as sure as I am alive.

"Good God, yes," he said, jumping half out of the seat, "I'm starved. Thank
ou. Thank you very much. My name is Killory. How do you do." He stuck out
is hand but Sally, of course, was holding the basket and simply nodded—a
ondescending nod. "How do you do."

"I haven't had anything to eat since about seven o'clock this morning," he
aid, pulling at the duck bone and munching the delicate meat. "You've saved
ny life."

"Where have you come from, Mr. Killory?"

"Well, I've been doing some work in Dijon. It's suspended now for a few
lays, although I'm through. I just go back to Dijon to sign the papers when
hey're ready before I return to the United States. All done," he smiled.

"I should think you'd go to Paris," Sally replied, speaking the obvious.

Frank waited to swallow the piece of good bread in his mouth, gulping it
nd grinning back at the handsome girl. "Well," he answered, "I've been to
'aris since I came over. But, you see, I've never seen any really big mountains
n all my life. I come from a small town in Illinois, Braidwood, and it's flat as a
ancake all around there. I've never been to the Rockies. So, with this chance

in Dijon, and being not too far away, I just wanted to come down here and
have a look at the Alps."

He took a folder from his inside pocket, pulled out a map and glanced
across it. It was a map of the Haute-Savoie and the Alpine complex beyond
Mont Blanc to the Matterhorn. "Incidentally," he continued, "I've been looking
forward to this all my life."

"Why, how nice," she said.

"But anyway, Miss—"

"Sally Bryce. I'm Sally Bryce."

"Anyway, Miss Bryce, here I am, mountain bound, and believe me, this
meal saved my life all right."

"Some milk?"

"Sure you have enough?"

"Oh, certainly. I'm really packed up with things."

Frank stood and opened his luggage. He brought out a collapsible cup
which he pulled into shape and offered to the girl. "I should have given you
this before," he grinned. "Forgot I had it." But Sally shook her head and he
poured the milk to drink himself.

She remained silent for a while in all the suction power of her summer
ripeness, closing her eyes. When she opened them Frank spoke. "Where are
you on the way to, Miss Bryce?"

"Well, it's been terribly hot in Paris. Simply awful," she grimaced. "I'm
on my way to the mountains. I don't know where, exactly." The man
might be a nuisance. Chamonix was small. If he dogged after her she might
have to pull out to some uncertain village in the Aiguilles. Anyway, by nature
and with the strong French common sense that seemed never to desert her
completely, Sally registered an option.

"No," she repeated, her head back and her pretty face shining with bland-
ness, "I really don't know just where I'm going to stay. Just some place up near
the glacier."

Frank looked down at the worn red carpet on the rumbling floor, in
thought. He raised his eyes quite suddenly. "Are you a mountaineer, Miss
Bryce?" he asked, groping, but in a voice full of interest.

He heard now her musical and altogether infectious laugh. "Oh, no," she
said, "I should say I'm not. *Téléphériques*, yes. I love to ride them and I'll go
any place the cable goes. I've been on half the *téléphériques* of Europe. But
climb those mountains, oh, no. About mountaineering I've reached the same
conclusions the Chinaman did about football: 'If it is a fight, it is not enough; if
it's a game, it is too much!'"

Frank chuckled. Very cute girl, he thought almost angrily; quite a woman.
And what a build! The pink of her nipples showed through the thin damp
cotton of her blouse. That's a funny joke about the Chinaman. No two ways
about it, these American girls have got what it takes. I wouldn't trade you an
attractive American girl for all the French women in the world; no, sir. The
French may be a little novel and unusual, but there's something about an

American girl that shines through. Just look at this woman, for example. And not only because I'm an American myself. Just look at her!

Frank's usual safe, suburban feeling—with life automatically rolling along in all its routine pleasures? It had vanished. She invoked an instant sense of gallantry and adventure and visions of the great nosegay never to be had.

"You're an American, aren't you, Miss Bryce?" he said, surprised at himself for asking the question on the heels of his own thoughts.

"Yes, you bet I'm an American. I love France; I love Europe, and I live over here. But I'm an American. Absolutely," she laughed, stretching her long legs widely apart. Neither spoke for a minute, listening to the panting heart-beat of the train. Then Frank broke out again.

"I don't imagine you have any language difficulty over here. You speak French, I suppose? I wish I did: would have helped greatly in Dijon, I can tell you."

"Yes, I speak French."

"Well, my dear aunt loved French. Called it the most lucid of all languages." Frank's face lit up. "She used to say, 'You speak French to the friend, Spanish to the gods, Italian to the women, English to the birds, and German to the horses.'" They laughed, as he added, "But maybe I have it mixed up, I don't know. Anyway, Miss Bryce, what happens if you married a Frenchman or an Italian or somebody over here?"

"Nothing happens," Sally answered, with a shrug. "I'd just stay American. You can, you know."

"No, I didn't know, for sure. I suppose I might have. I'm a lawyer."

"You are? Well, that's very interesting. Where do you practice law?"

"Braidwood, Illinois. It's a very small town in Will County, Illinois, which you never heard of. About fifty miles south of Chicago. That's where I live." He was alight with good fellowship.

"Braidwood? It sounds pretty." Sally smiled unconvincingly. She stretched her legs again, then sat up. She shook her head when he offered a cigarette. She took one of her own from a gold case in her bag and Frank fumbled in his pocket for matches; but she lit her lighter and didn't notice the matches he held out to her.

"It's in the prairie, as I said. A very pretty town, though, and wonderful farm land every place around there. Come and see us sometime, Miss Bryce. It won't take you very long to look at Braidwood," he laughed, "but it's a nice place. Hot as hell right now, I'm sure. And can it get hot out there! When there's been a dry spell and the sun heats up those cornfields and the wind comes across them all the way from Omaha it's so damn hot you can't even spit."

The train clanked across a bridge. She did not seem to listen. But looking at her Frank found her gaze fixed steadily upon him, that challenging, intimate, amused look that bound her to so many who talked with her about nearly anything. His mind tumbled with wild improbabilities.

"It can't be any hotter than Paris," she answered. "And anyway, we'r
going to the mountains, the high Alps, the glacier."

She talked of her parents in California, a bit, and then seemed to dismiss
them. She said something of her interest in sports. In naming a few she dis
covered that Frank played not one of them. She spoke of her life in Paris
issued a few *pronunciamentos* that were more startling than Frank had ex
pected, including casual references to what Frank construed as lush carryings
on among her friends.

Mixed in with this Sally suddenly caracoled into the fact that if a woma
became pregnant the thing for her to do was to go to Switzerland—by a'
means Switzerland—for the operation. As far as Sally was concerned that se
tled such a matter, and, as if all of one piece, they began to talk of Braidwood.

They next agreed that, well, they supposed anybody can be happy any
where if he's busy. Trite as the conversation was, Frank was blazing a trail tha
he hoped would catch fire.

Sometimes I talk all the time, she thought to herself, sometimes I sa
absolutely nothing and just stare steadily at a point two feet over somebody
head. I like treating boors or aggressive people that way. This man is filling i
the time very well; he's nice.

The conductor stuck his face in the compartment door, announcin
Annecy.

"My God, this air feels good," she said, leaning over to put on her shoe
which she had kicked into a corner, and straightening herself to get off.

A few minutes later, bag and baggage, they stood on the platform. Th
mountain train for Chamonix pulled in on the other siding. Frank dove into th
station buffet and came out with an armful of sandwiches and two bottles o
wine. Sally was already aboard to stake down their seats. "And a veal sand
wich!" called Sally. He went back for it. A-tingle as a hooky-minded schoolbo
and humming a tune, he handed up everything to her through the window
Then they were off again, in the slow climb upward under a pale and swolle
moon.

Her amused eyes and moist mouth seemed to tell him that she knew h
could not help thinking about the way her body moved and that she couldn
care less whether he watched her or not. Some men can make a good guess at
woman's age just by looking at her face and figure. Frank never could. In trut
her age did not even cross his mind.

And why should it? He was having a wonderful time and lapping up th
conversation—and appearance of Sally—in all-out excitement.

The colder air was fanning Sally's cheeks, making her eyes brighter, h
smile more glowing, as though a swarm of butterflies had suddenly started int
life in this beautiful body.

The wine was gone, the bottles thrown away, and it was well after mi
night when they reached the Chamonix end of the line. They piled into th
only vehicle waiting there, an old fiacre, bundling close together under th
thick blankets of the large carriage and gasping a little in the cold, thin ai

hey were up ten thousand feet and even though it was not snowing there was
night-bite that always comes with the altitude and the clear sweep of the
ind down from the rounded shoulders of the great Mont Blanc and its glacier.

The carriage had high wheels and strained springs and as these swayed,
rank found Sally's strong legs pressing him, and their arms were around each
ther in the shivering cold. The pair of small horses pulled them up the hill
om the station, across the narrow bridge, over the rushing mountain stream,
s spray steaming in the air, and on beyond into the small village, through it
nd to the far edge.

Sally had booked her reservation in the hotel beyond there, which faced
cross the Alpine fields and looked directly on the mountain. Frank had not
rranged a place to stay.

They were assigned rooms on the same floor. "And why not?" said Sally.
Why not, after all?" A muscular man who was the night porter, his head
ermanently twisted to one side, showed them up, sharing the luggage with
rank.

He let them into Sally's room first and they saw its balcony flooded with
ie light of the moon reflected from the vast snow cap on the crest of the
iountain. The top of Europe.

In the curious milky luminescence of the soft Alpine night, shadows flowed
ke waves up the mountainside, breaking the walls and great buttresses into
iangular shapes, tiering one upon the other like piles of Gibralters. As the
oon lit patches of the snowfields and cross-reefs crowning the higher faces of
ie rock, the shadows closed in around the gorges, séracs and perpendicular
ılleys in a moving, twisting pinnacle of contrasting colors like a giant and
uivering veil.

The mist was heavy now on the mountain. One minute, when the clouds
ould break, the reflections from the snow would make the mist glisten like the
)ray at a vessel's prow. Then the shadows again, with the shadow-mass and
ıe looming rock-masses above the gigantic base blackening each other into the
ırouded world of stone, danger and desolation.

"What is war?" Napoleon once asked, and answered, "A profession whose
ıly secret consists of being the stronger at a given point and time." On such
ıvoring terrain, Frank might have fought with success this night had he
ımediately closed in on Sally with the conviction that victory must be his. But
e did not. There are at least one hundred and eleven kinds of love and one of
ıem was his love for Janet.

Conscience is not an illusion, and Janet—loaded with love—was an invisi-
le hand on his shoulder. While he did not feel too sure of the strength of
ınet's invisible hand during every moment that might pass, he was powerless
) summon Napoleon's formula. In fact, mostly, he was flattered that Sally like
im.

Sally, on her side, had no more interest in having this man from Braid-
ood in bed than in a balloon. She had simply relaxed, glad to be out of Paris
nd free from her "stupid commitment" to the Belgian.

Maybe Frank's perception should have been alerted by the indifferent wa
in which she unpacked her luggage and threw her night things around. It wa
not. He was further illusioned when Sally casually remarked that she neve
slept in a nightgown or pajamas, hated them both, and always slept bare. Bt
after Sally had kicked off her shoes, loosened her hair into a cascade that fe
down her back, pulled her blouse up out of her skirt and was fingering th
buttons at the bottom to take it off, she linked her arm light-heartedly in hi
said the cheeriest of cheery "good-nights," and she paced with him to the doo
Frank gave her a hasty wave and went out, wondering: What's going on here?

He had promised Sally to wake her at eight-thirty. The church bells c
Chamonix, however, startled him into wakefulness much earlier. He had slep
little, but nevertheless felt light, alert. Altitude? he wondered; or happiness?

A solemn-looking mountain woman brought him breakfast, her grave, gra
eyes utterly vacant, her sleeves rolled up over her freckled arms. At last he ran
Sally's room. He could imagine her turning in the bed, her hair spread roun
her on the pillow, lifting the receiver with her long fingers.

"Good morning, my love," she said. "Have you slept well?"—this was t
become a ritual—"You're not feeling too tired?"

"Tired? I could climb Mont Blanc on one foot!"

"You are astonishing! So awake! It's the voice I like to hear first of any
thing in the morning. I like being waked up by this wonderful, wonderf
Braidwood voice! Good morning, my Lord Braidwood."

He had nothing with him but his city suit until they bought a pair of slacl
and a sweater in the village store.

Each morning he would hurry into the outfit and be smiling at Sally's doc
when she opened the creaking device and told him to come in while sh
finished dressing, her scattered objects of clothing lying all over the floor.

Or she would be in her bath and shout, "It's unlocked." She announce
that the tub water was always good and hot "and that's the way it must be, fe
me. But this damn bathroom must have been derived from the Aztecs c
somebody as modern as that."

Then the good breakfast on her balcony, Sally stretching luxuriously, h
arms high, her delicate fingers spread, their bright nails gleaming, her le:
flexing in her ski pants, her breasts always free under her bristling sweate
"Braidwood," she announced one morning, "I know there's a lot wrong with tl
world—and probably with me, too. But I'll tell you this. I never felt better
my life! By God, I'd have to be twins to feel any better. Now, what are v
going to do today? You name it and we'll do it."

This was followed, however, by the flurry of Sally looking for her mi
placed mittens, finding her small shoulder-purse, or discarding different ba
danas one by one. Then a fast look in the mirror, a tight pull of the chose
scarf, and away they went. To the maid she gave the smile. To Frank she sai
"Let's go!"

It was sheer joy to walk with her through the village streets. Sally clung
Frank's arm, looking contentedly into his eyes, laughing her infectious laug

ulling him over to the shop windows or helping to force their way through the
acationing crowds milling in the narrow streets.

The village men in their clusters would all stare at Sally. Sometimes,
earing their remarks, she would toss a high, ringing laugh and reply in French
o quickly that Frank could not catch a single word.

"He said you're a lucky man," she chatted away. "And I told him he looked
ike a bullfighter—doesn't he?—and that I like bullfighters." She told Frank she
aw one first in Malaga "close down in the arena where I could see every
esture; the whole beauty in the movement of the feet and hips. I adore
ourage!

"It's a sensual pleasure," she went on. "I feel no horror when the first burst
f blood comes. You see, my Lord Braidwood, I'm a gypsy. Yes, I am a gypsy.
nd I am superstitious. You must not defy me. I know some terrible spells."
Ier mobile face assumed a mock-menacing expression.

"You don't really believe things like that, Sal?"

"Yes I do. And I am very superstitious. You mustn't laugh," Sally said,
ervously. "No matter how, I have the power to feel people—feel the inside
vil if it's there. I can feel it in them just like you can feel a spider without
eeing it. Gypsies say these are people who 'cross' you. Everybody ought to be
ble to see this in wrong-made people. But they don't. I do. They don't even
ee their masochistic and sadistic urges and, least of all, how wrong-made
eople are affecting them. When that happens, something has already hap-
ened to anyone so blind.

"As long as a bullfighter stays in his own fighting terrain he is compar-
ively safe. Each time he enters the terrain of the beast he is in great danger.
here's a lesson in that, somehow."

Frank had never seen her so vehement, and he walked along, a bit puz-
led, until Sally halted him in the center of the little Renaissance square. She
ad an instinctive eye for beauty and, without any transition, was again gay
nd caressing as she pointed to a spot of red flowers circling the small fountain.
Look! Isn't that charming? Beauty is the best reason to love France." They
vere small Alpine roses and the breeze made them seem to be dancing.

Suddenly she took his face between the palms of her two hands, without
aying any attention to the crowd, and kissed him solidly. "'Adieu, moment
urtif, bonheur humain qui passe,'" she said.

"What does that mean?" Frank asked, bewildered, still holding her lightly
n his arms.

"Oh, something very pleasant and tender, Braidwood," Sally answered,
miling. "It's about a fleeting moment of happiness." Reaching down, she
lucked her talisman and put it in her belt.

Then, literally within minutes, sitting on a café terrace and watching iden-
ically the same scene, she had shocked him a little about money. It was one of
hose things that come up for no reason.

"Everything is on such a clear financial basis in France." she volunteered.
Few people make things complicated by becoming your friend for any ob-

scure reason. If you want people to like you in France, Frank, as I do, you only
have to spend a little money."

"Oh, Sal," he said, his face puckered, "you don't mean that. Just suppose
someone took you seriously when you blurt out a thing like that." When she
answered she was grimacing at the sight and noise of a small sheet of rock
ripped from the mountainside: "Oh, well, as Mediterranean people say, 'Have
joy!' "

Later, a noisy French band was playing in the square. "Order me a li
queur, Frank, a fierce liqueur," she suggested, somewhat absent-mindedly
Sally drank her liqueur at a gulp, in the Russian manner, and promptly stated
that if she were ill she knew he would take care of her.

"That's on the button, Sal," he said. "But are you trying to make 'good old
friend Frank' out of me? I'll be damned if I feel like that."

"No, but almost always, if I'm ill, I am alone; and then I wonder who gives
any medals for one's independence. I want to be close to you, Frank, and listen
when you talk," she added, looking at him with an affection that would have
melted the heart of a tiger.

Studying her was like taking apart a series of Chinese boxes, one inside the
other.

In any case, the days passed happily and the nights as did the first one
Except for the moment in the carriage while the wine was still on and in the
shock of the cold, when he found himself in this woman's arms, Frank was
locked at the companion level.

Sally yawning, stretching, pacing, climbing; fully dressed, half-undressed
and heaven knows what—was not teasing him. She was just being Sally, as on
then, and the heaviest dose of ether or all the champagne in France would not
have caused a ripple of change in the status quo. If one looks for rationality in
this, one risks madness.

Frank did, however, make a proposal. He suggested that they ride the long
téléphérique across the *Mer de Glace* and have lunch at the high inn above
Courmayeur on the Italian side of the massif.

"Why, that's a very romantic little place," Sally replied in a suggestive
voice, lifting her eyes to him with a smile.

His theory was that Italy—remote inn, and all—would shatter the
Chamonix environmental pattern and bring them together for the night. As the
morning advanced he had the look of a jockey on a winner. Everything had
gone well—according to plan, as the military say. "Come on, Sal," he urged at
the La Plaud terminal of the *téléphérique*. "We're almost there."

But when they arrived at the secluded hotel, disillusionment arrived with
him. So far as the changed environment altered Sally, they might as well have
been in an African wickup of mud and wattle ribs.

The inn's soup summed up all that is best in the Mediterranean. And they
were rewarded next by a dish snatched out of paradise; a fine *langouste*. The
results did not go beyond that.

"Did you know that Lafayette is buried at the Paris cemetery of Picpus in

Virginia soil brought from Virginia in the battleship *Virginia?*" Sally asked, cutting at the beautiful, highly seasoned *langouste*.

"No, I didn't," Frank said, glumly. And I didn't bring you over here to talk about a Paris cemetery, either, he thought. But he didn't say it.

"The rhinoceros grows extinct because savages—and the Chinese—think the hair of the horn is a medicine," he replied, with a grimace.

Yes, Frank's position was as fixed as the top of Mont Blanc itself in the way Sally had frozen it. Maybe on the last night, he thought to himself, for some damn reason of her own—but he knew better. In fact, in an odd way, his frozen status distressed him less than he imagined.

As for Sally, in turn, her resistance—such as it was, and if you can call it that—was utterly effortless. She merely found that her sudden retreat to Chamonix would have been a bore without him.

The following day they took the carriage that had met them at the station and brought them to the hotel, spurning the square's little cluster of taxis, and drove down the winding road toward Martigny-Ville. Frank wanted to see the Swiss border and at least take a short turn inside the country.

"Then you and I can say we've been in Switzerland, too," he laughed.

As vacationers drove past them, waving and laughing at these two enjoying themselves in the fiacre, or serious German drivers blew their horns from the rear, they drank in the scenery, bewitched by the wildness of the immense green grandeur.

Mostly there was absolute silence, broken only by the great tumbling waterfalls that came out of the high, gray faces of the cliffs and fell in long ribbons of water and spray into the river beside the road. The vast, eternal, twisted glacier was wedged far, far above these, like a frozen hurricane. Two mountain birds circled like quiet sails in a noiseless wind.

Suddenly Sally shouted, "Stop!" The old driver, alarmed, turned his head backward as he pulled the horses to one side. She jumped out and walked a few yards back down the road. A small turtle was inching across, and she had seen it. She picked up the little living thing and put it in the safe foliage.

A red-striped road barrier, flanked by the high wire fence that lost itself in the distance, blocked the frontier, guarded by trim green-uniformed border police of the Swiss army and a small company of soldiers.

Sally knew the country well, fortified by her school years in Lausanne, and when she talked to the chief guard in the idiom of the Vaud, they had no trouble at all in negotiating their short horse-drawn spin—paperless—on Swiss sovereign soil.

Returning to the barrier, she asked her usual quota of unexpected questions about the country today, and the serious looks on the guards' faces showed Frank that, obviously, they were trying hard to inform and satisfy her. Ah, yes, Sally's chemistry was international and worked at all levels. People liked to talk with Sally.

"Never mind, darling," she said to him in the midst of it all, interrupting herself, "I'll tell you everything when we get back to the hotel."

They left with Sally blowing kisses to the beaming guards and giving the tallest of the men a hug. He had told her graciously that he thought the bright Hermes bandana she wore was very pretty. He had buttressed the compliment with a hard effort at English, hence the hug; close up and long, her bosom pressing his tunic. Frank seemed suddenly to have been turned into a statue. All the soldiers laughed at her embrace and so did Sally, watching the expression on Frank's face.

That evening Frank received the wire from Monsieur Carraud in Dijon at the French leather cartel headquarters, notifying him the final papers would be ready to sign there the day after next. All was finished. The telegram brought him the joy of a yellow cholera warning.

At eight o'clock the following morning the mountain woman maid brought Sally some flowers, and on the card which she drew from the envelope she read the single word: "Wednesday."

"Summer flowers," the maid said, with accuracy, unwrapping the bouquet. "Where would madame like me to put them?"

"In a vase right there," Sally directed, pointing to the small table in the center of her room, "and now all I need is a hot bath, please."

At eight-thirty it was Sally who came to Frank's door, the telephone ritual omitted. She was wearing slacks and a sky-blue sweater, and he thought her more beautiful than ever. Was there in him now a reflective feeling of quiet happiness, or perhaps even satisfaction, fragile but soothing, inadvertent but warming, that—returning home—the great nosegay never to be had, in fact had not been had?

"Oh, Braidwood, Braidwood," Sally chanted in obvious delight, "thank you for the flowers." Frank, lifted on his elbow, laughed.

"Wednesday—off tomorrow," she said. "Well, I don't want this last full day to be overcast and gloomy." She sighed deeply. "But if you want to know the simple truth, I feel sad and depressed."

"All right," Frank answered, struggling out of the bed sheets, "there's something I particularly want to do with you this morning, Sal. I'd like to buy a present to serve as a reminder of me."

Her face brightened. Her musical laugh broke out in genuine delight. "Oh, Braidwood," she said, "what a very nice thought. You're a romantic. Well, darling, I've long wanted a little gold cross I could always keep with me, and I should love to have it come from you. I saw one yesterday in the shop on the square."

"Shall we go there now?"

"I can't wait."

She told the jeweler to take the tiny cross from the jammed window, and looked her thanks at Frank. When they were on the street again she clung to his arm. "I do so love living with you, Braidwood, going into shops with you, eating with you, having you alone like this. Couldn't we stay another fortnight —or even a week? Will you remember how sweet you were to me?"

They left the shop, hand in hand, to ride the series of *téléphériques* to the top station on the Brévent, transferring at each higher landing. It was chilly

nd the foggy air stuck to them like wet gauze until they mounted far above
he timber line. There the sun broke through. The air was crystal clear and the
now on the Brévent sparkled as they looked across the deep valley to the
ummit of Mont Blanc, seven miles away.

"Well, Braidwood," Sally said with a sigh, "it's worth coming a long way to
ee this." They shielded their eyes from the glare, and stared from this prized
ngle at one of the most matchless sights in the world.

A person must see the Alps from on high with his own eyes, just as he must
ear a concert with his own ears. Much of the charm derives from simple
hings; from the greetings of the herdsmen, always given and taken on the
nountain paths; from the tame creatures with their large eyes who raise their
eads in the beautiful foliage; from the quaint villages such as lay far below
rank and Sally, and from the ceaseless changes in the mountain vistas.

It is not at night or in the day that these towering Alps are most sublime,
owever. It is during the few minutes of change from twilight to the full day
hat the eternal mountains rise from their purple beds and Mother Earth holds
  jubilee.

Frank put his arm around the girl, her breath coming faster in the thin air.
he raised her eyes and gave him a faint smile. They turned slowly together as
hey peered from one end of the horizon to the other, Italy, Switzerland,
rance in the far distance.

They could make out their hotel, separated from the houses that dotted in
ittle clusters around the square and along the river cutting through the flat,
reen pastures on its way to the lowlands, and the limpid, languid lakes.

Then the close-packed trees on the vast slant of the enormous massif, the
rees stopping at the jagged timber line and giving way to Mont Blanc's snow-
atched rock. Then the great glacier—"The snow creeps," the Alpine peasants
ay—lying in its two-gorged spread down the side of the mountain, like a two-
ointed robe of fleece, rough-topped, gray-white, relentlessly eroding the great
ock below and renewing itself through eternity from the snows above. Age?
enus de Milo is so beautiful we forget how old she is; older than Paris, older
han Caesar, older than Christ and all Christian thought. And they were look-
ng at a living thing far, far older than that. "I think it's more frightening than
eautiful," Sally said, "the glacier, I mean. But look, Frank, where it stops and
he snow begins."

The vast dome arose in its series of four peaks. The lower pair at the far
houlders did not confuse them, but which of the other two was the summit?

In the Alpine world the wind's velocity increases with altitude; but, in
ompensation, is steadier. This is the rule in the mountains. Three French
uides stood outside the small shelter, nearly frozen by the wind and hooded
ike the muffled trio in Goya's "Winter." Frank worked his way down the icy
splanade below the steps of the *téléphérique* hut to ask one of them to come
ack up to Sally with him. The man had about thirty feet of red rope coiled on
is shoulder, avalanche insurance to help rescuers find him if he fell, sometimes
nder twenty feet of snow.

So now the Frenchman was standing there beside Sally, his face tanned

the color of a good light cigar, his hands thrust into his pockets, rocking bac
on his heels and grinning broadly. A formidable man who knew this mountai
and the Aiguilles like he knew the back of his hand—the broad, gnarled han
of a peasant—waiting to answer Sally's questions.

"Oh, yes," he said, "the summit is the farthest of the four peaks, to th
right, nearly flat across itself. It's the top of Europe, you know." Sally stoo
thanking him, full of optimism, energy and eager eyes.

"I'd like to climb it one day," she said. At the moment, she meant it.

The guide pointed out the three main climbing routes that could be see
from the Brévent side, with the alternate branch routes near the top.

Huddled close together, Sally holding Frank's hand and pressing on hi
arm, they were enthralled as they urged the guide to go on.

"My God, I'm glad I came here," Frank murmured. "Imagine missing thi
Just imagine missing this." Then he added, which he need not have at all, "An
imagine missing you. I'll never forget our standing here as long as I live, that'
sure. Oh, no, Sally; not standing here with you, Sal."

The pleased Frenchman pointed out the route that Jacques Balmat,
young crystal hunter, and Michel-Gabriel Piccard, the village doctor pioneere
in 1786, the first ascent ever made and among the most remarkable in th
whole history of mountaineering.

"Very dangerous," said the guide. In the flickering glare of the snow pla
teau he could see that the word *danger* had brought an alertness into th
handsome woman's face and eyes.

"The ascent itself was magnificent," he enthused to Sally in French, whil
she translated for Frank in bits and pieces.

He tapped his pipe on the escarpment ice and went on. "Few people, an
certainly not me, although I've spent my life on that mountain, would care t
do it even now with comparable equipment, or to make a moonlight descent o
the lower glacier; the two climbers unroped and without ice axes, heavil
burdened with scientific equipment and with long iron-pointed batons—and b
a route, of course, never before explored. They went up and won."

Then he told them of the bitter dispute between these two that ha
marred the triumph, as well as the deliberate misrepresentations of Piccard'
embittered rival, Marc-Théodore Bourrit, who wrote a spurious account Duma
accepted in his *Impressions de Voyage* in 1833 and which was credite
throughout the world. "Forty years passed," the guide explained, "before Pic
card received the recognition Balmat should have shared with him. Only the
was a medallion honoring Piccard placed in the Hotel de Ville down there i
the village."

"Poor man, poor man," Sally sighed bitterly, in a burst of outrage tha
surprised Frank. "I've known sons of bitches who would do exactly a thing lik
that if they got a chance," she announced. "Real, true, honest-to-god sons o
bitches."

Suddenly she gave a low cry like a lonely, desperate animal. It was s nvoluntary that her face looked completely untroubled and before Frank could quite realize what had happened she was staring at him blankly.

"Sally!" he said, urgently. "Sal, what's the matter?"

She clung to him, her long fingers clutching his arms as though she needed to hold something by sheer force.

All her gaiety was gone. She moved back from him, her arms folded across her chest, her heavy knitted mittens hugging her shoulders and breasts.

"I'm cold, Frank," she said, with a little tremor. "I'm cold. Let's go down."

And when he said goodbye to her the next afternoon at the Dijon junction and the train to Sally's Paris rolled out of that station, she also rolled right back out of his life.

# 4

THE TWENTIETH CENTURY LIMITED was passing through the Indiana sand dunes on the shore of Lake Michigan—great billows and mounds of tufted sand which reminded Philip Allen of the Egyptian Sudan, except that they were stark white in the morning sun—when the porter shook him.

He was bringing the breakfast tray to the stateroom and had the receipts for some telegrams Allen had asked him to send from Buffalo during the night.

"That will be $5.84, Mr. Allen," the porter said. "We'll be in Englewood in twenty minutes." He smiled broadly, busy laying out the linen and dishes. "No refund today."

The proud, confident train gave its passengers a refund if it arrived late and Allen often joked with the porter that he never seemed to collect it. "You're making a poor man out of me by always being on time, Jim. But wait until winter. Just you wait for the snows."

"Makes no difference at all to the Twentieth Century Limited, Mr. Allen," he laughed. "No difference at all. No refunds. Never any refunds on my train. Now you better hurry, sir. The observation car is four cars back."

The porter knew Allen enjoyed seeing the remarkable rendezvous of the Century and the Pennsylvania's rival Broadway Limited. As if at the signal of a starting gun, they had left New York at the same moment. Each had thundered for a thousand miles through widely separate parts of the country, one across the mountains, the other along the lakes, to reach the end of their race at the same time. Now they would join one another on parallel tracks, like a tandem of horses, and make their slow, majestic way, side by side, through the vast Chicago trainyards to their separate stations.

He finished dressing and walked back to the observation car to read the morning papers put on at Elkhart and see the great red train of the Pennsylvania accomplish this rendezvous in a concert of accumulated engineering and human achievement that stretched back to the first day of the wheel. Then Philip returned to his car, ready to get off.

The Chicago Club was only ten minutes away, on Van Buren Street. Allen sent his bags ahead by the club's automobile that met him at the station and walked there in the fine lake air. He went directly to the red stone building's large reading room on the lake front, where the busy life of Michigan Avenue surged by its broad windows.

Philip Allen liked Chicago and had large interests there. Years ago he had conceived of an amalgamation of Midwest farm equipment companies. He remained chairman of the firm's board and took pride in reminding anyone how America had fed the world again and again after catastrophes. "This couldn't have been done without machinery. The American farming I knew as a boy is now as old-fashioned as making payments in beaver skins and bears' hams. The Russian farmer feeds himself and two others. The American farmer feeds himself and fifteen others. In spite of all our agricultural problems we should be proud that the American farmer is—literally—the most productive man on earth." The pun gave him a slight amusement but the fact gave him great joy. His lower-cost machinery had played an important part in bringing it about.

Everything about the city quickened Allen on these visits. He felt that the magnificent view from Grant Park along the whole solid face of Michigan Avenue and Lake Shore Drive had no equal in America except New York's skyline approached from the sea.

Very old cities have the charm and formation that centuries lay upon them. In Florence one can say, "Driver, to Galileo's house," or "Is this where Michelangelo lived?" or "Who spoke from that rostrum there?" "Dante, signor." But Chicago was the great, surging mass advance of a dauntless people who had built there on the plains, in spirit and fact, so much that had come to mean to the world Mighty America.

One of the giant ore ships passed in the distance, among the largest vessels afloat on any lake or ocean, sailing south in the deep water that reached close to the boulevard along the shore. The sight never failed to stir Allen, teamed, as it was, with the nation's railroad miracle of which Chicago was the hub.

The famous *Onaka* had been launched in the Cuyahoga at Cleveland as early as 1882, and Allen had seen this pioneer ship from that very window in the Chicago Club when he was young.

She set the pattern to this day: well over three hundred feet long, shallow-bottomed, a staunch prow for ice-breaking—useful until the Lakes froze in too tight. Her wheelhouse and bridge stood far forward, at the very tip of the bow. Her engines and crew were aft, clustered at the base of her tall, black funnel. The flat deck, a hundred yards long, stretched between these two superstructures and gave her the stretched-out look of a toy boat made of taffy. The hull cradled the ore she was bringing from Duluth to the Gary steel mills.

These pioneers were not waiting for the breaks of good fortune, he thought as the sight of the *Onaka* came back to him, they were making them. There is always someone or something that goes out ahead and leads the way. They redeem the hopes of the past and save the hopes of the future. Theirs are the personal victories of the men and women who keep the Faith. And it is the law which has preserved it. He saw man, not as fated but as struggling. And he saw law as the fundamental protection in the struggle.

The long ship was leaving Allen's sight now in the direction of the bend beyond the Illinois Central railroad station.

Frank had defended the Harpers shortly after his Herrin success and now it was the Wednesday morning after the day the phone had rung in the Killory house; Shaw's long distance call from New York.

There was a humming of bees, the abundant bees of Illinois gardens, and the air was sweet. Janet was far from the house, deep in the center of the flower bed. She was turning the earth with a small trowel, pushing aside a mole trap to reset it when she finished. But, finally, she heard the persistent ring. (*Mektoub:* It is ringing.)

"Janet? Margaret?" she called, although certainly the girls would have answered the telephone before now. Poised in a single long step out of the flower bed, she stepped onto the gravel path and walked resignedly toward the house. Insects were darting over the garden pond, among the trembling butterflies. But the phone stopped. Janet shrugged and turned back again. The persistent ring began once more. She hurried, exasperated, to the kitchen entrance. Wasn't it ever possible to do anything—anything at all—without some kind of interruption? Why are children always there when you don't need them, never when you do?

"Who?" she asked, as she picked up the receiver. "Who is this?" The connection was clear, but surely over a long distance.

"Oh, why hello, Mr. Shaw. So you are back in New York all right, are you? Why, yes, Mr. Shaw, I'm certainly sorry, but I was in the garden. And how are you?"

No, Frank was not home. He had gone someplace down in the county today. Could Frank be in Chicago next week? Janet didn't know. She asked Shaw to wait, please, while she got a pencil. Then she wrote very deliberately: "Mr. Philip Winston Allen at the Chicago Club at ten o'clock Wednesday, the 13th."

"Mr. Allen is your partner, I'll tell him. Oh, I'm sure Frank must know where the Chicago Club is. I'll ask him to send you a telegram, Mr. Shaw. I know he'll be glad to hear from you. We had such a nice time when you were here; why, Jan and Margaret have been living on what you said about their table manners ever since. Oh, no bother at all, Mr. Shaw, none at all. Goodbye, Mr. Shaw, goodbye."

Philip Winston Allen looked at his watch. It was ten minutes to ten.

Frank came promptly at ten. The two men sat at a large Italian table near one of the tall twin stone mantels under the immense brass chandeliers at the end of the room.

Killory's first remark did not entirely surprise Philip, although the well-known event was long ago, but it was a rather curious opening at that. "Well, Mr. Allen," Frank said, "I suppose you are the only man alive in America today who ever refused an appointment to the Supreme Court."

Theodore Roosevelt had offered him an appointment to the Supreme Court and he had refused it. Allen had answered "Why?" a thousand times since "T.R." had been initials spoken on the lips of the world.

"Well, I didn't like Teddy Roosevelt," he said. "I always thought T.R. looked out for himself first too often when others needed him. Otherwise he certainly never would have split his party that elected him President by herding up his Bull Moose following and turning the government over to the opposition. Self-interest may be human, and to err is human, but to be that deep in error is dangerous.

"Naturally, this was not his motive and he did not intend to lose himself. But he knew, none the less, that his own try for the Presidency outside the party might well elect Wilson, who was not only the minority candidate against Taft but received a minority of the nation's vote and still became President—thanks to T.R."

Philip Winston Allen speaks bluntly, Frank thought. I can practically hear him telling this to T.R. himself—and I'll bet he did!

"The public acquires its own history, often different in each generation. Churchill rode with the 21st Lancers in Kitchener's gallant, pointless charge at Omdurman, revenging General Gordon's slaughter thirteen years earlier. The British people and the world still had a conventional picture of Gordon's Khartoum disaster and of General "Chinese" Gordon, which journalists of the day crystallized for years on end. Cromer's accurate *Modern Egypt* gave them a very different Khartoum and a very different Gordon. And had Strachey published his study promptly after Khartoum he probably would have been lynched. The public wasn't ready for any other aspect of its hero-martyr.

"No, T.R. was a brave man and had many good qualities, but I never liked him from the very beginning and could not feel beholden to him in any way," Philip continued, "and I say this in spite of my affection for Wilson, about whom I was interested to hear that you, Mr. Killory, made a charitable and splendid speech not long ago." An expression of surprise crossed Frank's face. He had forgotten that Janet had told Shaw about this at their dinner together.

"Years later, Wilson appointed me an adviser at the Versailles Peace Conference. I was glad to go, and deeply honored. We sailed on the *George Washington*, you know. I wonder if it might have interested your Braidwood audience to know that the President was always superstitious about the number thirteen? Strange thing, Mr. Killory. He thought it lucky. Wilson actually timed the *George Washington* to reach Brest on the thirteenth. He emphasized the importance of Article Thirteen in the League Covenant. By coincidence, he put in twice thirteen clauses. He announced the Covenant's completion on the thirteenth of the month. Moreover, his name had thirteen letters; which probably strengthened his superstition, I suppose."

Allen smiled the little folds at the corners of his eyes puckered into a cheerful squint as those very clever eyes took in the younger man like the transforming mirror of a painter's stare. He liked Frank on sight. Others would, too. A man with a certain soldierly gallantry but a natural manner that was direct and easy. An able man, surely. Shaw, you are right. This is a good man for Allen, Van Biber, Caxton & Shaw to have in court.

Philip had ordered some coffee and the waiter brought the cups. Now he grinned, a wrinkled grin, and lifted a cup as if in a toast to the younger man. "Good morning, and good luck," he said, "and thank you for coming here today."

Frank started to speak but the older man continued. "But that happened in the past, a long time ago," he said, "and what you and I are going to talk about is the future. What I want to talk about, of course, is you."

"The United Motors–Harper case?"

"Oh, no, Mr. Killory. Heavens, no. That's water over the dam. Our firm will just have to see what Shaw can do to win it on the appeal. But Mr. Shaw spoke very highly of you, and I am also deeply interested to realize that you are young and have your life before you."

"I felt very sorry that case had to be lost with Mr. Shaw, sir," Frank answered, with obvious sincerity. "Both my wife and I enjoyed his stay in Braidwood, enjoyed it very much. I'm sorry I wasn't home when Mr. Shaw phoned. Janet was happy to talk with him and I hope he'll come back."

"I'll tell him, and he'll appreciate that. We were both very interested in your theory of the case, Mr. Killory."

Frank paused. "Well, sir," he said slowly, "I feel there are many things the law doesn't reach, at least I don't think it does. The law can deal with much more than the facts, and with the rules. But behind these and outside them there is so very much which the law tries to reach but doesn't always quite cover. In short—and this is the way I saw the Harper case—I think the law never is able to catch more than a part of life; an equally important and vital part usually defies and escapes legal definition."

Allen spoke. "De Tocqueville said that, Mr. Killory."

"Well—yes," Frank answered hesitatingly. "Yes, he did."

"The law has always been the interest of my life, Mr. Killory," Allen said. "Who made it, why they made it, what it is, and how well—or badly—it works. The law is to me what hay is to a horse. It sustains me. I love it and I live on it," he chuckled, "any kind of law and all kinds of law, including Indian law. I'm very much interested in the American Indian, Mr. Killory."

"Why, that's fascinating," Frank said, "and surprises me, in a way. I wouldn't have imagined, sir, that you would be particularly interested in Indians."

Philip sat back comfortably in the broad, light tan chair, his hands folded across his lap. "The American Indian is my hobby. But it's a large subject. In fact, for the last few years I've been writing a book about the Indians who lived here and developed here for many centuries—possibly several thousands of years—before we came. I'm afraid I'm not doing it very well, of course, but all my ancestors came from Ohio and my dear father was an authority on the Indians, bless him."

"Ohio?"

"Yes, the climate in the wilderness of Ohio furnished an excellent home for the Indians, and Illinois about the same. The usual view of the Indians—these remarkable people—as lurking savages, infesting the forest and living without laws, is both erroneous and unjust." The giant relaxed in his chair. "This is where the law comes in, young man, interesting you and me." He smiled.

"The crimes generally recognized and punished by these immense tribes are not far from those dealt with by our own laws today. They were chiefly murder, treason, theft, adultery and witchcraft. This last is surprising, Mr. Killory, but it was true among most tribes and certainly among those in Ohio. Witchcraft was punishable by death, either by stabbing or burning or from the tomahawk. As late as June 1810, old Wyandot Chief Leatherlips—the Indian name is Shateyaronyah—was executed by his tribesmen under the charge of witchcraft. He was dispatched with a tomahawk.

"Theft was punishable by twofold restitution. Treason was punishable by death. For the first offense of adultery by a woman, most tribes cropped her hair. For repeated offenses her left ear was cut off. They just knocked the poor woman's ear off with a knife after the tribe's elders passed the verdict—very carefully passed it, I might add." Philip described a wide circle in the air with his heavy arms.

"Here was a jury system, young man, thousands of years old and practically universal among all except the tribes that were marauders. Also they employed what is today another fundamental feature of our jurisprudence: that justice must not only be done but be seen to be done.

"Outlawry was generally regarded as consisting of degrees," Allen went on. "If the Indian convicted of the lowest degree committed a similar crime again, it was lawful for any tribesman to kill him. If the outlawry was of a very high degree it was the duty—not the right—of any member of the tribe to kill him on sight.

"Across the whole range and variety of tribes the laws were well obeyed and remarkably uniform."

Frank was smiling broadly in the way that came so naturally to him. So this is Philip Winston Allen, he thought. In his—our—profession, as in the broad world, all the wines of honor have gone to him, but never to his head. Neither Janet nor I pictured him as charming. We imagined that he was probably not very warm; rather cool, aloof and probably quite austere. I knew, of course, that he had enormous knowledge of the law. And I caught the spirit of justice in his eyes the minute I saw him: he fears God and nothing else on earth. But there's a lot of altruism in this man too, and I wasn't prepared for that.

Allen lit a cigar—"My morning cigar," he said, offering one to Frank, who raised his hand in a No, thank you. Then Philip went on. "The worst was not the Indian subjection. We forget that not only the Americans but the French and the English made them pawns in our wars and corrupted them horribly in the process.

"The French treated the Indians best. We come next. But the use the British made of the Indians is a terrible tale. In this period—1740 to 1758— even Benedict the Fourteenth issued a papal bull demanding better treatment for the American Indians. This side of our progress here as Europeans is as comforting as a crocodile in a canoe."

Surely his visit with Philip Winston Allen, Frank mused, wasn't to talk about Indians. Surely Allen must be getting his impressions of me in his own way. There is a lightness of touch behind this man's thinking. And underneath there is something else; a moral resonance which gives his judgment density. Perhaps this is what gives Philip Winston Allen's opinions their cutting edge into the public consciousness and brings him trust. No matter what comes of this meeting, Frank felt, I am deeply honored. And obviously Allen was the last man in the world to be hustled.

Allen checked himself in his running narrative and he was chuckling as he said, "Young man, I'm sorry. You'll have to forgive such a long recitation of my hobby. But, you know, come to think of it, today's world doesn't seem to have changed greatly in aggression or in the tragic use of power and the rewards of power, everywhere, since man first made sharp points out of stones. But now the world is smaller, the points are larger and longer. There's no distance any more, except in men's minds. And it is obvious that the weapons make war mutual suicide."

"Well, sir," Frank replied, "I just hope that the people of the world can live together in a smaller world, at a higher level of prosperity, without wars. But we face aggressors."

Frank was speaking with growing emphasis. He saw that Allen was listening intently and he slowly began to wonder how any words by a small-town lawyer from such a different pond must sound to Philip Winston Allen.

"Meanwhile," he continued, "we contemplate healing the world when we are not decently governing ourselves. Whatever the cause, most people throughout the world are all but broken by the machinery of modern government. Yet our own politicians ask more power here, as if they were not already so strong that they, too, can all but break our backs with their own bureaucracy."

"I agree," said Allen. But Killory gave Philip a tentative look as he exposed his views, like a hurdler who, the first obstacle jumped, assesses his progress and the obstacles ahead.

Allen, in turn, assumed Frank was pondering further remarks. But what

Frank was to say was ready-made—even perhaps a little mechanical. He had expressed it many, many times.

"There is too much emphasis on personal rights and not enough on personal responsibility," he stated, "and too many of our office seekers stimulate this instead of discouraging it."

"I agree," Allen nodded, "and it is a profound disservice."

"Why, even in the town where I live my political friends are little different than what you see at the federal level. The game they play at the polls is, most often, a self-serving exercise in how to win without the intelligent consent of the governed. Nine out of ten are trying to by-pass the rational side of the public."

Allen smiled. "Well, Mr. Killory, we're sitting right here in a great city where William Hale Thompson ran for mayor on the promise, if elected, he'd punch King George of England on the nose. Remember? My, my, and Thompson was elected, too. Oh, yes. Old Ho Chang, the benevolent Chinese magician, is a friend of mine. He once told me—wise man, Ho Chang—that magic depends on leading the minds of others away from the true basis for the tricks. So does politics, with many men. But don't forget, this field also contains some very great men. It's a very human business, and I sometimes feel it's a little too easy to condemn so many who are in it."

He also knew that men are sometimes captured by what they chase. If you asked him what it was he chased, he probably could not have told you—except, perhaps, that he chased his own convictions. You could see in his blue eyes, clear as Alpine lakes, that he had long since won the inner battle which is the lot of those men who are committed to convictions.

Allen shifted his bulk in the chair, and, leaning forward like some well-groomed giant, spoke to Frank very slowly. "But politics is not for you and me to decide," he said in a low voice. "Very happily for us, it's a different world, and for different people than we are. They're in one business. We're in another: the law business. And that's that.

"Mr. Killory, let me come to the point. My firm and I are interested in you. I wish you could drop down to New York one day soon and spare a little time with me to meet my partners. Yes, I do. Those of us who are senior in the firm talk things over together and I'd like to introduce you to them. We want to come to know you better. J. P. Morgan and Company—it's an old tradition—always take in new partners, if any, on the first day of a year. Allen, Van Biber, Caxton and Shaw have no special time for it.

"Van Biber and I founded our firm long, long ago, and he has been dead many years. Caxton and Shaw will head the firm together when I go. But there would have been no firm without Clarence Van Biber, and his name in our firm is the best reminder of that; the finest scholar of the law I ever knew, bless him. I loved that man.

"Come and see us, if you will, Mr. Killory. Just come down and have a little visit. Bring Mrs. Killory and do some shopping and see some theaters while you're there. Come when you can. I'll tell Shaw. We'll be happy to see you. But I must be going now," Philip said. "Goodbye, Mr. Killory, goodbye and good luck."

Frank discovered himself standing, saying something in farewell, but when he told Janet that night he could not remember how he left the invitation except to say "Thank you" and except that Allen was gone in a vanishing sort of way and he found himself sitting alone in the large room, looking up at the ceiling.

Janet stood still a moment, pressing her heart, for she knew instantly that fate was taking a hand.

# 5

FRANK AND JANET moved to New York that spring to take up his partnership in Allen, Van Biber, Caxton & Shaw.

Philip Winston Allen's interest in Frank represented what Aunt Margaret called, years ago, "Opportunity—the big chance! The trademark of America!" But Janet left their home with the reluctance of the last touch of fingers in a lover's goodbye.

She hated to sell it. She loved this home made from so little and simply could not bear to see it pass from their life forever. "All right, honey," Frank had said, "we'll hang on to it for a while. We should be able to get more for it later anyway."

Briefly, they considered asking Aunt Margaret to move there and, in a way, keep the house for them. But that was impractical, not only for Margaret —it was too far from the library—but because they would take their furniture with them.

No, this was goodbye to Braidwood: Sam Welsh and his family had gone on ahead so that Sam—good, familiar, faithful Sam—would be waiting in Frank's office when Frank arrived; working for him with the ardor of a disciple.

There was the poignant assemblage of things to give away; the astounding accumulation of white elephants that can build up through the years. Of these the children's baby toys, the Flexible Flyer sleds and so many other things that had marked the children's growth were the most difficult to pile on the back porch in a heap, ready for the neighbors or the Salvation Army.

There must have been at least twenty dolls, and Janet could not look in this box as she softly closed the lid. There was the banjo Janet had given Frank on their first Christmas, a surprise purchase from Lyon & Healy in Chicago, and he remembered unwrapping it and how at that moment the rebuilt fireplace failed them, as the contractor had promised it would not, and filled the whole house with smoke. There was a suit of plus-four knickers, introduced by the Prince of Wales when he stirred the hearts of all ladies alive from coast-to-coast on his visit to America in 1924. The Braidwood Golf Course was opening and Janet had insisted, to Frank's dismay, that this suit she had given him was the only possible thing for him to wear on opening day. "After all, dear," she had said, "they are to play golf in, and even if you do not play golf, that is why our town has the Braidwood Club. Everyone will be wearing plus-fours." Frank had been the only man in plus-fours, and at the poker nights at Braidwood's Masonic Hall it was a long time before they let him forget the hilariousness of this spectacle. "Frank in his English jumping pants" was the usual summary, and the vision was enough to collapse the gatherings of his friends for many years. He tagged the suit: Salvation Army.

"Oh, Frank," Janet was saying, "where have the years gone? It's like sweeping our lives away."

Frank, too, was surprised to realize how many times in these last days he wished to turn back from leaving this house.

Yes, they would miss Braidwood—and Braidwood would miss them. There was universal regret in the town and county over this departure, and even some tinge of wonder that Frank could make the move away, and of all places, to New York; the city they summarized with the exclamation of so many throughout the nation. "New York! I like to visit New York for a few days. But I wouldn't live there if you gave me the town."

Frank and Janet had joined in this appraisal a hundred times. "Everybody there is in such a hurry," they agreed, "pushing, pushing, pushing. Why, people live in the same building for years and don't know each other. It's a rat race. No, not for me."

Sam Welsh had kept several Long Island real estate agents busy and had located, among others, a house in Glen Cove which they could rent, with an option to buy. They chose it on sight, just as Sam thought they might.

"What on earth could we have done without dear Sam?" Janet asked Frank shortly afterward, for loyal Sam was constantly being sent, like a fire engine, or summoned like a lifeboat, to the scene of some household crisis.

In a remarkably short time, the Killory family were established in general surroundings which, with the lovely trees and the privacy (trees sheltered the back of the house and the front faced Long Island Sound), were more similar to the atmosphere they had left than they ever imagined. "Why, I don't feel as if I am living in New York at all," Janet said, and this feeling became her happy solace from that minute on.

A proposal for membership in the Creek Club, made by Shaw, had placed them in the club's ranks promptly. With the swimming pool for young Jan and Margaret and the neighborliness of the cabanas, there was a strangeness to it all, of course, but there was also a sense of new excitement, and even a sense of belonging.

Young Jan, however, took all the developments with a small, annoying touch of scorn. Any interests she had seemed to have been left behind in Braidwood and they found it impossible to break through her odd diffidence.

Frank discovered himself as promptly acclimated to the 17 Battery Place office and downtown New York. His office, of course, was on the partners' floor, for his partnership in the firm had been a part of the move. Not only the public elevators but a series of internal circular staircases connected this floor with the firm's two other floors below it.

Sam Welsh's office adjoined Frank's large and pleasant work place. Allen had graciously given Frank his own Mary-Louise Bracken when he arrived, which was an enormous help. She had moved in with Sam, invaluable for the countless new problems, internal and external, which faced Frank in operating as a new comer to the immense firm and big community.

Frank broke into the grin which was already famous around the place and thanked the old man, but he was really touched, as was Sam. He thought to himself, It's the promptness of his kind gestures that touches you, that you immediately find so appealing in him—his spontaneity. Ready-made phrases and the ritual of etiquette are absent; his thoughtfulness for others is pure improvisation, and it resembles the little inventions that affection inspires. He is personified by simplicity—complete simplicity. I owe him a great deal. Yes, I owe him a great deal.

Membership in the Lawyers' Club nearby, and an application by Alfred Caxton for Frank's membership in India House, although this would take a long time, completed his downtown acclimation. Use of the firm's permanent Hotel St. Regis suite when he worked late and preferred to stay in the city was a valuable stand-by convenience. The transition eastward, begun at Braidwood with so many heart-tugs, contained fewer sadnesses and more joys for Frank and Janet and went much more smoothly than their Braidwood friends could realize when they so often spoke of the Killorys.

As these years progressed Philip Allen had taken a warm pride in the man who had sat opposite him that morning in the Chicago Club. He often said that the brightest thing he had done in his late years was "to bludgeon that man from Braidwood to come on here." He would recount that "Frank wouldn't have pulled up his roots out there in Illinois and come East if I hadn't sat there in Chicago and talked to him by the hour like a Dutch uncle and persuaded him."

Then he would add, with a smile, "Well, it really didn't happen that way. Bill Shaw picked Killory smack out of the blue when Killory beat us hands down in a United Motors case. As a matter of fact, nobody had to persuade him at all, and certainly I didn't. No, nobody persuaded Killory. Although Killory had never had a big-city, big-firm experience for a single day, when he got here he took to this place like a duck to water. The point is, I'm glad he came. I just couldn't be any more glad. He's able and a real star, Killory is. And those don't grow on trees. He's a man of strong conviction who believes in his own thinking and is prepared to support it. A man you can feel certain of; that's Frank Killory."

The firm's purpose in Frank's partnership was not to have him serve any specific clients, or prepare the cases. These were the responsibility of other partners and the firm as a whole. The primary purpose was to have Frank in court. He was a specialist for the firm; the voice at the bar. This was his talent, there was no question about that, and this was Allen's intent.

It meant that the great body of the law that had to be consulted was combed through by others. And, most important, the basic legal philosophy on which the attack or defense of the great cases would be made was thought out by others, most often by Allen.

There was efficiency in the method, and a sound application of the wise rule of selection. This melding was essential, indeed unavoidable, in most of the intricate legal jousts for which such large firms were employed.

It was the task of the organization as a whole to function in this flexible way and to come to the court with the most comprehensive and updated case that could possibly be prepared. But, once in court, if it was a very large case, the court had seen Shaw standing there for Allen, Van Biber, Caxton & Shaw. Now it saw either Shaw or Killory.

Unavoidably, however, Frank's own thinking was on the periphery of the large issues at which he appeared to be in the center. In fact, there was a disembodiment there. The power of the language before the court, the power of the tone and the timing before the jury, the power of the personality and the persuasion, these were Frank's. The power of the mind was Philip Winston Allen's. In short, it was important for Frank to be intelligent, but he was not required to be wise.

Killory stood out front, backed by the assemblage of specialists and minions with which he was intertwined. Killory was the man in court when the flash bulbs went off and the news pictures went to the public. Killory was the man at the bargaining table, speaking for the firm's client. When reporters wanted a statement Frank was the man at the client's press conference. If a legal event involved enough public interest to justify radio forums, Frank was the man at the microphone. But, in the deepest depths of it, the brain was the brain of Philip Winston Allen.

Frank had a nearly uncanny knack with the press. They liked him, admired him, believed him and wanted to help him. He had the talent and sense of fitness in this, and the sense of drama, too, many said, that officers of most the clients' companies lacked abysmally. Moments with the press made most corporation spokesmen as nervous as a coffee-drinking cat. Frank often served in their place. Frank was in his element, as natural as an old shoe. He made the most of each possibility so that the public could have Allen, Van Biber, Caxton & Shaw's client's side of the case clearly, convincingly, sympathetically.

He liked newspaper people. He had an actual yen for them; not to utilize them particularly, although he frequently did so, but because there seemed to be inside him an affiliation with this craft that gave Frank a great deal of personal pleasure; he was as attracted to newspaper people as the proverbial stage-door Johnny is to the chorus girl.

Some accused him of driving by bluff and horn, but not many. In any case, this special attraction's value to Killory in personal pleasure was great, and the value to the firm's clients was even greater. In fact, the ladies of the press danced in Frank's wake like scraps of paper behind a thundering subway train.

"Your Killory would be the greatest public relations man in New York," old Potter of United Motors once said to Allen, "an absolute natural. I just don't see how he does it and if he wasn't making umpty-ump dollars a year and didn't have his future with you and your collection of ambulance chasers we would hire him right from under your nose. No wonder he beat you in that dealer suit. I think he could have done it standing on his head."

Allen said, "Killory has more brains than to work for you. He would know you ought to be working for him, you dumb baboon."

Sam Welsh, however, was fretful. But this was Sam's nature. Dogged, loyal and fiercely faithful to his Braidwood idol, he was touchy as a bear with a sore nose regarding any infringement on his services to his mentor. He was marked through all the floors of offices by his pale face and excited eyes in quest of something for Killory. Nevertheless, Sam fitted in well with the rest of the junior staff serving all the partners. If he seemed possessive of his boss this more amused than disturbed them, and Sam never knew that a few called him, not unkindly, "the panting heart."

To the mystification of everyone, entirely on his own initiative, Sam had distributed an office memo to telephone Sam first if Killory had to be reached at night—a requirement Frank had merely humored. Then Sam was to locate Frank and say who was trying to reach him. If Killory wished to talk he could reply to the call, or Sam could tell the caller to ring him. Sam's plan worked fairly well in keeping Frank undisturbed at home, although, of course, Allen never used it and had no occasion to use it, nor did Caxton or Shaw.

In fact, when Sam went to see Miss Brent to explain his system to her for the senior partner's use, Allen saw him standing beside his secretary's desk and called out the door, "What's the matter, Mr. Welsh? Come in."

"It's about Mr. Killory's telephone," Sam said, a little flustered in front of this big bulk of a man in whose office he had never stood alone before.

"Is he having trouble with his telephone?"

"Oh, no, sir, it's so that Mr. Killory will not be disturbed at night."

"What are we supposed to do, use carrier pigeons?"

"Well, sir, we have a system now."

"That's good. What is it?"

"Well, anybody telephones me first. Then I telephone Mr. Killory."

"Oh, I see. Sort of like calling police headquarters and then they call the cop."

"It's just that I generally know where to locate Mr. Killory if he is here in New York or Glen Cove, or even if he's out of town, and then, too, there are calls, including many newspaper calls, he would not want to talk on. You know how it is, sir."

"Yes, I know how it is. Why, that's fine, Mr. Welsh, and very alert. This your idea?"

"Yes, sir."

"But suppose the caller can't reach you?"

"Then they would call Mr. Killory."

"What time in the evening does this system start?"

"Whenever the office closes, I suppose, Mr. Allen."

"Where do you live, Mr. Welsh?"

"Right now we're living in Atlantic Highlands, New Jersey."

"Well, I think the thing for us to do is to figure out how long after the office closes it takes you to get home to Atlantic—what is it?—Atlantic Highlands, and right then is when we'll get tied into the system. How's that?"

"Oh, in any case, Mr. Allen, this wouldn't apply to you if you wanted to reach Mr. Killory. Naturally you would just call him in Glen Cove and Janet would tell you where he was if he wasn't there."

"Mr. Welsh," said Allen, his poker face as sober as doomsday, "you lay out your system. I follow the system. Don't you worry about me kicking over the traces. Hazel," he said, "we're in a system. Pay attention. Thank you, Mr. Welsh, thank you."

Mrs. Welsh heard the report from Sam that night: "There is no question, Min, Philip Winston Allen is a decisive man." Min agreed, if Sam said so.

Yes, Frank was increasingly busy. He was either preparing to go into court, or in court, or preparing to go into next court in a succession of trials as regular as his heartbeat itself and, also like his heartbeat, his work was going smoothly. There was a rhythm to his persuasiveness in court which the jury, the judge, the spectators and newsmen seem to catch, and it carried them along with him.

It was not only the feeling of sincerity and conviction, but that indefinable something which turned observers into rooters and skeptics into believers. Frank had what the British call "the Nelson touch"; what he did impulsively, what he said spontaneously, and how he did it or said it was, somehow, just right.

His voice was more than a voice; it was an idea. His vigor was more than strength; it was a guarantee. His good manners were more than good manners; they spoke for humanity and justice.

But all cannot always roll along with perfect smoothness, of course, and the first even slight touch of discord came one noontime after the partners' lunch meeting in the firm's dining room adjoining Philip's office.

Perhaps it is in the nature of history to declare itself through small events. In any case, Frank was talking to Caxton, and Allen heard the younger partner raise his voice in a brisk attack of excitement. He did not know what the discussion was, but he did hear Killory say, "I can understand that some corruption is inevitable in a big government, or nearly any government. But the thing which really burns me up in the history of the Harding regime, for

xample, is that even the leaders in the administration condoned it, they con-
oned it. That's the point."

It was customary for the partners to rise if Allen finished his lunch ahead
f them and left, as he generally did. When Philip came to his feet on this day
nd started to the door, he touched Frank on the shoulder as he passed him
tanding there and said, "Frank, if you're not tied up, I wish you would stop by
iy office for a minute when you're ready." Shortly after, Hazel told the senior
artner that Frank was there, and Allen waved him to a chair.

"Frank," he began, "I was very interested in what you said at lunch. You
ounded so sure, and certainly you were. But, you know, Bernard Baruch has a
avorite saying, maybe you've heard it. Bernie says: 'Every man has a right to
is own opinion, but no man has a right to be wrong in his facts.'

"Facts are not partisan things, nor is history. You said what 'burned you
p' about the Harding regime was that the corruption was condoned. Now,
'rank, you had your facts wrong, and that's always serious. You were talking as
f you knew what you were talking about, and, Frank, you didn't. That's a
itfall for any eloquent man. It worries me a little."

Never before had Frank felt uneasy with the old man. But he accepted the
ebuke with sportsmanlike detachment and with grace.

"Oh, no," Allen continued, in the tone more of a friendly observer than of
critic. "Such corruption as is symbolized by Teapot Dome was not condoned.

"This problem began on the May morning in 1923 when Harding received
he first evidence. I can give you the chapter and verse on this, because I
vorked on it later with Owen Roberts and Atlee Pomerene, but it's all part of
he record and has merely been distorted by politicians to cash in on the fable
f condoning corruption.

"Two months later Harding himself died without knowledge of the widen-
ng trails down which the future evidence would lead. Coolidge followed
hrough on everything which developed."

Allen was demanding Frank's concentration now and he was getting it.

"It was restitution which prevailed, my boy, restitution. The corruption
vas not condoned. Not a million miles from condoned. In fact, this case should
e regarded as a classic example of exactly the reverse.

"The most sensational revelation involved former Secretary of the Interior,
Albert B. Fall. Fall had given his resignation to Harding in January 1923, to
ake effect two months later, because he was 'tired and wished to return to New
Mexico.' There was no knowledge or even rumor of Fall's dishonesty, or even
is involvement, until December twenty-eighth of that year. In fact, the news-
apers sympathized with Harding on losing Fall from his Cabinet. The *Times*
vas typical. The *New York Times* bade Fall farewell in an editorial ending:
Everybody will wish him well.' Look it up sometime, Frank, it makes interest-
ng reading.

"After Fall's retirement, his earlier resignation did not shield him. Oh, no,
iot at all. Coolidge immediately appointed two outstanding men as special
rosecutors—Owen J. Roberts and Atlee Pomerene. The two best men in Amer-
ca for this tragic and essential task. They worked their hearts out on it.

"Although Fall persistently denied his guilt, Roberts and Pomerene procured an indictment. I presented the evidence with them to the Grand Jury. They then fought the case against Fall year in and year out and well into the Hoover Administration until Fall was finally convicted in October 1929. He was sent to prison and fined a hundred thousand dollars.

"In fact, only nine main figures were involved in toto in the Harding Administration scandals. Six of them were government officials, three were not. Two non-officials were acquitted. Of the remaining seven, four were sent to the penitentiary, two committed suicide and one died awaiting trial.

"Condoning corruption, or denying that it existed, was not the official performance. That politically profitable charge is as false as it is shabby. I shouldn't have trapped you, Frank. Just remember what Bernie Baruch said about facts; very important. I'm sorry if I seem to jump at you in this. I don't mean to. Excuse me, Frank, for getting so excited about it."

Allen never knew whether Frank excused him or not, although surely Frank did. But when you give advice and consolation it seldom occurs to you that it may come back to you some day, mocking, like an echo.

That very evening Father Rice also touched Frank on another rather tender spot. Frank's somewhat frequent references that he wanted "to know what the people are thinking" about this or that, nettled him on visits to Glen Cove when he would come East on business.

"I'm not so sure how much people think, anyway," Mr. Rice huffed, "and here's what I mean about people's brains. Take this big city of New York," he said, picking up a newspaper from the table.

"Getting ready for New Year's, I see this enterprising paper asked its readers a question. It says here: 'If you were banished to a desert island in the New Year and could take with you only ten books, which ten would you take?' The response was tremendous. Now, if it is permissible for me to break into a New York literary fiesta at such a high level and to question the choices, let me shove myself into the intellectual parlor, Frank, and tell you what surprised me most in the list of books.

"In all the answers, not one New York thinker mentioned a book on astronomy. Yet, remember, a man on a desert island has around him—what? A little sand, miles of ocean and nothing else in sight. But, above him, and on the line of the horizon, the great universe is spread out. Wouldn't you imagine a man starting the New Year on a desert island and living constantly in contemplation of God's real work, would want to study it? Why, the greatest book on men ever written, *Hamlet* and all Shakespeare included, is only an analysis of the emotions and actions of us imperfect human beings. But a good astronomy text is a guidebook to the universe—our real home."

"Well, I don't see much to that," Frank answered, "It's just that nobody thought of it."

"That's what I mean. When many people say 'I think,' do they really think? No, Frank, people really don't think too much." Then Father Rice chided Frank for often being "so optimistic as not to be realistic."

Frank stared hard at him, and Janet shot them both an apprehensive look. "But that can also apply to the pessimist," Frank said in a sudden burst of temper which always surprised even Janet, amazed that he could take so seriously, and like a bolt out of the blue, some of the things that angered him.

If his father-in-law was taken aback by Frank's vehemence he did not show it as Frank went on. "Actually, I think chronic pessimism may sometimes be a form of self-coddling, self-pampering, self-indulgence. It may come from a hidden, unconscious desire to be saved from hurts and disappointments in case things don't turn out right. Well, believe me, I'm not going to hide behind anything like that. And they don't give prizes at the finish line to people who do, Father Rice."

He was speaking with slow deliberation and a worried glance from Janet was unable to stop him. "Pessimism can get to be a protective habit; really more emotional than intelligent. Sam, my own Sam, in my office, is a Brooklyn Dodgers' fan—roots for the Dodgers, always wants them to win. But he never fails to tell me before each game that the Dodgers are not going to win, even though he bets on them. His team just isn't going to make it. 'I guess that's the end of their winning streak,' he says. Certainly if the Dodger players felt that way, they'd never win the World Series."

"Well, Frank," Mr. Rice replied, "I'm sure you're right. I suppose anybody just has to be careful what it's right to be optimistic about. I've seen optimists who commercialized their optimism horribly, and at uninformed people's expense, politicians particularly. In fact, I think automatic optimism makes one a little suspicious, either about a man's motive, or character, or both."

Frank eyed his father-in-law closely. "That's the trouble with you, Father Rice," he said in a voice that stung, "you just don't understand people. You just don't understand what it takes to get on in this world. And you never will."

"Perhaps I don't," the older man replied, and there was a firmness in his quiet voice that gave Frank a little start. "I think you understand people, most people; I really think you do. But, Frank, I don't think anybody understands you, or knows you, quite as well as they think they do." He said this with courage and dignity, for he loved his daughter and, through her, Frank. Then he got up and went away without another word.

It was an angry passage that had taken place between them. It left its mark. Although Janet visited Oak Park several times and Mrs. Rice came back to Glen Cove often, Janet's father seldom returned, and never for long.

The scar went below the surface and had not healed in the years before Mr. Rice died. For Janet and her mother, stricken beyond consolation, it was as St. Monica said to her son: *Nil longe est a Deo*—Nothing is far from God. Janet bore the ill wind, but it was difficult nearly beyond endurance.

The awful emotions of her loss washed across Janet again and again like the bitter waves of the sea. "Frank," she said long afterward, "they say you can get over anything, that time cures everything. I don't believe you can and I don't believe it does; but, given enough time, maybe I can put this where it belongs, at the back of my mind, somehow, and beneath the present." And then, in the close-coupled way that tragedies sometimes strike, Frank's Aunt Margaret died, quietly, in her sleep, but quite suddenly.

It was a hot Sunday afternoon and the heat was rolling across the Illinois prairies. It was quite shady where she sat in the wicker rocker Frank had known as her favorite chair from the time he was a little boy; the sun could not get at her but it made the rest of the world bright and let her see out into the secluded street and hear the few footsteps that sounded on the pavement as they passed. She was sitting with her small sewing basket on her lap, her half-knit stockings in her hands, plying her needles and glancing at the brightness outside when she fell asleep. It was the end of her life.

The tragedy was, of course, the direct and awful blow to Frank that her father's death was to Janet. Yet he was to find that there is nothing higher and stronger and better for life in the future than some good memory of home, especially a memory from childhood. Some good, sacred memory, preserved from childhood, is required. If a man carries many such memories with him into life he is safe in may respects to the end of his days, and if he has only one such memory, as Frank did, even that may sometimes be his anchor in the winds. In our similarities lies our humanity. But our differences depend upon our inner selves, and they are born in the heart and shaped in the mind by the heat of emulation.

The awful blow to Frank was shared, in turn, throughout the little community which had always been his aunt's home, and she passed away leaving there the warm memories of a close freind which make it so hard to believe that anyone we have ever loved is really gone, or that life itself is much more than a dream.

# 6

THE YEARS PASS into other years and we count time in private rhythms which may have little to do with others or with the world. But, in the after-light, there can be no doub that Sally Bryce would never have been a meteor in the newspaper world had she not moved to Rome and had Neville Chamberlain's problem of defending Britain's faulty policies not become monumental.

Prime Minister Chamberlain (preparing for his famous umbrella) had told the hushed House of Commons there was a last chance for peace.

He announced that he had taken an important initiative and had asked Mussolini to mediate. What, Chamberlain intoned, would Mussolini's answer be to this effort he was making? A moment later a note was passed along the Treasury bench. Chamberlain read it in dramatic tones. Mussolini would mediate. Hitler had agreed to the meeting in Munich. The House went wild with emotion. The cheers for Chamberlain rocked and rocked the great hall. "Peace is saved!"

But it was a staged effect. The message had arrived, and Chamberlain had read it, before he began to speak. The drama was a shabby, self-serving stunt unlike Chamberlain and totally unworthy of the hour. And thus a luckless piece of parliamentary fraud in a moment of national life or death remains to this day beyond understanding or excuse. But the contriving occurred. It was true.

This is now a secret everybody knows. And they know it because Sally Bryce revealed the staging of this soggy escapade at the highest levels of the British government.

To those who said that Mrs. Charles N. Benson, writing in the papers as Sally Bryce, had knocked herself upward so early in this competitive field by brute force, high connections and an elastic body, there can be only one answer: they simply did not know what they were talking about.

True, she had entrée. It probably made her success possible. But countless others have failed—the majority have—who started with this advantage. True, Sally possessed her telepathic power to discern who was of value, or would be in the future. This certainly accelerated her advance, because it saved much lost motion. Further, she could snatch opportunity out of trouble, which is the hallmark of feminine statesmanship.

It is also true that she had become somewhat intoxicated with the incense of important men. Moreover, it is demonstrable that contempt and hero worship can be equally unhealthy and that both can lead to mischief. But she never judged the fairness of her attack by the unpopularity of her target and felt distortion is dishonest no matter whom the distortion distorts. Yes, a good journalist, as much as an honest politician, must engage in a little motivation research all the time. But, beyond all else, Sally had the thing without which there is nothing: talent.

It was deposited in her as truly as a sense of balance is born in an acrobat. And she developed it as fully and faithfully as the best man on the highest wire. Her writing had content. Moreover, she wrote with the rich, possessive pleasure of a discoverer.

Most interesting writers are interesting because they think for themselves. Their brain has not been fitted to thoughts ready made. In addition, a good writer is by profession a good audience and so can be mistaken for a charming guest.

With this she contained another ingredient of the good journalist: the ability to take another person's point of view; to put oneself in another's place and see a problem from an approach different from one's own. Her own security notwithstanding, she could always see on the faces of the poor and the helpless all the melancholy of their secret arithmetic.

A good writer thus adds a cubit to the human race—by respecting its dignity, its strengths, its needs for advancement. In time this became Sally at her best, and that best became very good indeed.

But, also, it was her resilience—her ability by sheer persistence to wear others down—which in the end astonished one the most about her.

There are certain jealousies in every profession, however, and this intelligent, hard-driving, attractive woman did not receive the general credit she deserved; possibly because her other attributes were so to be envied that the pyramid simply could not support this capstone on top of the rest.

Enthusiasm can sometimes be sweeping as well, and to creative people there always remains the world they may create, more real to them than what really happens, passes, and is gone. As one result, in these days Sally did have, like a careless jockey, a tendency to come unstuck at the turns and soar off into a few wild guesses.

A militant rival editor, at odds with her own paper's editor, the famous Vincent Emery, parlayed the rare occurrence into a biting, unjust witticism. He called all her writings "Sally's Fables."

She did not take this happily. In fact, one evening when the rival editor's description was repeated in the Savoy bar she announced to some thirty listening colleagues: "That Hercules with the brain of Einstein. I'll take him apart, finger by finger, right off his funny fat hand, and tooth by tooth. The son of a bitch says what I write is not true!"

"Profile" articles about prominent personalities were her slow start before she broke into the vault of the Chamberlain treasures. But this taught her a fundamental, namely, that no newspaperman is any better than his sources.

London was the cradle where Sally first benefited from that awakening, and London remained her place of action for some time. But Rome was the conception chamber, for there she made her union with the source that resulted in the Chamberlain exposé when Mussolini led him to Hitler's footstool.

She arrived in Rome as Mrs. Charles N. Benson. The idea that she marry Charles Benson, on post at the British Embassy in Paris, had not flashed out finished and complete from her mind or his. But they had been wandering around this central idea for some time before he was transferred to Rome.

This young Englishman, beginning his diplomatic career, was a man of extraordinary appearance and had the handsomeness people speak of as Byronic. Fresh out of Cambridge, rich, well-bred, well-mannered, he was widely regarded as the catch of Paris. He was also an urbane and valuable convenience. Sally could call him and, on no notice, or little to speak of, he materialized at her rue Capucine apartment as magically as a beautiful dolphin arising from the sea—ready to take her anywhere.

His whims were hard to follow sometimes, but the preoccupation of his life was horses, and heads turned at these two in a chain reaction on the bridle paths of the Bois.

The least assertive of men, Charles caused pleasant comments, as well, at the edges and corners of many Paris drawing-room discussions and was welcome everywhere. Doubts plagued this masculine man in a womanish sort of way, nevertheless; a constitutional dilatoriness, an inability to carry anything through from beginning to end without the constant intervention of unresolved doubts and afterthoughts had been a part of his character ever since his Eton days.

They should not have married, of course, and this is simple to see when you think of it simply. But when they stood among the flowers in the thronged Paris church there was at least equal folly in their "I do" on both sides.

In Rome, Charles, very Foreign Office by now, ranked a vague third under the British Ambassador; and Sally, as his wife, swam in the political life there on a balanced and beautiful keel that transported them well above Charles' stated official position.

She knew twenty times as much as Charles did about what was happening although he seldom asked her. Thus the British government in London missed another major opportunity for information merely because a diplomat's wife was so much brighter than her husband that he shut her off from his views and duties; a not uncommon situation long observed in most capitals of the western world.

Statesmanship is the art of creating policy; diplomacy is the art of executing it. A statesman should be by nature and temperament the most unquarrelsome of men. Charles qualified. But when a statesman finds it necessary to quarrel he should and must do it with a stout heart and a cool head. Charles had neither. He would never be a statesman, and, of course, had no such intention.

Nevertheless, Charles' intellectual equipment—and the important lacunae in it—served him well. His elaborate mediocrity was an asset. Was there not some sense in his treating his diplomatic career as a perpetual journey? He passed through it so gracefully—smoothing this over, smoothing that over, and always achieving the bureaucratic goal of never, never being recorded as wrong—and he was on each post such a relatively short time, that few had time to see through him. He was excused for having studied nothing deeply that had to do with the nation or its people and for having understood nothing properly, and he made observers forget that he was incapable of doing either.

Sally had handicaps. She was American and married to an Englishman. This put a double barrier across the road to information. Moreover, the adder of her resentment against the Fascist system had sunk its fangs into one official tunic after another. This was bad enough. But to high Roman men there was something worse. Here she was, beautiful, provocative, dynamic, desirable in the extreme in every male Italian eye—and yet independent beyond assault. They could not touch her.

Sally was as welcome in the eyes of Rome's swains as the ace of spades to a gambler. They desired and angled for her, but they could not trust her. They envied Charles, but the standard field of track runners pursuing this foreign wife was forced to fade. The only Italian who they believed had disarmed her (it was at Como) was a middle-official in the Ministry of Foreign Affairs. While the singleness of this phenomenon, from the Roman viewpoint, was an agony—perhaps even to Il Duce himself—it was nevertheless a solid fact.

It was summer and the sunlight was hot and hard as it worked on the broken crags of Rome's ancient face: one epoch building on the ruins of an earlier one, and now all of them time-blended by Mussolini into a common ruin.

Many, many years earlier the dictator had arrived, eleven years before Hitler. Mussolini's famous March on Rome was in truth, however, made in a sleeping car. He put on his Black Shirt as the train drew into the station. Then he wore a top hat and striped trousers in the afternoon when the King made him Prime Minister. Oh, yes, the Dictator seemed to have been absorbed into the constitutional system, but he came into that system with treachery in his heart and lies on his lips.

His ferocious egotism would one day end in a moment of revenge unrivaled since the snarling Roman rabble enjoyed the tossing of early papal corpses in the Tiber; this pompous man who was to become a mere thrown-together collection of dead weight, shattered by falling from the heights of his illusions and sunk into upside-down formlessness on the portico of a Milan filling station. Yet here he was: Mussolini! Il Duce!

To thoroughly understand dictators one must know all the evils they cause. Sally, young as she was, grew to know these well. She saw it like a surgeon who, performing a local operation, discovers the whole body is diseased.

She was watching the blind, the powerful and the important pushed down to the Fascist tyranny that awaited them—the selfless along with the self-seekers, the clearheaded along with the muddled.

She was watching the many exquisite women who were congregating from everywhere, nourishing their hard eyes and sharp tongues. On the way to this stage of development, the interim steps, like steps in the graduations of Freemasonry, seemed to have been skipped entirely—in their ocean-bound, sky-bound, train-bound travels, often with their shameless young men.

She was watching the Germans there, clucking their Teutonic tongues in unison over the backwardness of the non-Germanic world.

She was watching the British and American business executive group, a rather tight little drawn-together band in supplication to the money to be found in Mussolini's Corporate State. Their negotiations consisted chiefly of attempts at concessions in Libia, Asmara, Tripoli and other Italian overseas possessions, requiring contacts at a very high level. Humbug deserves humbug, and that is what they were giving and getting in Rome.

Sir Hugh Drury, representing certain British and Canadian oil interests, more or less dominated the British wing of the group, looking as imposing as Nelson in Trafalgar Square.

The Japanese were just a grazing herd.

Archibald A. Scriver, an ambitious, sycophantic, corrupt and corrupting man, was Drury's counterpart in the American wing. He had married his main chance instead of earning it. He was in Rome on a semi-permanent basis seeking motion-picture distribution rights for a Hollywood contingent and their New York backers. His philosophy of life was not complex, his pet phrase being, "all animals, except man, know that the principal business of life is to enjoy it."

Scriver, with his Cassius look, officer's mustache, a sort of watery, tallow softness to his body and a walk as if he had springs on the soles of his feet, immediately and continuously bombarded Sally and Charles with invitations, setting dates too far ahead to be refused. For he and his bright-eyed, babbling, rather witless wife, Grace, with her little ticking cat heart, who had provided his original source of wealth, entertained often and extravagantly.

Both Scrivers had the faces of restless wanderers from many countries and the assurance of money in the bank. As a fellow American, Sally found them annoying. At their house on the Via Giulia the carpets were twice as thick, the silver twice as heavy, the pyramids of petits fours twice as high and the dinner guests twice as numerous as in other households as rich as theirs. Everything was doubled and Sally said, "Hell, it's double or nothing there, I guess."

At their dinners Scriver, dressed with eccentric pretentiousness, always had Sally seated next to him. Then, nodding his foxy face with a close-lipped smile, he went about the process of quietly measuring her body and bosom with his eyes. Those old and familiar sensations repulsed her with this man. Moreover, he had a conspiratorial tone with her during any slim opportunity.

"Excuse me, Sally. Excuse me," his sensual lips would whisper gently, close to her ear, as he pressed against her body on some excuse and her eyes shifted just a little to him, or she would see him boldly drooling down her décolletage. The man's lewdness left her furious and brooding. At one of the Scrivers' most glittering dinners, Sally finally put a stop to this. She just threw up her hands and laughed. Scriver looked as if he had eaten some tainted boar ribs in a Greek diner. Thereafter this swaggering rooster left Sally alone.

But it was not so easy to control or avoid the exotic vagrancy and exhibitionism of the Fascist leaders and Roman male aristocracy. They knew much that Sally—questioning, questioning Sally—wanted to know. What kind of people are you, you Fascists, who would explode the moon, mine the stars and slaughter the angels? Have you a timetable for catastrophe?

She had guided most of them—including Il Duce—into a chair. The questioning began in the candlelight of her eyes. What Sally had started as a casual habit in Paris finished as her purposeful custom in Rome.

Her first encounter with Mussolini occurred at a Foreign Ministry reception and was Rome's best topic before the next morning. You seldom saw a gathering of more serious, important, irresponsible people. Sally knew Il Duce had inquired who she was, for everyone knows everything instantly at a Roman reception, but few expected Mussolini's circulation among the guests to halt, for Il Duce to entrench himself at her side when the chief of protocol—psssting gently—presented Sally to him.

Lean, long-legged, handsome Sally was dressed ravishingly in a Patou

gown, low-throated for just a glimpse of her breasts, her important jewelry
aglow, her hair coiffed high, her graceful hands and long bright nails as fragile
and delicate as a Chinese print. Her wide-set eyes looked excited, and looked
exciting to Il Duce, as he came forward in the stalking gait of an animal in its
hunting.

Sally's hand applied its mild judo and, promptly, Il Duce was sitting
down. They were sitting on a small red-and-white upholstered sofa with gilded
arms, their feet sunk into a thick rug with a Spanish corrida design. Those
around them moved away from the couple like bees from a crowded hive.

Like many Italians, Sally had a natural poetry of speech and she launched
into the subject of Bonaparte, a rather startling choice of subject, Rome
thought, although Mussolini's roaring hatred of the French was famous and
this was allowed as an explanation for Sally's tour de force. Punctuating her
words with her infectious laugh, her eyes imparadising this famous man, she
spoke in an unmistakable parallel which, if some called it impudent, was at
least interesting.

"I have always been more interested in the decline of Napoleon," she
purred to the entranced man, "than in his advance. Napoleon, a master strate-
gist, was incapable either of computing the days or of forecasting the effect of
the climate, which everyone in Moscow computed and foresaw. I am only
speaking from a woman's point of view, of course, Your Excellency, but this has
always mystified me." Her Italian had the slight harshness with which the
French use that language.

Fixing his eyes on the animated woman—ophidians have these eyes but
they are rare in human heads—her turned hip tightening her skirt, Il Duce
nodded but did not even interrupt her.

"Ah, yes," Sally went on, tilting her glass of champagne and looking into it
as if it held tea leaves. "And finally, there on that British rock, that remote
piece of England, lay the man who had left the soil over which he spread as
much suffering as glory. The giant enchained on St. Helena! He had the world
at his feet and all he got out of it was a prison for himself."

If Il Duce saw sly attempt to offend, he showed not the slightest sign.
Sally's sorcery was foolproof. He did, however, promptly vanish from the little
sofa like a pricked balloon.

But diplomats are confirmed chatterers. They can be counted upon to drop
endless bricks—diplomatically, conscientiously—and with a soft skill. Masculine Roman society also has always had a standard atavistic recourse when its
bright, stony eyes confront such a humiliating impasse as Sally presented. It is
traditional. It is expected. It began soon: the carrying of tales about the handsome American woman along with the conventional high-Roman lie, graciously
whispered, that they had, in fact, taken Sally to bed and that she was a
disappointment there.

Hysteria in gossip is sometimes cruel, often indecent and always unjust,
and the topic of Sally reached almost the point of hysteria among the clanking
Fascist taletellers as she paced, unconcerned, across the booted-and-belted
scene.

The stupid risk in an attachment with any of these braying men was so obvious that, for her, they might as well have been identified by walking down the street ringing a bell, like lepers in the Middle Ages. But by some feminine chemistry she divined that Alberto Monaci was different. She was right. And she took him with a gusto as native and powerful as any Roman could conceivably ask.

He was a true child of the Italian sun, the last of what French detractors call Rome's exhausted aristocracy. But his career on posts abroad had taught him diplomacy's hardest and most crippling adage: never utter the disparaging thought aloud. He was not an important man. But Sally could trust him.

Monaci had a proud, sad Labrador-dog sort of head. His eyes were warm and comforting and uncompromisingly brown, with small crow's feet under them, and Sally was struck at once by the noticeable beauty of his graceful hands. Although Alberto was an old campaigner in the ups and downs of luncheon parties, he was a very informed official and always brought knowledgeable insights that were a sheer joy to Sally when they met in the official rounds. He fascinated her at once.

He lived in a house that had the beauty of centuries upon it and stood on the slopes of the Tiber. Below lay the whole of sad and beautiful Rome, like an abandoned eagle's nest. Far beyond, the river described a wide curve, with meadows and woods on either bank. In its day the Imperial City had many silly and regrettable features, but it was the hub of the universe, the palace of the most powerful men, the seat of the most important government in the world. This was the part that appealed to Sally. Sitting with Alberto on his terrace she could practically see an emperor riding out of the city at dark, leaving the town on the heels of conspiracy, galloping over the wet stones and then into the woods that came so close to it.

He spoke of her confrontation with Mussolini one afternoon. Drawn there by her love of flowers, they were visiting the gardens of the Villa Borghese, leading each other through the masses of flowers, exotic trees, ancient rocks and cool ponds and the Japanese midget forest.

"For reasons best known to your lovely self," he said, smiling, "or probably no reason at all, you spoke to Il Duce about Bonaparte. All Rome has wondered why. I do not. Surely this just popped into your beautiful brain. With you, charming one, that requires you to say it." He laughed quietly and reached over to take Sally's hand. "There is a super-fast flow from that rapid, kinetic mind of yours to the lips. You've an oral mind, really."

"Oh, Alberto. What I'm thinking is that evident?" She was listening intently.

"It's more than evident. It's verbal. In my business this would never do. The business of diplomacy is to think it, but not always to say what you think."

Sally felt a small stab of resentment, for he was touching on something that had caused her to say to herself, again and again, It's always my tongue that gets me into trouble. And much of my blurting is nothing but a bad habit.

They stopped to listen while a gaunt, long-haired Italian played his violin and his fat companion sang *"O Sole Mio,"* as Alberto went on. "May I tell you something surprising, however? Napoleon said 'the history of Rome is largely the history of the world.' Yet in all Napoleon's travels, all his career, all his life, Napoleon Bonaparte never set foot in the city of Rome." Did an instinct tell him Rome would shrink him?

A smile came back to her lips and a touch of light made her eyes gayer. Alberto had information in him. He had secrets in him in a city of hearsay and danger. He had discretion in him. He had romance in him, as well.

He also had a wife. In matters of piety, she was an angel; a tall Roman woman, poor and beautiful. Clara. Afterward when Sally's thoughts would turn to her she could see Clara only as a distant, obscure figure. Asked her philosophy of life at this time, however, she would have replied in the words of the condemned man who paused at the steps of the gallows to inquire: "Is this thing safe?"

She decided it was. But the change in their relationship came almost imperceptibly; she did not quite know how. They had never spoken of it, but at a time that was practical for both of them he had asked her to drive up to Como for three days and Sally had accepted.

Sheltering the Villa d'Este and framing the rounded end of the lake where it flows into the river, the old town of Cernobbio is a city of trees and bells and flags and bridges and the gentle, charming variations of color and light that a beautiful lake always gives the buildings and foliage that circle its shores and are mirrored in its shining surface.

The moon made its mirages as they made love on their bed pushed toward their balcony, the lips of the lake washing the quiet shore. The low hills of the landscape and the far-off mountains were caught in the limbs of the colorless blue. The earth and their bodies were lit with the night's light and shade and she felt able to count every speck in the midnight sky.

His pajama trousers and overturned slippers lay scattered on the floor. Her dress had fallen in a circle and her underthings were near it in a froth. He had drawn her roughly to him, with his lips open, a solid sunburned body, his wide chest on her breasts. Her eyes were half-closed, but seemed to be looking out from under the lids. She clasped her arms around him low on his back, feeling the smoothness and pressing him closer with her delicate hands. She quivered as he whispered Italian longings and then, turning her slightly, cupped his hand and put his lips on her breast. Sally lifted her shoulder for him; running her fingers through his hair she held his head down on her, her back arched, watching him, and in time brought his head to her other breast. Her eyes were placid, as if she wanted to go on comforting him, rapt in this lovely moment, and then she smiled.

She circled her fingers around his lips and lifted them gently from her moist breast. She took his hand and drew him to the bed. He lay on her lightly, taking care not to hurt. Hurt? Alberto found himself in the arms of a devouring woman.

Her hands played over him, her legs held him, her whiplike body engulfed him, her hair framing the small back-and-forth motion of her beautiful face on the pillow, her eyes in ecstasy, her lips murmuring and whispering until, in an all but uncontrollable frenzy, she spent herself with the moans and low cries of complete and shattering release. And sometimes in these moments of her deepest release Sally would speak as if he were not there at all and only the stars were listening.

Her passion was unfeigned, as truly as an implacable sea is unfeigned. Her satisfaction through it was absolute. But the hunger to know any man, a passion to get inside him, to be a part of him—that had never happened.

Even when Sally had lain in Alberto's arms in Como, and in many places elsewhere, ardent, they had been two individuals, separated by consciousness of self, satisfied by the feelings received and only slightly by the feelings given. The need to communicate, to melt herself somehow into somebody's very soul, simply was not there.

In these moods her standards, principles other than that of discretion, and all the cautions that served her well—and quite consistently—in daily life and were especially needed in the quicksands of Roman society, were, of course, utterly reversed. Yet these violent reversals left not a trace on her impassive face or on her mind. Moreover, she made the common feminine mistake of imagining that a man who is in love can pull himself up as easily as a woman who is not.

This was more than a seductive, insatiable woman with a compulsion to be satiated and capable of using up a man's strength and life. She was not that selfish. But she was a singular person—a loner—nevertheless.

As Sally leaned against Alberto, spent, pressed close to him, she once pointed through the windows of a hotel on the high cliffs of Sorrento to a little hut on the slope toward Amalfi. "Look," she whispered. "Look. I would happily live there for the rest of my life. There in that little hut."

He answered drowsily, smiling, and in a mood to deliver a typically Italian flippancy. "It's probably not for sale," he answered.

He heard her infectious laugh, but he might have noticed that Sally had not said, "There in that little hut with you," and that, strangely, she had never, at any moment, said that she loved him.

In less than two years, Charles' Rome Embassy assignment was finished and he was transferred home to the Foreign Office before eventual reassignment abroad. Soon thereafter, Alberto left Rome on a Geneva assignment, in similar rotation.

When Sally encountered him in England she did not know that his negotiations in Switzerland were to be brief and that Count Monaci was now on post in London. She simply ran into him by chance at an Italian diplomatic affair at Claridge's.

In this encounter did she foresee new—renewed—delights, perhaps at some early opportunity, in one of the inns on the Sorrento-like cliffs of Scotland, when the night would be full of prickly moisture and salty foam? She did not. Did her surprised face and the smile in her wide-set eyes conceal images of Como brooding in its blackish-gray twilight, or the prospective sunshine of the south of France? No. Did she visualize them lying again on the ancient stones of Taormina, below Aetna? Not at all. Sally had cut the knot and she had no wish to see the frayed ends spliced together.

"Why, Alberto," she said, overjoyed to see an old friend and as free from any aftermath of their affair as if it had never happened, "what on earth are you doing in London?" Then she turned to Charles at her elbow and remarked, lightly, "Dear, you remember Count Monaci in Rome?" which was perhaps the most unnecessary remark of the year. Charles wheezed his greeting through teeth muffled by a small sandwich and Sally promptly drew Alberto aside. They stood protected by one of the pillars.

When Charles was rotated to London Sally had decided to write feature profiles of people in the public eye. She had a reservoir of material among the important people she knew in Paris and Rome as well as London and simple entrée to many she did not. Vincent Emery, the editor of one of the big national circulation papers, and a prestige paper at that, told her to try a few profiles and show them to him. She did this, painstakingly and well, and seldom in the long record of the historic "no" to newspaper applicants has anyone received a job so fast. Emery knew he had something before he finished the first paragraph, his face breaking into a broad grin. "Mrs. Benson," he said, in open pleasure, "we want you on our paper."

"I'm Sally Bryce in the paper," she replied.

"Pretty name."

"It's my name," Sally smiled. "My, I'm glad you like my work." It was as simple as that. Her first piece appeared the next Sunday: a full-dress piece on Lady Nancy Astor, and the remarkable thing about it was that Sally made the worn-out subject sound fresh.

Italy had been an Ally. Now, of course, under Mussolini relationships were badly strained. Alberto, Sally realized, knew much. This Italian was also a solid friend of England and her United States. "Profile" popped into her mind the instant she saw him. The idea had cleared itself within the interval that Charles gulped the sandwich and wheezed his hello. Action.

"Alberto, dear Alberto," she said in genuine friendliness, "I want to do an article about you in my paper."

"Me?" he laughed. "Why, Sal, I can't imagine such a thing; who would want to read it? I'm not famous, you know, Sal. I can't imagine it."

"Well, I can," she answered. And when her article appeared in the mass-circulation paper the way she wrote it, this was the best thing that ever happened to Count Alberto Monaci, officially, socially or by any other yardstick.

Alberto, of course, was Sally's private source on Italian matters regarding what was happening in Rome during the crisis which resulted in Munich, and whether Mussolini would accept Chamberlain's urgent call to mediate with Hitler. And, at last, when the dictator replied and the House of Commons went wild with "Peace is saved," Monaci had delivered this note from the Italian Embassy to the British Foreign Office the moment it had been decoded.

He knew Chamberlain had received the paper and read it before he made his self-serving speech on the last chance for peace, and had so dramatically interrupted himself with the "information" in the middle of it.

Monaci had the facts. Sally had the typewriter. And these were the first words of her piece: "Prime Minister Neville Chamberlain yesterday perpetrated a parliamentary fraud . . ."

# 7

FRANK HAD SAID a hundred times that he would stay out of politics, and Janet had been quietly relieved by each declaration. In Braidwood, as early as the acclaim for his arbitration of the Herrin strike, Frank had been spoken of for Congress. A Will County Citizens' Committee felt him out. The *Braidwood Star* even made open references to these feelers. Most importantly, old man Mayo tried to persuade him to run.

"You would have the support of the Committee, Frank," he had said, "because you would have the support of this town. Do it, my boy, we all want you."

"No," Frank observed pedantically, although naturally pleased by such a warming sign of affection and respect, "that's a different business, Mr. Mayo. If I went to Washington I would regard my election as the constituents' mandate to use my judgment and not theirs. I think this is the real meaning of representative government. Then, if this community did not like what I did in the House of Representatives, I would think they should throw me out at the next election. While on the job, I would not perform on the basis of bewildering voices from the folks back here at home. That only leads to pressure groups, and government by pressure groups is the least democratic government of all. Government by appointment or by special blocs, loud and howling, is not American Democracy. But, Mr. Mayo, that isn't the way voters operate. Politics is not for me, and I just don't want to get mixed up in it."

Mr. Mayo had tried again after Frank's defense of the Harpers, this time with Jim McCarthy, the grateful Harpers themselves, and several others. As they clustered in Frank's office, his answer was the same: "The politician who is not free, or is afraid, to have a mind of his own and do what he wants based on his own convictions but, instead, tries to puzzle out the weights and counterweights of organized groups is not leading the life for me. He is merely a paid agent. And he is an agent, furthermore, of whatever group is the most articulately greedy.

"This could even apply to the United Mine Workers of America, my own client, sometimes. What about that? You know I would never patronize organized labor or any other special group just to win votes. I don't have to be a Congressman, you know. Politics is just not for me, friends, not for me." Those urging the hope finally realized that this was the way it was to be.

But Frank's conviction, spread across his mind like the varnish that covers an old painting, was wiped away by the rubbing-off process of an important event.

Conviction? Contradiction? Contradiction is a cardinal element of life and of itself it may be no contradiction. Contradiction has its place in human nature. It is neither true nor false. It *is*. And in the time and place that this contradiction occurred, Frank did not think of it as a contradiction at all.

On the national political scene the field of action was clarifying itself; as in Shakespearean versions of medieval battles when opposing armies take up their positions in full view of one another while the generals ride about from place to place making declamatory speeches. And then an electric thing had happened.

The President seized the coal mines of the nation.

It was a Sunday evening. Philip Winston Allen was at Sea Island, starting a shooting holiday on the dunes of this retreat off the Georgia coast. The miners' union and the association representing the coal operators of the nation had failed to reach agreement on new contracts, after long and intense negotiations.

The union gave the previously agreed ninety-six-hour notice of a strike call, effective at 12:01 A.M. that Monday. Three hours before the midnight moment, while the press of America stood in the White House corridors, the President of the United States issued his Executive Order.

It directed the Secretary of Commerce (a Mr. Billings) forthwith to take possession of the plants, facilities, and other properties of more than two hundred named companies. It stated that the seizure was made "by virtue of the authority vested in me by the Constitution and laws of the United States, and as President of the United States and Commander in Chief of the armed forces of the United States." Billings was to decide the wages and working conditions. All must obey under penalty of arrest.

Alfred Caxton was in Europe. But before Allen could reach him by cable from Sea Island, he had a message from Caxton that he was coming home. "Incredible," Caxton wired. "Will be aboard *Aquitania* tomorrow." And by the time Philip reached the Whitehall Building Monday afternoon, nineteen of the thirty-nine partners were waiting for him in the conference room. Allen, Van Biber, Caxton & Shaw were the attorneys for the coal mine owners association.

The Sunday night radio flash had activated one of the great and significant cases of Allen's era.

There are some who do know the frightful cost of historic errors which quickly become impossible to correct. Allen regarded this Presidential action as one. Yet his thesis was only as good as its provability. That set the task in this room.

Churchill's sense of words was drawn from his own special reservoir, from which Lincoln also drew, fed by Shakespeare and the Tudor clerics who wrote the first prayer book for Edward VI and their Jacobean successors who translated the Bible. Allen's words were Blackstone, interpreted by Philip Winston Allen. He wanted to shorten the suspense, and spoke at once.

"The President has acted in an emergency, true. But there is no right way to do a wrong thing. The nation's leader relies on a doctrine of executive necessity: Presidential immunity from constitutional limitations in the emergency. If the present executive can define the emergency himself and then so perform, what is the result? A clear precedent is established by which this President or some future executive can by arbitrary action compel obedience to whatever conditions he may choose to impose. Who is to define every emergency? If such power is restrained only by a President's own definition of an emergency, what independent restraint is there? And, how long will restraints remain, in other directions?

"Our system of government has no place for any such concept of arbitrary powers. If once established in this free land, these must be finally fatal to our liberties. And if we do not intend to create free and independent citizens this nation has gone to a great deal of trouble and expense for nothing.

"This seizure of properties, including the President's threatened unilateral changes in wages and working conditions," the bristling giant continued, "is unlawful. By God, it is unlawful.

"The Constitution does not need to be liked or approved; it has to be obeyed. I believe these seizures are completely without authority under the Constitution and laws of the United States. They are, in my opinion, at least, contrary to the traditions of the common law on which the Constitution was founded. They are not warranted, and cannot be upheld, I believe, by the Constitution itself—either in its terms or as construed from the beginning of our Republic until now. The big battle at issue here is regarding the worth of law; the worth of law."

Frank sat at the end of the table. Shaw was on his right. Sam sat close behind Frank to take notes for him as Allen went along. But to Allen what he had said was the whole of it. The rest would be explanation. It would be an explanation, however, that would summon the work of many, many people, and under the intense pressure of the brief time allowed before the pleading in this emergency action.

It would involve eight of these Allen, Van Biber, Caxton & Shaw partners directly, the supporting staffs of twelve more, and six additional law firms from various parts of the nation as associate counsel and as direct representatives of various defendants demanding consultation. Surely a thousand men, all told. Allen's policy would also involve the whole bibliography of the legal world from the very beginning of common law, in the great and contradictory problem of finding and annotating and documenting the laws' creeds. And, finally—in the end—it would involve a decision.

Frank would plead the great case; his voice would be the voice speaking to the Supreme Court.

The central responsibility for Allen's policy and the authority behind it was Allen's.

Sam Welsh had rung for Mary-Louise to help share the note-making, for what Allen outlined now, legally buttressed by the case-findings, would be the wisdom Frank would plead when the curtain lifted and he stepped before the Supreme Court.

"This claim by a chief executive is not a new one, of course," Allen said quietly. "It is precisely the claim which was at the root of centuries of bloody struggle to overcome the absolutism of the British Crown. It was precisely the threat against which the founding fathers established safeguards here by specifically limiting executive power in the framing of the Constitution of the United States.

"It is precisely that claim which was made more than three centuries ago by James the First of England when he asserted that it was treason to maintain that the King was under the law. It is precisely the claim for which Charles the First lost his life and James the Second his throne. And, most importantly, it is precisely the claim for which George the Third lost his American colonies.

"In short, it was the continued effort of the British Crown to exercise unfettered prerogative that culminated in the War of Independence and the establishment of the United States under the government provided in othe Constitution.

"The founding fathers made it clear that, in establishing the office of the Presidency, they were creating a position of far more circumscribed powers than those then attributed to the Crown. This idea remains a sacred poem, and it is the safety hatch of all our liberties. Obviously, without it human nature would run amuck; just as our President did Sunday night.

"The provisions of the Magna Carta were absorbed into the principles of the common law. They were well established as a part of that law when Sir John Fortescue, for eighteen years Chief Justice of the King's Bench, somewhere around the year 1468 wrote his famous treatise, *De Laudibus Legum Angliae*.

"Gentlemen, in a matter as complex as this and with the enormous power of a government already committed against us by its action, we must find and select a central theme, a keel for our approach, hammer at it, document it, stick with it and prove it. For if we choose the right fundamental, because we have chosen an applicable fundamental, and prevail, the government's entire position falls like a house of cards. Gentlemen, we will fight on the magnificent foundation of *De Laudibus Legum Angliae*. And, by God, we'll win."

Allen looked the length of the table. "Mr. Killory," he said, "will you please do me the favor of intense study or restudy of an old man's choice: *De Laudibus Legum Angliae?*" Then he went on, slowly, his eyes roving the ceiling.

"Our thesis will be to contrast the limited constitutional powers of the British Crown as they existed even as early as the War of the Roses, with the arbitrary powers of the kings on the continent. It is still sanctified, gentlemen, by the island's eastern channel, whose floor is white with the bones of Englishmen.

"We must go on and point out that the controversies between the Crown and Parliament came to a head under Charles the First in the celebrated *Case of Ship Money—The King v. John Hampden,* in 1637." He turned to William Shaw. "Mr. Shaw," he said, "correct me if I am wrong, but I think this is reported in 3 Howell's State Trials 866."

"It's 826, sir," Shaw answered. "I'll work through on that, and I'm sure Alfred will want to as well."

"No, Bill, no," Allen said. "I want Alfred—and by the way, when does the *Aquitania* dock?—I want him up to his ears in the *Case of Prohibitions,* 12 Coke's Reports 63. Hazel, remind me of that, please.

"In the reign of James the Second the controversy broke out afresh," Allen continued. "The King claimed the power in cases of urgent necessity to dispense with the laws. Finally, when the King pushed the matter too far by indicting for seditious libel those who opposed his views, there was, as you will recall, a reaction.

"In the *Case of the Seven Bishops,* Mr. Justice Powell declared that the claimed royal prerogative 'amounts to an abrogation and utter repeal of all the laws.' "

Eying a specialist at the far end, he said, "Mr. Ashley, will you please supply this case fully for all of us.

"In any event, the culmination was the exile of James the Second and the passage under his successors of the English Bill of Rights." His big hand stroked a heavy book on the table. "Thus, by the start of the eighteenth century, the English people, after a long and frequently bloody struggle, finally established that the Crown was under the law and it was clear that the seizure of property without the authority of the people through Parliament was illegal. The President's seizure of this property was illegal, and all the law in the meanwhile, I am convinced, will support a contention of tyranny here.

"It was against this background that our founding fathers drafted our Constitution. The constitutional debates, as reported in Madison's, reveal with graphic clarity and as plain as a blue whale that the delegates had firmly in mind the recent excesses of the English Crown against the colonies and the long and costly struggles that had been waged by the people of England and other European countries, such as Holland, before the royal power had been circumscribed and placed under the law.

"Some delegates had differences about a few of the Constitution's provisions, but on this provision against tyranny, they were unanimous, clear, and exceedingly concrete. Wouldn't you be, had you been sitting there among them? Well, they were, and we intend to have the President of the United States find that out.

"It was in this framework that the delegates drafted our Constitution—all men who knew at first hand the evil and danger resulting from personal power in unfettered exercise, and many of them lawyers deeply read, I am happy to say, in the law of the mother country. It is against this real fear that the provisions of the Constitution must be considered. This was why, and this was the moment, that Houdon said of Benjamin Franklin that 'he snatched the thunderbolt from heaven and the scepter from the tyrant.'

"Good Franklin's hot liver swole with angry bile. Ours do now. I want no man working on this case who is not angry about it, for, my good dear friends, any man who loves the United States of America must be angry on this day."

Allen meant it; and he said it with a roar of indignation and outrage. Shaw looked at Frank. The younger partner leaned toward him. "Bill," he whispered, "I don't like to see the old man get as mad as this. It's just not good for him."

Allen went on, his tone low but each word as clear as the clap of a hammer.

"Lincoln's Emancipation Proclamation was purely a war measure, *flagrante bello;* eminently legal. It recited that it was to operate solely against enemy property in Confederate territory. The Supplemental Proclamation of January first, 1863, by which the original Proclamation was put into effect, specifically exempted all of Tennessee and West Virginia then occupied by Federal troops.

"Slaves in those areas, as well as the border states of Kansas, Delaware, Maryland and Missouri, did not receive their legal freedom until the Constitution was amended by the Thirteenth Amendment. Constitutionally, the initial Emancipation Proclamation in its effect on slave owners in the area of rebellion, was no different from Sherman's destruction of property on his march to the sea.

"Yet our nation's present chief executive, in an immodest, I might even say irreverent, aside to the Great Emancipator, in the petition for certiorari, has the unmitigated gall to cite among the precedents this action by Abraham Lincoln.

"It would take a scryer to look into his mind and that of his Attorney General. Our task is simpler. All we have to do, gentlemen, is to look into their actions, and with great rapidity. Our mission is freedom; our cargo, truth. If we can find their law, we can beat it."

Frank and most of the other partners laughed at this, for Allen's powerful arms were swinging in big arcs and his head was tossing like a lion as he went on. "The Constitution speaks a better language than that. These officials will discover, as Macbeth discovered, that you can murder Banquo but you cannot lay his ghost.

"They know full well that the government is not powerless to deal with the

reat to coal production. Nor did the crisis arise overnight, although I per-
nally think both the mine owners and the union have been incredibly stupid
id stubborn in the long negotiations.

"Congress provided the President with various means for dealing with the
rave matter. But neither the Congress nor the Constitution provided this
resident with any such means as he used Sunday night: seizure.

"I would certainly like to ask the present Chief Executive, and we will ask
im through the Justices on the Court, whether this President doubts that the
amers of the Constitution believed firmly that in a tripartite form of govern-
ient lay one of the surest safeguards of the people's liberties.

"Can it be that liberties have become distasteful to him since he has drunk
om the cup of power? I hope not. But power is heady wine, emergencies are
npelling, and here we are. Yet, Article I, Section 1 of the Constitution unequiv-
cally vests in Congress alone all legislative powers granted. In this action the
resident refers to 'the authority vested in me as Commander in Chief of the
med forces of the United States.' Rubbish. This is mere tripe, and utterly
nfusing to the public.

"It is indisputably clear that the President's military power as Commander
i Chief is limited to a command or executive function—the direction of the
med forces. The President's military functions, so help me, do not encompass
ny power to legislate on war or related questions. It is high time we helped to
ut a healthy stop to the country's mixed-up thinking about a President as
ommander in Chief, smacking as it sometimes does of the implication that he
somehow Commander in Chief of the nation. Not this nation, oh, no. Nor has
ie judiciary in the past felt itself powerless to declare the illegality of Presi-
ential orders delivered on the point of his military sword.

"In *Little v. Barreme*, 2 Cranch 170, 179—Mr. Schwartz, will you please
ipply this case for all of us, if you don't mind?—the Supreme Court observed
f an unlawful seizure order issued by the President to a naval officer, as
)llows: 'The instructions cannot change the nature of the transaction, nor
:galize an act which, without those instructions would have been a clear
·espass.'

"Court further held that since the President's order was illegal, it furnished
o protection to any naval officer who acted under it, and that the Captain
ittle involved was therefore liable for damages, poor man." Allen chuckled.
This will show all of you," he said, "what can happen to you when you obey
·ders.

"I think the case is especially noteworthy as a decision in our battle since it
·as rendered by a great Federal Chief Justice, speaking for a unanimous
·ourt, declaring invalid a wartime order issued by the very Federalist Presi-
ent who had appointed him to the bench. As you know, it is cited by Cooley,
·rinciples of Constitutional Law, and it is sure as hell going to be cited by
llen, Van Biber, Caxton and Shaw!

"The government cites, as substantially their sole authority on this branch
f the argument, *Mississippi v. Johnson*. Rubbish, again. Utter rubbish. That

decision, I may remind you, held only that the President could not be re
strained under specifically cited conditions, not one of which is a million mile
from this issue. Neither *Mississippi v. Johnson*—why they dug this up I haven
the faintest idea—nor any other case can be twisted into meaning that th
Supreme Court of the United States cannot perform its historic duty of holdin
subordinate officials of the government to account for their unlawful or uncon
stitutional acts. And, by God, we will tell them that, too.

"Probably we shall never know what arguments the President used t
persuade the Attorney General, or vice versa, in this seizure, for it is improb
able that either of them will run the risk of immortal ridicule by giving awa
the secret. But the law—gentlemen, the law—is the only bugle call, the onl
cockcrow, the only armed archangel that can chase a politician from the artif
cial paradise of his own self-aggrandizement and of his own rationalizations.

"A free nation cannot wait for a man to discover for himself that he
employing tyranny. If so, it would be already too late. This applies even whe
a man's intentions are of the best and he fails to realize the direction in whic
he is taking the nation, or the direction a successor in the White House coul
take it under the conditions he sets.

"No man is the government in this greatest nation on the face of the eartl
The people are the government. For the moment our opponents may seer
strong, but they are also wrong. Gentlemen, your road lies ahead."

Allen's gaze roamed along the faces in this group. Some of these are youn
people, he thought. Good. Good. He put his hands on the edge of the tabl
and arose.

"My warmest congratulations go to you," he said, "accompanied by prid
in my small association with a most important event in your lives."

The meeting broke up. As the group reached the door, Hazel came in an
handed Allen a radiogram. Pausing, he opened the envelope. It was a brie
message from Alfred Caxton aboard the *Aquitania* at sea. Allen chuckled as h
handed it to Frank. "TELL KILLORY TO SATURATE HIMSELF WITH DE LAUDIBU
LEGUM ANGLIAE," it read.

# 8

RANK WON THE CASE. By a decision as consequential as any in the present ntury, the Supreme Court of the United States rebuffed a President's seizure power.

This complied with the national mood; overnight, an intelligent, fearless d dedicated figure walked into the hearts of countless millions. In Frank the tion saw, as the Braidwood courtroom had seen, a Patrick Henry. He em-died a classic example of American individualism; its hope, its history, its ritage. Here was a magic merger of erudition and eloquence, supported on e solid foundation of integrity.

The valor, the gallantry, of Frank Killory standing for America against the reat of great individual power, the democratic spark in the American soul hich rallies to the defender of our liberties, the voice which was more than a ice because it was also a conscience—all these factors and the political cli-ate itself brought about one of those electric upsurges which occasionally veep nations and find an instant response in the minds of millions: Killory ust be President of the United States.

Nothing could have been less realistic or politically more improbable. Yet, an by man, family by family, somehow the grass-roots blades began to grow this desire. And in the forefront of the growth were the women. Frank was rne on the shoulders of the Supreme Court.

Then a visitor entered his life, prophetic as the three classic knocks before e curtain goes up in a French theater. He had never seen Walter Karnes efore Karnes walked into the office; a triangular man with a triangular face, a ell-shaped nose, a firm mouth, intelligent eyes, and a note of cordiality in his ice. In his handshake his fingers were like steel clamps.

An atmosphere of civic virtue surrounded this visitor, and it was justified. rank knew Karnes was a man of brains, fiber and character and that he was a ower in national politics. All this was attached to Karnes' business reputation. urther, he was an important member of his party's National Committee; a arty regular.

"Mr. Killory, hurrah for you!" he said. "By God, I didn't think this country ad anybody like that around any more."

Frank's answers to such sayings had long since been reduced to mumbles. Ie could only again mumble his thanks. But a new note came into this con-ratulation that distinguished it from all others. Karnes put an official touch ito it: the first. "Mr. Killory," Karnes stated, "my party is hopelessly divided. enator Means and Senator Willis are both able, honest men. But they seldom

agree on anything. Both are great Americans, really. Yet because their view
personalities and appeals are so different they have, as you know, very differer
followers. Actually, in my small opinion, either of them would make a splendi
President of the United States."

"I know what you mean," Frank said, for this was the famous dilemm
Karnes' party faced.

"It is a tragedy that the lines within the party are crystalizing," Karne
continued, "and, frankly, I do not blame either of the candidates as much as
blame some of their followers. If Senator Means is nominated at the conventio
next July, it can be only over the dead bodies of Willis' delegates. If Willis i
nominated we'll be lucky of Means' delegates don't all but walk out of th
convention hall. The feelings may not appear on the surface to be that stron;
Mr. Killory, but they are underneath. Moreover, these antagonisms are boun
to grow as the nominating time comes closer."

Frank interrupted him. "Mr. Karnes," he said, "I know both these mer
not well, but I know them. I'd trust either one of them with the Presidency, :
anybody can perform that impossible job at all."

"Absolutely! Absolutely!" Karnes stated. "I couldn't agree with you mor
But emotions kick this fact downstairs. First, there's the bitter rivalry abou
who should be nominated. The real horror in this is that the followers of bot
candidates are convinced—and claiming it from the housetops—that if th
other man is nominated he cannot win the election. 'Why nominate a loser'
they're yelling. That's a fine kettle of fish. It ruins the after-election willingnes
of the party's workers to work together. They are split into committed faction
at the precinct level. It's party fratricide, Mr. Killory, and fratricide with
vengeance. The only possible solution would be if Means or Willis won in a bi
enough way at the convention to unite the party. But there it is."

Frank laughed. "Well, if I were the opposing party and its candidate I'
figure I was in the catbird seat."

"Exactly."

"What do Senator Means and Senator Willis say about this?"

"Each is determined not to give in to the other—thinks the party woul
make a fatal mistake by nominating the other. Each thinks he can unite th
party after the election. They're human, and they think this because they war
to think it, and because it's been done several times in the past." Karnes spok
ruefully. Frank fell silent and pressed his hands across his eyes as his visito
continued. "It was before my time on the National Committee, but the part
became united even after the Chicago convention when Illinois' Governo
Frank Lowden and General Leonard Wood were deadlocked beyond any pos
sible concession, one to the other.

"It's always sounded as if the delegates to that convention were just sittin
in the auditorium like trained apes while the politicians in the Blackstone
famous 'smoke-filled room' chose a President of the United States, as if that
the way both parties are run. The nonsense ignores the fact of the deadloc
entirely, and that Senator Harding, Ohio's favorite son, was the only candidat

committed in all the Lowden-Wood countercharges. Thus Harding was, in
t, the only candidate on whom the Lowden and the Wood delegates could
ree."

"You think it's as bad as that this time?" Frank asked.

"Worse. It used to be said, 'You can't make the White House from the
nate.' The reason was sound, and remains sound. As far back as Webster,
lhoun and Clay the Senate usually contained many men of far greater sta-
e than the man chosen for President. It still does. But by the time you climb
gh in the Senate you are publicly on record about so many controversial
ues that both the party and the nation are divided about you, as is true of
ans and Willis today.

"Warren Harding never committed himself to anything in an important
y in the Senate, which is how the nomination could go to him under the
adlock circumstances. This allowed Harding to be the first Senator to bypass
e 'prominent Senator' obstruction since Senator Benjamin Harrison was
cted to the White House in 1888. But few men in public life today are
mmitted to more things, and for longer, than Senator Means and Senator
illis."

Frank was completely absorbed. It was late and Mary-Louise had waved
om her door that she was leaving, but he did not see her. His chin touched his
est and he was holding his head in both hands. Every once in a while, he
ought to himself, you run across someone who clearly knows his business, is
turally wise and level-headed and who has no axe to grind, and this man
rnes is one of them. "And who do you think can be nominated?" he asked.

"You could, Mr. Killory," Karnes answered, as quietly as in a commonplace
eeting to a friend in the hallway.

Frank opened his mouth, but no word came out. Then he said, "Well, Mr.
rnes, I know a little about politics, as everyone does. It's a business of its
n. I have no illusions about this bubble that has put my name in the papers
ice the case in Washington. Do you know a more popular American indoor
ort than talking about who should be President when elections approach?"
e shook his head. "Oh, no, Mr. Karnes, I've no standing whatever in the
rty, or in the nation, really, and, if you don't mind my saying so, I am
aazed that, with your practical experience, you would come here and talk
out it, kind as you are."

Frank suddenly heard, loud and clear, a strong oath come from the lips of
alter Karnes. "Mr. Killory, I didn't come here because I'm a dreamer, or
cause my friends who think as I do about this are desperate. We believe it
uld happen and we believe it would be a wonderful thing for the country if it
d."

Who is to know how well off he is when he is well off? What dismays,
astrations, elusive yearnings and uncrystallized ambitions—and what erosions
an lie latent in the blood. How easy it is to forget sometimes that the wish
r progress toward one's goal and the cost of the wish can be two different
ings. When is it that something more is too much?

It was 4:35* in the afternoon on that November day. And it was at t
moment, as on the day that Napoleon left Elba and invaded France by hims
that Frank's life found its sharp and apparent need. From that moment forwa
he devoted himself to becoming President of the United States.

The first contact from out of town came from Chicago, and it came ve
fast. Jacob Morton was on the telephone. "Hello, Frank, hello, you so and s
he shouted. "Walter Karnes was out here. Frank, my boy, I want you to co
out here and make a speech. Yes I do, you come and we'll take good care
you, that we will! I'm on the program committee of the Executives' Club. Y
know the Executives' Club. Best platform in the Midwest; one of the best in t
entire country. They'll be overjoyed, my boy; all the newspaper and air peo
will cover it. No doubt about it. Walter Karnes knows them all. Every wc
you say at the Sherman Hotel here will go every place in the United States."

"Wait a minute," Frank tried to interrupt. But Morton went on. "I ne
about two weeks to get ready. If the club has a speaker for its next regu
lunch—and I'm afraid they have because they work pretty far ahead for th
program—I'll bet I can get them to have a special lunch day for the occasion."

"Jake—Jake, wait a minute—"

"Oh, Frank, I'm just talking. But don't tell me there's no chance. Wal
Karnes has forgotten more about practical politics than ninety percent of th
fellows will ever know. And, there's another thing—"

"What's that?"

"Well, you know most of the Mid-Continental area managers across t
country from your old days. We have a good many more now. They're in l
cities, of course: twenty-eight big centers, all told. I'm bringing every one
these men in here next week. We're going to put on a regular pep-talk to the
and it's going to be about you, Frank boy. That's what it's going to be about."

"Why, Jake! My God, you really—"

"Our whole central office is going to send them back where they ca
from with a program; a program to make the biggest, loudest holler in t
U.S.A.—they and their friends and everybody they can collar in the twen
eight cities!"

What a great crowd they really are, Frank thought as he listened with
warm feeling of pride which Janet would share with him that night.

"As you realize," Jake continued in his husky voice, "they know all t
newspapers in their cities and the public forums, if any, and every kind of ci
organization there is. They'll tie them all in like a Buffalo Bill roundup, or r
name isn't Jacob Morton. But, Frank, all of us out here think we should pit
most of this activity around the local women's associations, and I think tha
right. Tell me something; for heaven's sake how did you get such a high-pow
appeal with the females—my wife included? So help me, they think you lit t
moon!"

"Hey! You're way out ahead of yourself."

---

* Secretaries leave early in that office.

"I'm ahead of nothing. By God, this country needs you. The crowd that's nning this country is ruining this country and we're going to hell in a basket. at's the way it is: just as you said in the Court, the President of the United ites has gone hog-wild.

"Frank, you're a big man. Yes, this country needs you—and how! Take it sy. Watch your health, boy. You've got friends. I'll wire you the date we line for the starter here. Make it a good starter. We know you will. Make that eech ring, boy; you can. It will kick off a chain reaction across this country e Patrick Henry on a bicycle. Our men will be set in the twenty-eight cities then. They'll be ready to roll with all the other things."

"Roll with what other things? What do you mean, Jake?"

Jake paused a moment, as if closing his eyes and seeing the vision. Then went on. "Within one minute after you go off the air; exactly on the button, ere are going to be phone calls throughout those twenty-eight cities, letters to e editors, Killory speakers volunteering all over the place, paid ads endorsing u by the best citizens we can find. And, Frank, listen to this," he breathed. 'wo days later, because it has to look like we had time to do it after—not fore—your speech, two days later in the downtown districts in all twenty- ;ht cities, at lunch time that day, the prettiest girls our people can grab are ing to pass out ten million campaign buttons, Frank. T-e-n—ten million. LLORY FOR PRESIDENT.

"Make it a good speech, Frank. Make it sing, boy! Make it sing! And, just e more thing." There was a pause. "Bring Janet with you," Jake said. "We'll ed her for the photographs, you know."

Frank stared at the phone as he put it down. This was Jake—Jake Morton alking like this about him. He could see Jake waiting for him in his office in e Forrest Building, his big brief case in his lap, on only the third day after he me back from the war. The Mid-Continental account made possible the use—Janet's and his house, where Margaret and Jan were born—the founda- n of their life, really, which Janet spoke about often, even to this day.

It is always nice to be honored, even by people and organizations who do t know you, he thought, but to be respected and honored by men who have own you all these years, worked with you, gone through a great deal with u in good times and bad—this is the most touching thing that can happen to nan, to a worker with others. We pass this way only once. If those who know best can feel like this, it puts some purpose in life, after all. "There are no ysical scales to measure a man's worth to his fellows, but those who know u best must respect you and believe in you." Aunt Margaret had said that. s, he mused, the test is not how far I have got, but what do good people ink of what I am doing. Very slowly, Frank bent over across the desk and his ad dropped into the crook of his arm. The catch in his breath and the isture in his eyes came from the tenderness and gratitude in the good heart a very good man.

"Dear, dear Jake," Janet said when Frank reached Glen Cove that night d she met him at the Long Island Rail Road station. "But, Frank, I didn't ow Jake had anything to do with politics."

"He hasn't, honey. I'm sure he never has—any more than his father ev
had or than I ever had. I think Jake and the Chicago crowd just got themselv
all excited somehow. Anyway, Jake is no politician, that's certain. But, hon
isn't it nice of the headquarters gang to feel like this, and think up all this a
want to do it!"

"I think it's just absolutely wonderful of them. Oh, Frank, they're so pro
of you. And they ought to be—they've known you all these years." Her ar
reached around him, holding him close in the car. "But there isn't a living so
and there never will be a living soul, as proud of you as I am."

"Hey, look out," he bellowed. "Want me to run this car up a lamppos
They both laughed and there was a great deal of gaiety and satisfaction wi
each other as they drew into the driveway and blew the horn to let Jan a
Margaret know they were home.

"Amateurs!" Frank said, when they started into the house, his arm foldi
her to him as they walked, just as it had under the fairyland lights in Cent
Park the night before their wedding, years ago.

"Hello, folks," the two girls called from their upstairs windows.

"Hi!" And then Frank repeated to Janet: "Absolute amateurs! What do y
know, honey: amateurs fooling around in the big league!"

"They're not fooling around, Frank dear. They're your friends. They knc
you. Who ever heard of anybody knowing anybody who ought to be Preside
of the United States. Why, darling, I'm just proud they think that much of yo
no matter what happens. I think Jake is just wonderful. And I'll bet h
absolutely right about Mr. Karnes. Mr. Karnes is no amateur."

"No, he's not."

"Anyway, it will be the best speech they ever heard, dear. 'Make it sin
he said. I know what he means."

"Janet, I want you to come with me; and Jake wants you to come. You'
in this as much as I am, of course, honey. If Karnes' idea gets off the ground
will be because of you as much as anything."

"Oh, Frank. Stop it!" she laughed. "I'm just a prop, but I'd like to be
good prop. For heaven's sake—it's already happened. Myrtle Jones called r
up today to ask me for lunch. I haven't heard from Myrtle Jones for ten yea
and I don't care if I don't hear from her for ten more. But there she was, on t
phone.

"Well, Myrtle never did anything in her life without a purpose, nev
since we were girls in Oak Park. I thought to myself: Well, well, this talk abo
Frank must be getting around if it gets Myrtle on the telephone with me. O
yes, darling, it's already started and I've already started being a prop."

Sam Welsh was in Sam Welsh's heaven. All this recognition and approv
simply endorsed his knowledge of Frank; his prideful knowledge of him a
his abiding affection for him.

"Who has worked with Frank Killory as long as I have, Min? Nobod
Since the day we started in the Braidwood office, who has seen him in his u
and downs like I have?"

"Well, Janet, of course," his wife replied.

"Oh, I don't mean like Janet. I mean—things in the office. Frank's prog-
ss, you know. Who?"

"Nobody."

"I told you way back then, when I hadn't been in the Forrest Building a
lid thirty days, that Frank Killory was a big man. And I told Frank, too. I
member one day like yesterday. He was plenty sunk that day!" Sam chuck-
l, "It was the letter from Jake Morton's father. Wow! I'll never forget it.
ank Killory is my oldest friend."

Sam had talked shortly before with the Allen, Van Biber, Caxton & Shaw
fice manager. He explained that some of his boss' extracurricular activities
eant that he, Sam, would need another office to take care of these properly.
uld he use the room opening on the opposite side of Frank's office, the one
at had the door to the outside hall? Could the manager have the files re-
oved and a phone put in, or, better, two phones? Then a little furniture
ould finish off the problem and everything would be fine; nobody inconveni-
ced or disturbed. The deed was done the same evening.

So there Sam sat from early morning until night—earlier trains in from
tlantic Highlands and later trains back—for Sam, pale and perky, now ruled
the man you talked to before you talked to the man everybody was talking
out.

Philip Winston Allen was not involved in all this, and, in fact, hardly
vare of it. He had left, gleefully, for a long holiday immediately after the
'ashington decision; released on Decision Day from the hours on hours of
aseless effort that had cooped him in the Whitehall Building office.

"I'm off to Antibes," he bellowed to Hazel the very next morning, so early
at few of the staff were even there and Frank and the other partners on the
se were, of course, still in Washington. "Cable me at George Hanson's villa if
ey want anything. Goodbye, sweet Hazel, good luck. Goodbye," he said,
ving her the bear hug of a happy man.

He allowed neither her, nor anyone, any time to blurt out congratulations;
isappearing like the Sahara lion that hides himself in the rays of the sun to
oid being seen by the dazzled hunters.

Caxton and Shaw were in charge of the firm. They had met Walter Karnes
hen he came to see Frank; both knew Karnes and both—especially Shaw
approved Karnes' mission. As for the rest of the partners, and the staffs up
nd down the three floors of the office, all degrees of excitement seized them,
nging from Marion Thomas, the chief switchboard operator, who felt as if
ie were preparing already for White House duties, to young Johnny, a file-
om boy and his unidentical twin brother who viewed any enthusiasm for any
artner with utter disgust.

"I don't think he's got a Chinaman's chance," Johnny would insist to any-
ne not too far his superior. But as his forum was largely his twin and the clean-
ng woman, the damage to office morale was not noticeable. On the whole, there
as a stir of excitement, good will and general pleasure in the whole "esca-

pade" (as Caxton called this development). It was too early for a feeling
anxiety.

That note was to come from Janet. And the source of it was a woma
About a week before the Chicago speech, scheduled for December fifteen
the phone rang in the Glen Cove house. Jan had come in and answered it. T
voice said that Mrs. Archibald Scriver was on the line and wanted to speak
Mrs. Killory. Janet was only passingly puzzled by the name, strange to her; b
when she said hello she knew at once that she was speaking to the Mrs. Scriv
she had met at a Creek Club skeet match only the day before.

"This is Grace Scriver," the babbly voice announced. "We met yesterd
when you were with the Dillinghams. I'm so sorry not to have had a chance
talk with you."

"Oh, yes, Mrs. Scriver. I had to leave just then, I'm sorry."

"Well, I did want to speak to you about your husband."

"Yes?"

"You see, my husband is an immense admirer of your husband. They ha
never met, but like so many people both Arch and I feel as if we know him
we do one of our own family. We think he's just wonderful, Mrs. Killory."

"Why, thank you."

"But we are worried about him, dear girl, very worried—"

"Oh, why, Mrs. Scriver?"

"—because this campaign will be a terrible strain on him, surely, and
will be on you too, dear girl. We've been through this sort of thing many tim
before, my husband and I, and we know. You see, my husband is on t
National Committee."

"Oh, he is?"

"Yes, for many, many years. He knows the ropes, so to speak, of cours
and he knows the pitfalls. And we both know how much mothering, after
fashion, it takes to be sure that a big man like your husband who is new to t
business—if I can call it that, which it is—doesn't find himself making gaffes
offending the wrong people in ways which would mean nothing in business lif
but which are fatal—absolutely fatal—in politics."

"Yes, Mrs. Scriver."

"So, Arch and I were talking last night and I told him I had run into you
the club. 'Who was she with?' he said. 'The Dillinghams,' I said. 'Oh, that's ;
right. The Dillinghams are all right.' So, there you see; but Arch and I began
wonder; because all kinds of people will be confusing you, dear, and we ju
thought that perhaps there might be some small advantage, some small a
vantage, in you and I setting up—oh, I don't know what you might call it—so
of a clearing house, not on friends, heaven forbid, of course, but on sort ‹
strangers that will surely be, in a sense, moving in on you and could really l
very, very damaging, especially now when so many of the important politic
figures in the party do not know Mr. Killory and, after all, have known bo
Arthur Means and Grant Willis for many, many years."

"Why, Mrs. Scriver, I hadn't thought—"

"Oh, I know, dear girl; but you and your husband are both in a very
erent business now, and this is what came into Arch's mind. It so happens
h is going to be in Chicago at the time your husband makes his speech.
ere is your husband staying, dear?"

"The Blackstone, I think, he always does."

"Well, the Blackstone, or wherever it is. Will you tell your husband that
h—Archibald Scriver—is looking forward to getting in touch with him
re, and to a good visit together? Will you do that please, Mrs. Killory?"
ere was a touch of condescension in the voice; a woman very proud of the
e and eminence of her family.

"And then, dear, if you can have lunch with me Thursday—that's day
er tomorrow. We live in New Jersey, you know. I'll be in town Thursday.
ppose we meet at the Colony and have lunch there. It would be delightful."

"I would—"

"Oh, surely come, Mrs. Killory. There will be just you and I alone, and I
want to talk to you so much. And, oh yes, Mrs. Killory, I mean the Colony
ib, not the Colony restaurant, you know." Janet accepted and then she
ephoned Frank.

"Archibald Scriver? I know Archibald Scriver, honey. He was the high
lder on an important painting sold at Parke Bernet not long ago. Must be a
y rich man; paid several hundred thousand dollars for the picture, if he's the
e who bought it. Yes, Archibald Scriver. Well, honey, tell Mrs. Scriver I'll be
ppy to hear from her husband out in Chicago. It's the Blackstone Hotel;
t's where you and I'll be. Jake Morton telephoned me yesterday. He's re-
ved our suite."

Mr. Archibald Scriver had opened another door.

Such men never seem to obtain quite what they wish from each useful
or they open, but important men should blame only themselves for these self-
ving satellites—and for the success they attain with their same old props of
ttery and specious self-denial.

This was a man of position and vitality; a man with a condescending smile
d perceptions as quick as a gypsy fortune teller's. He also had the easy
anner of an established bon vivant.

He lived in a golden world and would hardly be thought to have an
terest in money, although there were some who suspected that it ruled his
e—which it did.

He sat on the ballista of his wife's money and hurled himself upward: to
ore money, to influence, to circles which were whirling with significant busi-
ss or political activity, to the excitement of the theater world and the great
astelands of the motion picture industry, and, most importantly, to a little
ower here, a little power there, a little power all over the place. And, as he
w it, the Killory political outlook was as full of plum as a fruit cake.

The pack Scriver carried on his back, like Bunyan's pilgrim, was the bur-
n of utter selfishness. How could Frank give his confidence to Archibald A.
river?

# 9

Janet and Jan sat near the radio in the Blackstone suite waiting for the minu
in the Sherman Hotel ballroom that would bring Frank to them over the a
And Mrs. Rice, of course, had come in from Oak Park.

The three sat quietly. Janet could forget qualms, and she was forgetti
her qualms regarding the whole great change that was engulfing this fami
since the Supreme Court's "DD"—Decision Day—in Washington. All th
flooded her mind was that Frank was determined to raise the country and th
some millions of people, good people who loved this land, would be wanti
him to do so; her Frank, dear, dear Frank.

The toastmaster was tiresome. His introduction of Frank was long ar
pedantic.

"Who wants to hear all that?" Jan remarked, with the note of irritatic
that was nearly always a part of her voice.

Then Frank came on, speaking low at first. Janet rushed to turn up tl
dial. Her eyes were dim and misty as she heard the surge of his voice:

"Fellow Americans across our broad and mighty land. I want to speak
you about some things that are on my mind and heart.

"We have a power in this country which must not go to sleep. It is tl
power of an informed public.

"We are the victims of a mistaken leadership. There is no worse ar
unworthy mistake in public leadership than to misinform the people and ho
out false hopes and false promises soon to be swept away. Our people can fa
misfortune or peril with fortitude and even with buoyancy, but we bitter
resent being deceived or finding that those responsible for our affairs are then
selves dwelling in a fool's homestead or a politician's paradise. This situation
intolerable, unsafe and unsound in the national interest."

Frank was speaking from his full and manly heart. A roar of applau:
crossed the assembly, deafening the set. He had to pause while the toastmast
asked for quiet, quiet. A rustling sound told Janet and her mother that tl
audience was settling down.

"We need facts. Honest facts. For this nation's basic faith in the ability (
people to govern themselves implies that the more truly informed they are, th
wiser will be their decisions. If I did not believe this I would not be a believ
in America. Because that faith is America.

"Today this spirit and our system are both under attack. Are we to b
come a nation that, in our failure to defend sound principles, ceases to knov
what sound principles are? People of America, I say no!

"Not only in economics but in all phases of life, today's revolutionary sformation in the government's role sharpens the government's need to cipline itself in the basic truths and the laws of human experience. We, in , should re-shoulder our moral responsibilities as individuals and stop pass- the buck to 'forces' and 'conditions' eloquently defined by politicians but er solved by them."

Again the ballroom shook with applause. Janet and her mother and Jan the waves burst in a solid roar.

"We can only meet our nation's problems as each of us does his or her t. And the part we must play is in political action. For political difference is d democracy. It is political indifference which represents our dangers.

"When we, as citizens, do not believe in what is being done our opposition uld be honest and clear and acknowledged and on a plane and of a charac- that returns the authority in our nation to the people themselves, which is ere it belongs."

Janet's mother reached over and took both her hands in hers. Janet was ing openly now; tears of fine, deep pride that it was Frank, dear Frank, of the people in the wide, wide world, who was speaking to fellow countrymen rywhere.

"Is Pa tired?" Jan asked nevertheless. "He sounds tired."

"No, your father is not tired. Sh-h-h."

But Jan would not drop it as new applause roared out of the set and nk waited for it to subside.

"Pa sounds as if he were preaching," she said.

Her grandmother was a picture of complete indignation. "Janet," she an- red, "your father is not tired and he is not preaching. He is making a very and important speech to many millions of people all the way from coast to st. Please be quiet, and for heaven's sake pay attention. That, I think, is the st you can do."

Again the applause hardly died down before Frank continued:

"With the people's active—dynamic—participation in the affairs of our n nation wrongs can be righted. For this country was built for Faith, not r. We must make a beginning—and a great beginning—but no beginning is ugh. 'It is not the beginning of any great matter but the continuing of the e until it be thoroughly finished which yieldeth the true glory.' This was ake's prayer before the battle at Cadiz. It must be ours before the battle ay."

Then, as he drew toward the conclusion, Killory spoke what were, for the rposes of his address, the most important lines he delivered. The significance s not lost on all who heard it in the groups waiting to spring into action in ob Morton's twenty-eight cities, or all who read it in newspaper accounts, torials and air comments that followed.

There and then, Frank threw his hat in the ring.

"I am not personally disinterested," he said, in the pin-drop silence of the m. "I intend to be directly involved. And I intend to inform you of my ideas

as often as I can between now and the Presidential nomination in July. I co
only march with a party that marches to the music of the union. March with
March with me. For my party makes the music of the nation! Help us. H
me. Thank you. Thank you."

The twenty-eight cities and many, many more lit up like rockets. 1
spontaneity of the response had the crackle of a prairie fire. The whole feel o
surprised everyone who had assumed that, in any case, a Killory movem
would take an enormous amount of staging just to get it up off the ground.

They had not dreamed that the country was so ready for a leap i
nowhere, so ready to try the untried, that the combination of the politi
climate, the frustrations the country felt in choosing between the leading car
dates, and the national restlessness as a whole would ignite such a conflagrat
as this. A ratio existed between experience and bafflement. The more exp
enced the politician—knowing how very long it takes to condition the pul
mind—the more puzzled he was. Bafflement is a distasteful feeling in prof
sional politics, if not a downright derisible one, and the prevailing tone was
brush off this Killory event. Only Karnes seemed to accept Frank's Chic
results as understandable.

"It doesn't have the feel to me of a flash in the pan," said Karnes, "and
very important." Scriver, always ready to pick another's brain and always re
to rush to the aid of the victorious, summarized to Killory what Frank was
hear from then on: "Something's happened in the country," he said with
usual pompous and satisfied air.

There was a Christmas-like snow. A crowd, ignoring it, had pres
around Frank's car as it left the meeting place. Scriver announced this puff
the car on the way back to the Blackstone. "I don't know what it is, Killory, 1
I know it has happened," Scriver said, his face puckered up in a sly smile.
don't care what anybody says, they are wrong. You have a damn good chan
of being President of the United States. Killory, put it there." Scriver stuck
his hand. "I'm with you," he intoned. But Frank was distracted—the "bi
watcher mood" was upon him—while Scriver was talking. The flatness of
sponse brought a puzzled look to Scriver's face, but he said no more for
moment. This man is going to take a little knowing, he thought, watch
Frank now with a glum expression.

After about a minute Frank broke into a smile. "Walter," he said, "how
you really think it went?" Frank was speaking to Karnes.

"I think it was everything we could hope it would be. Speeches are rar
as important as the speaker thinks they are, unless he holds an official posit
and the speech has a direct bearing on events. Yours is a start, the start, an
good one. A very good one. Frank, miracles happen.

"We need the multipliers—the sources that comment on what somebody
saying: the newspapers, editorials, air comment and all. A good kick-off he
immensely in supplying the multipliers."

Frank was all attention, concentration complete. He had turned in the s
to face Karnes directly. Here was a man—a political veteran—who knew wl

was talking about. Frank's head was half forward, his eyes half closed,
ning.

"For example," Walter continued, "many a hopeful has been killed off fast,
ore he really started, by laying an egg at the Gridiron Club Dinner in
shington. The multipliers have helped others who made an early hit there.

"Men in public life become surrounded by an atmosphere. Sometimes the
osphere is undeservedly bad. Practically nothing they do or say seems to
e mass appeal and create satisfaction. Others, equally undeservedly, are
e to breeze home in the cocoon of the atmosphere which somehow sur-
nds them. The public wants them to succeed, wishes them success, and thus
s that they are a success.

"This first speech could have killed off any Killory miracle as dead as a
k in a bag. Undoubtedly, this is still a possibility. But at least we start now
h the foundation that this miracle must have."

"I agree with Walter," Scriver volunteered, without response from either
n.

"Walter," Frank said, "you feel we're off to a good start. What next? What
I do next?"

They were approaching the hotel. As they came to the canopy and the
rman opened the door, Karnes paused in the seat for a moment, the picture
lving in his mind.

"Well, Frank," he answered, "now let's not press it too hard for a while.
's let this sink in; really sink in. I wouldn't make another speech for quite a
le. Just remember a man in politics is not obligated to explain anything he
not said. And no press conference here at the Blackstone before the train
evening, Frank, or at the station either. Just how glad you are to be in
icago with so many kind and hospitable friends. Don't compete with your
n speech for space in the papers. Photographs, yes; but no more talking, I
uld suggest." And then he said a final word. "And don't forget, Frank,
ody ever listened himself into trouble."

Killory nodded. "Thanks, Walter," he laughed. "Thanks a million."

The Blackstone suite was full of Frank's Mid-Continental Insurance
nds when Frank, Walter and Arch arrived. As the cheers went up, Frank
ld hardly press through to the bedroom where Janet was backed into a
ner with Jacob Morton telling her, as he had so many times in the Braid-
od years, about that first day in Frank's office when he gave this local man
Mid-Continental account. But a reference Jake made this time touched
et deeply, and tears came as he said the words that closed in around her
rt. "Mr. Rice would be very proud of you both today," he said, "and I know
wish he were here." Janet's mother heard this from nearby. The women fell
o each other's arms, sobbing.

This is the way Frank found them. "Honey, honey," he said in some alarm,
hat's the matter? What on earth is the matter, Mother Rice?"

Janet lifted her head. "Oh, Frank," she said, "we're so proud. I don't care
at happens. You know that. But we're just so proud."

Within four days the commotion brought James Usher, one of the
tion's most important magazine publishers, to the office. And Sam Welsh I
answered telephone calls from three newspaper publishers, one of whom Fr.
knew well, who arranged visits with him.

Usher came to dinner at Glen Cove. He came alone—which of itself v
extraordinary—and he brought with him a pasted-up dummy of the foi
coming issue. He and Frank traveled to Glen Cove together and Janet took
girls out before they arrived, so that the two men could have a dinner unin
rupted by family talk and the distractions of the young people.

Generally, a meeting like this out of the city made it so late by the ti
the men could get through with their after-dinner discussion that the Glen C
trip was a great inconvenience for anyone who had to return to New York. '
formula for the disappearance of the small family was to become stand
practice in the Killory household, and even Jan did not grumble, for sv
evenings were filled in by visits to her friends or the movies.

Before that night, Frank had never seen but once the sandy, wizened li
man with the haunting expression and the flickering eyelids who afterwa
became so familiar in the councils about Killory.

"Mr. Killory," Mr. Usher said, "our people watched the effect of yi
Chicago speech with great interest. This is a very exciting development
anyone to see who is supposed to feel the pulse of the country. Sometime
think our people's pulse-reading, and certainly mine, gets very cockeyed. M;
times, I'm sorry to say, we have been as far away from what the people w
really thinking as the Happy Valley Race Track in Hong Kong. Sometimes r
Moreover, of course, it will be some while before you have any promising pl.
at all in the Gallup poll. But we think something has happened across
country and, whether it has or not, my magazines are going to give it a hell c
push."

Usher's lack of enthusiasm for both Senator Means and Senator Willis v
not intense, although his antagonism to the adminstration was famous. To p
up Killory, however, represented a major decision. It could only be the prod
of long and hot debates behind the high windows of his editorial office, a
was, beyond doubt, a prize no politician's last drop of blood could buy agai
Usher's best judgment. This meant Usher's mind had revolved in endless ı
cles, round and round, and then settled the matter with a final solid thund
clap of decision.

The pasted-up dummy he carried was a Killory biography in pictur
Page after page showed the Braidwood office and the town itself (a real sho
a view up the side of the Whitehall Building—"from this to this"—a reprint
three pictures taken outside the Supreme Court on Decision Day, Frank del
ering the Chicago speech (a close-up behind the microphones) and shaki
hands with people afterwards across the rostrum. Frank did not know all t
publicity was being processed to be read by millions the following week.
was obviously taken aback.

"Mr. Usher," he said, "I always knew you people could move fast a

ep; and I remember the night, at Kitty Barret's dinner, that you told me how
u tied in your organization to do it—the photographers, the writers and
itors and all. But, frankly, I'm amazed. And, of course, my friends and I
ank you, Mr. Usher, we thank you very much. May I keep this dummy?"

"Certainly."

"What could help even more, however, would be some guidance from you
om time to time. Politics is new to me. I don't want to fall in the black hole
st because I don't know my way in the dark, you know. If you will help me,
r. Usher, it will be a great favor."

"I have had a great deal of experience with men in politics," Usher re-
ied, "and I would like to be helpful. But that is not easy, Mr. Killory; at least
have not found it easy. Most men start out wanting advice. They get much
ore than they can use. In fact, they would have to have ten heads to even
ar all the advice they get. Most of it isn't worth a damn, because it's too often
rely proffered. I have learned this much: unless a man in public life directly
ks for specific advice it is an utter waste of time to volunteer it."

"I've asked directly, Mr. Usher, and I mean it."

"All right. But perhaps I can go a little further. You may want some of my
ople to help you on speeches, perhaps; or some of our experts—at least they
end their full time trying to be experts, and that's a start—our experts on
litics, economic issues, the state of the country, the Washington scene. I have
o in mind; a first class statistician and another who is a very brainy man. I'll
ve them get in touch with you, Mr. Killory, and they are yours as long as you
ed them."

"Well, that's certainly a real vote of confidence, Mr. Usher," Frank said,
mbly and sincerely.

"I think you can be nominated, Mr. Killory; I'll be damned if I don't,"
her answered, banging a broad palm on the table. "My magazines won't
clare for anybody. But read the magazines. It's time for some new excite-
nt in the public prints, Mr. Killory, and I don't mind telling you we relish it."

Killory laughed. "You make me sound like a movie star on the make."

"Well, not too different, perhaps, but the purpose is different. You said
mething that struck us all in that Chicago speech. You said: 'Political differ-
ce is good democracy. It is political indifference which is our danger.' You
e right as hell, Killory. What this country needs is a grass-roots sense of
rticipation in our government.

"Every editor hears every day from subscribers: 'I want to do something,
t what can I do?' Well, what they can do is to get interested, and get their
ends interested, in government. That means they need a wish. The wish must
productive. That means a man. The man must be interesting and, if pos-
le, unique.

"You are both, Mr. Killory. No matter what happens, whether you're nom-
ted or not—and I'm not even thinking of the election because that's a differ-
t problem—your underdog try for the nomination will be all to the good. Our
ople think, and I am amazed to say they agree among themselves, that we

have a duty to stir up that interest. We propose to do so as dramatically an
effectively as we can. Frankly, what your results may be is secondary, becaus
we feel that the effort itself is valuable all around whether you win or not."

The issue that came out the next week hit the nation with a terrific smas
The affiliation with Usher was the prime payoff of the Chicago day. The pow
of consistent, favorable, nation-wide publicity—no holds barred—was in th
picture now.

Among other key potentials for such support, three important newspape
chain publishers showed varying attitudes. One impressed Frank as indifferen
Frank was wrong. This man was an opponent. A staunch admirer of Senate
Grant Willis, he had stated to many others—and insisted—that Frank's talen
were "really limited to blandishments, easy language and a nice sense of th
favoring moment."

The second of the three bluntly told Frank his papers would suppo
Means and oppose him. "Further, Mr. Killory," he said, firmly but not imp
litely, "you have no possibility whatever of winning the nomination."

Frank gained more ground than he realized by treating this challenge wi
his natural humor and grace.

"Well, sir," he answered, "maybe I'm like the man in the poem. 'They to
him it couldn't be done; He smiled as he started to do it; He tackled the jo
that couldn't be done; And he couldn't do it.'"

The publisher laughed, and up-graded his ideas about Killory, as Fran
nudged him and grinned that he was going to try anyway.

But the third, Marshall Putnam, whom Frank knew well, came aboar
with flying colors. He also joined Karnes in warning Frank against anoth
major speech and multi-city appearances too soon.

"Let the public prints expose you, my friend, but don't expose any mo
concrete ideas for a while," Putnam advised, "Just let the normal course
publicity about an interesting and promising man find its own way—unpressed

"But if you doubt that it pays to advertise just consider the fact that
Colorado there are twenty-six mountain peaks higher than Pike's Peak."

Frank smiled as the publisher continued. "And, oh yes, so long as we're o
the subject of advertising, I might tell you, too, that surveys by my advertisin
people demonstrate that the ten most persuasive words in the English langua;
—and in this order—are: You, Easy, Money, Save, Love, New, Discover
Results, Proven and Guarantee. For ad headlines, that is. Use 'em, Frank, u
'em in your speedrun. And don't forget to watch your camera angles, too."

Frank's face turned sour. "Marshall," he interrupted, "you know as well
I do that that's exactly the kind of thing I abhor. I simply cannot and will n
do what doesn't come naturally to me. And I'm too old a dog to teach ne
tricks."

"Well, Frank, you have a good life and a fine reputation built throu;
many hard and creditable years. I'd say you were very well off indeed, a
doing your good share in a field where you fit marvelously. Good for yourse
and Janet and everybody. You didn't have to get into this political thing—th
special business, as you call it. You know, sometimes I wish you hadn't.

"I've watched big league politics a long time. In businesses as well, I've seen a lot of strange things happen when somebody gets a thousand percent concentrated on some particular goal—money, power, the top job in a big company, some public office or whatnot. Not just to fast operators or smart schemers. They're hardly more than a damn nuisance. But to good men—really good men. I tell you, human nature, concentrated like that, can create mighty unexpected changes in men you thought you knew well, and understood well, before this hit them. And the most lethal time bomb of all in that respect is politics."

"Well," Frank said, somewhat wanly, "there's a lot about it that I don't understand, and that I don't like. That's why I've always said politics is a special business and needs a special temperament. Out in Braidwood or any place else I never wanted to touch it with a ten-foot pole."

"Now, look, Frank," Putnam interrupted, with a note of exasperation, "in any case, my friend, you are in it. Don't blow hot and cold on this. Janet told me there was a little now-I-want-to-be-in-it-now-I-don't going around in your head. That's a waste of time and as self-defeating as anything I can imagine. You are in it. You're in it, and you're going to stay in it, at least through the convention. And the only way you will not be in it is if the Kansas City convention throws you out. Meanwhile you're going to express yourself as best you can about what you think our government should do to serve the country. Yours is a very honorable effort no matter what happens to you if you stay on the level with the American people as, of course, you will. More power to you, my good friend. By God, you're serving America, not yourself."

"Marshall, that's a very nice way to put it."

"You know who told me that, and I agreed?"

"No."

"Janet, bless her heart. Janet. My boy, you and I are the two smartest men know. We both married above ourselves."

The human and personal aspect of Putnam was famous in the newspaper field. He had a sort of perpetual agitation of ideas, and instead of progressing steadily and continuously, he was impelled to advance by leaps and bounds suitable to his kangaroo nature. In this way he threw himself on all daily developments and shook them; which meant he threw himself on the nation's leaders and shook them.

Journalistic visits were mostly forays by the editors, publishers or columnists, for Frank had become excellent copy on any score. But the affiliation between journalism and all political developments is by nature so close that these exchanges between a lively man the newspaper people liked and who liked them became the basis for his judgment on how to increase his popular appeal for the hard road ahead.

Several Midwest farm-journal editors and a most influential Southern California urban publisher (Willis territory) and another in Pennsylvania (Means territory) came to get their impressions of this newcomer and his ideas. The editor of a large women's magazine and his wife, and a very hard-boiled

Sunday supplement baron bearded him, too, about the time that Usher's smash article hit the country.

Frank wanted as much leisure as possible with each of them, and they all came out to Glen Cove, as he preferred. Janet, Jan and Margaret disappeared after a polite greeting. "Don't hurry off, honey," was Frank's ritual; but hats and coats would already be on. The little plan had not yet been swamped in the backwash of the New York center's demands on Frank's time, his movements and his mind.

Karnes, however, continually warned Frank that while his popular appeal was indispensable, it was not decisive. His national popularity would be vital at the Kansas City convention. But the nation would not be voting there. Only party members, of course, sent as delegates from each state, would be voting.

Politics was not a once-every-four-year spurt with these nine hundred men and women. For the most part it was their daily life and, to this extent, they lived in a world apart. Many would be office holders with their own re-elections to consider. This would dominate the thinking of most such delegates regarding who the Presidential nominee should be: the effect of the man on their own prospects in their own localities. While they would very much like to see their party win the White House, their even greater anxiety was their own re-election. Which candidate for the nomination would strengthen them the most locally?

These mayors, governors, congressmen, senators and other office holders, local candidates and their supporters, past and present, sitting as delegates, represented the true core of party responsibility to the party as a whole. Nearly all would be beholden to, and loyal to, the chosen leader of their state delegation. How could Frank break into these loyalties and into the multiple fortresses of self-interest?

Means and Willis both had a solid political base supplied by their Pennsylvania and California delegations. The gravitational pull of each of these bases was approximately equal. The two rivals could count on the solid support of enough other delegations to split the convention.

As Karnes had pointed out to Frank repeatedly, he had no base at all. New York State, now his home state, was foreclosed. Its governor, who controlled the delegation—the largest to sit in the convention—was a political ally of Senator Means. Somehow, Killory must revive his position as an Illinoisan, for he had no other choice.

Fortunately he had retained Braidwood as his voting residence, or even Illinois would have been impossible. Karnes had let out a sigh of relief on learning that at least this slim tie existed outside New York.

Walter went to Chicago. "The faster Killory gets to be an Illinois boy again the better it'll be," he told Jacob Morton, "and until we can lay some roots for Frank in what will be the Illinois delegation he will have no base whatever in the convention line-up. The most critical place in the United States for this whole thing is Illinois." He hardly needed to tell Morton that he had this at the top of his head in urging that the opening speech be in Chicago.

So, the problem would be delegates, and national publicity that would eap national popularity was important now only to the extent that it influnced delegates in Frank's favor and impressed on them the idea that he had a eal chance to win the nomination. And on the day of the Chicago speech the dds against that outcome, taken by a LaSalle Street bettor who made a pecialty of sporting events and elections, were a hundred to one.

With the party workers so heavily committed to either Means or Willis it vould be especially hard to generate much enthusiasm among the rank-and-file or a complete outsider. "Most of them will not want to appear disloyal to the egular party leadership," Putnam had pointed out. "The only way to stir any nthusiasm in the working ranks of the party is to have a fuse lit and a torch arried by the so-called independents. That's the only available source at this tage.

"If enough people who have never had party interests or affiliations show p at party meetings in the towns, join the party, carry the torch for Killory and 1 other ways promote the sound idea that neither of the two senators satisfies hem, and that their man is this man who can save the country, they will have a trong impact on the delegates by convention time.

"The delegates won't say so, but they fear a deadlock, too, and if our man an be established by the independents as the Deadlock Man, the right man, re open up the only hole in the line that we can go through. That's where your trength with the women counts, Frank," he said, "because the women are by nd large more disposed to be independents than the men. The independents s a whole and the women in particular are your key to the convention."

When the newspaper publisher pointed this out Frank chuckled. "Well, 1arshall," he said, "if we're going to depend on the independents you'd better tart with the ladies in my own family. They're not for any party; except they'll e pulling for their Pa."

When Putnam repeated this to Karnes it exasperated him. He told Janet nd Jan—especially addressing his remarks to the daughter—that if their lives rere to be involved in the political world they might as well understand the andamental value of the vehicle—the party—which was indispensable to the .illory's future if Frank was to serve the nation.

The occasion arose when Jan announced to him that she was an indeendent, which she did with even a little unexpected shyness, realizing the etachment this implied in relation to her father's efforts. "You know, Mr. arnes," she said, "if I could vote I'd vote for Pa and I'll shoot anybody who oesn't, but the whole idea of party membership, and declaring myself a Reublican or Democrat, is something I can't even imagine."

"Well, Jan," Karnes replied, "you will have to ask yourself, in all honesty, this is really a good definition of good citizenship, combined with the shock-1g fact that so many citizens do not get out and vote at all."

"Oh, people ought to vote—"

"Yes, but if all citizens remained independent our type of government mply could not function. I wonder if you take into account what would happen if the rival party system and party responsibility were liquidated; at the polls, in state legislatures, in Congress, and for the Presidency? In short, if everyone were, like you, an independent.

"Have any of you who speak of yourselves as independents really estimated the good that could come if a far larger proportion of the whole national body joined the party of their choice and voted in the primaries as well as the elections?"

There was nothing Jan could do to slip away. All she could do was sneeze and interrupt by asking, "Isn't there a draft, from some place? Mother, I think I'm catching cold."

"It is obvious that party government can be abused," Karnes continued. "Sometimes it is abused, and your father, among others, is making that charge today against the present administration. Both political parties you or your mother or I could choose need mending and will always need mending. Thinking people will never agree in every detail with either party's political philosophy or legislative program. But if you, Jan, are talking about how this country is served best, the so-called independent should join the party wherein they find the lesser difference of opinion with their own thoughts.

"That we Americans have been spared Europe's curse, the curse and tyranny of one-party rule or the chaos and ineffectiveness of numerous splinter parties, is frankly not due to citizens who refrain from joining either of our two great parties. To quote your father again, Jan, 'political difference is good democracy. It is political indifference which represents our dangers.'

"Pericles wrote of civic duty: 'I do not say a citizen who takes no interest in politics minds his own business. I say he has no business at all.' That's what your Dad is saying."

This became the keynote for, and motif in, Frank's campaign for the nomination. This was the keel of the strategy ship and it was laid. But the weeks were passing, and Frank was dancing on the edge of time. Moreover, as the French would say, he had an ocean to drink up in his new activities.


So did far-off Sally; purposeful Sally.

There was not a sign of a cloud passing by with Charles. It was all a steady drizzle. The best diplomacy in a lifelong diplomatic career is to avoid allowing your superiors to keep score. Vague progress, and always the appearance of vague progress, is the wiser road to ultimate happy retirement. Charles had always managed to keep his results abroad unscored in the career section of the Foreign Office. Now there himself, he puffed contentedly, and enjoyed his relations with others in the establishment and his daily hours on horses. His elaborate mediocrity was his salvation.

But Sally had the gnaw, itch and bite for more effect, more range, than her writings now supplied or, of course, than anything having to do with their life in their house on Regent's Park.

"A stately house," Charles called it. It seemed to her, however, that an architect who tried to achieve too much, even if he succeeded, was rather a bore. It had been built seventy years before by Charles' father on the site of an eighteenth-century mansion; formed in a square design with courtyards in front and back; three stories with a fourth half-story. Made of brick, it was perfectly symmetrical, with innumerable gables cutting the roof line and a forest of chimney tops.

You could almost feel the architect's hatred for lightness and light. It was hard to heat, gloomy to live in, and—with the scarcity of good servants—nearly impossible to keep clean. Sally detested it.

But Sally liked the British people. In fact, she had once written, and meant every word of it: "The glory of England does not lie in her flag. It lies in the justice and quiet independence of her average citizen. There has never been a good cause, no matter how distant, which has not found Englishmen among its courageous champions. If his country fails in its duty or its honesty, the Englishman stands and says so, and the government he attacks will defend him. It will, in fact, protect him against the very politicians he so often criticizes and whom he frequently surpasses in courage and intelligence."

Vincent Emery had put these words by an American on page one, but such treatments of Sally's writings were rare, and somehow the steam seemed to have gone out of them.

Alberto had long since been transferred, to the Far East, and even during his short assignment in London, Sally had never resumed the affair which ended its passionate course in Rome. Nor did Charles show suspicion of any other deviations by her, of which there had been few.

Sally understood that urge for satisfaction and answered it with fierce compulsion. But she could not understand the equal urge that came to her at times, a haunting feeling fully as compelling.

It was more than a resentment against frustrations bred by her view of the world. Surely it was more complicated than general dissatisfaction or mere vanity or a desire to live a more interesting life of more consequence in compensation for her dull marriage, although that was undoubtedly a part of it. She knew women—smart, pretty, fashionable women—who wanted to marry her Byronic-looking husband for his money. Nor was it bred of idleness. Sally was always busy. Was it a positive urge for power? Was this the masculine tang in her that she prized and cultivated? Well, it was at least the power to influence events and people, and to do so in a hurry, to plan what others would do, to make uncompromising decisions of her own that counted for something, to be responsible for things that ought to be done, or at least that she thought ought to be done.

Consciously or not, this was the true root of her devotion to her newspaper talent—a means to this end. What other avenue was as open for a woman? It was the wellspring that fed her instinct for action, always action, even in the minor "Do something! Don't just stand there!" quality which was her hallmark. It was, in fact, the compass of her life. And now?

"All I know is that I'm bored as hell," was Sally's unstudied summary to

Vincent Emery. "Here is a time for clear-headed, courageous men to come forward—and be written about. There isn't a single damn statesman in the whole of Europe outside Winston Churchill; and he's been thrown out, defeated! Kicked away! *Arrivederci!*

"The hope isn't in Europe at all. Once more, it's in America. Obviously anything decisive—and anybody decisive—will come from there."

She offered Emery a cigarette but he said no. "So what, Sal? So what?" His pale eyes looked serious and pinched in a red face. "What are you leading up to?" Emery asked, as old man Mayo in the Braidwood bank might have asked some good friend beating round the bush about a loan.

"Emery," she said, "tomorrow is my birthday." Sally often wondered what she would do if one day she should get old herself. She never quite felt this could happen to her.

"Tomorrow should also be the beginning of spring," he smiled. "Your birthday should announce the beginning of spring. It would be a graceful legend."

She was sitting on a couch before a low fire. The weather had turned cold and wet. She was wearing lounging things, a Chinese house coat, and her legs in the trim blue pants were stretched out, soaking in the warmth. Her head was bent in her arm and she had not seen the reassuring sympathy in Emery's eyes. Born of her brooding, the strong compulsion was on her; it had been growing and gnawing, of course. It had taken nothing to bring it to a head and propel her now, except that she was finding herself increasingly adrift these days, unusually lost, and filled with a corrosive apprehension. Sally to float becalmed on the unfavorable drift of her life? No. This was impossible for her.

Sally turned to face him. Emery had never seen her on edge like this. She stood up straight in front of him, her long legs spread like a sailor's on a rolling deck, her hands on her hips, her remarkable head thrust forward.

"I'm not leading up to anything, Emery. Nothing," she said, with petulance. "I'm just talking and feeling. If I can't do that with you, what am I supposed to do?"

"I'm sorry, Sal," he replied softly. "I thought you wanted to do something and were telling me about it."

"Well," Sally answered, looking out of the corners of her eyes, "I am. I'm stuck in a rut, Emery, a rut. And as sure as God made little apples I'm in the wrong place here and now."

"You mean in this house or in England?"

"Both. Emery, I'm going to America." She stood with her arms gathered across her, her back planted to the fire. "What I'm really saying is that I want you to help place me on an American paper. I want to write for the paper over there."

Emery reached out his hand and caught hers; he did not want to lose her as a worker and friend. "But, Sal," he said, with tenderness in his voice, "you haven't been in America for years."

"I know," she said quietly. "But that's part of it. I want to go. I cannot stay asleep in the earth like a nocturnal owl and not wake up. You've said it yourself, Emery; I'm a woman of Spain! *O extremada o nada*—all or nothing. You know that. I want to work on those American papers right now so bad I can taste it!" She bent over and kissed him gently on his forehead as his black eyes met hers. "Please."

He did not answer her at once and seemed preoccupied. Sally waited, her hand firmly in his.

"What about Charles?" Emery asked. "What would he say to all this?"

Sally had long ago, and easily, exhausted Charles in her own imagination. If her husband had had a sense of humor or a philosophy, what fun she could have had with him. But his philosophy, she knew, was a pompous evasion of real things. Nothing whatever in his romantic or philosophic trappings could conceivably provide attachment to her heart. In her life's course she did not want to hurt him but she knew she could not help him. What can you do with a man who is always inspecting his tongue in a looking glass?

"Charles?" she answered. "Charles does not figure in this at all."

"Sal, Sal, my Sal," Emery said at length, "the papers over there are loaded with extra people."

"I know." She was brought up short by his obvious reluctance.

"Moreover," he said, rising and turning away from her, "we don't want you to leave here. We really don't, Sal."

"What can you do to help me, Emery?"

He gave a shrug of his thick shoulders, and then walked over to the fire to stir it up with some tongs. Sally took them from his hand and pushed at the logs herself.

"What can you do, Emery?" she murmured again. "I don't want minor outlets there or space work on an article-by-article basis. I've a record here that I hope somebody will respect. In leaving you, you know it's much better if I can change from you to some other paper; not simply quit here and then try to get lined up in New York or Washington."

"Yes, that's right, of course."

"So, if Editor Vincent Emery can bridge the gap, we're set."

"What do you mean 'we're set'?" he said, a little impatiently.

"Well, I'm set, I mean."

"That's better," he grimaced.

"Maybe they'll treat me like the speaker in a cowboy town who was alarmed when the audience pulled six-shooters until he discovered they weren't gunning for him but for the man who sent him. But, anyway, Emery, no big paper or good syndicate is just going to up and hire me from London." She paused, and then exclaimed excitedly: "What I want is some sort of word from you to the right paper that I'm coming, that you don't want to lose me and that you are sending me to them with a view to their taking me on. For their own good," she added, with a little laugh, "before somebody else does."

"Sal, of course that's the way to do it," he said, smiling. He looked up at her. "If you want to know the simple truth, I do think it's as good for them as it is for you. Yes, I do, Sal. But what you need is to be syndicated. That would let you cut across all the lines, appear clear across the country, and write in any paper that will buy you from the syndicate."

Sally brightened, all business now, and touched by his wholeheartedness.

"My pick would be John Bixley's Liberty News Syndicate," he continued. "Fine, fine people they are, Sal. John—everybody calls him 'Curly'—can add you to his stable if he thinks the newspapers his organization solicits will buy what you write. I'll tell him that if he has a single brain left in his funny head he ought to take you on."

Sally was rubbing the palms of her hands together. She was sitting on the couch, her knees tight up under her chin, looking at him with almost love in her eyes, but tauntingly. "Emery. Why in the name of God didn't you tell me that in the first place? What did you keep me waiting for? You had me wondering."

Slumped in a chair before the fireplace, Emery looked up. "Oh, nonsense, Sal. You know as well as I do that you're not lined up yet."

"The hell you say," she cried triumphantly. "Emery, we're in!"

"You're in, you mean. Sal, we don't want you to go."

He looked around over the back of the chair to the door. Charles was coming through it, blowing into a handkerchief. Emery caught Sally's eye in a quick glance. She shook her head, warning him.

"Hello, Mr. Benson," Emery said, "I'm sorry it's late. I was just leaving."

# 10

WHEN SALLY CHECKED INTO the St. Regis Hotel, she registered as Sally Bryce, 15 Regent's Park, London. They had reserved a charming suite for her, small but bright and airy, looking along Fifth Avenue and to the sunlit corner of Central Park.

"Oh, this is lovely," she told the assistant manager who showed her up, half excited and pleasantly surprised by the light-tinted brocade walls, the inviting furniture, the gay crystal chandeliers and fragile sconces.

"Thank you, Miss Bryce," he replied as he helped her with her coat. "We are very happy to have you with us."

The porters brought up the luggage, the stream of assorted cases marking a seasoned traveler who wants everything with her but packs so that she knows where everything is.

"Two trunks are coming from the pier," she said to the two porters, "and the drayman promised they'd be here in a few hours."

"About noon, ma'am, I would say," one replied, "and we'll see that you have them right away."

How easy it is to get things done in America, she thought; what a wonderful, wonderful convenient place to be, this country.

She tipped the waiting men, fingering the crisp green bills in her delicate fingers as she took off her gloves. "My first American money in a long, long time," she said, giving the porters the smile. "It seems so solid after Europe, you know. Why, it even feels solid."

Sally was simple and friendly with servants, and sometimes would exchange gossip with them as long as they would talk. She was not only kind on such occasions but actually had a self-effacing manner, as if each time she asked them to do a service she was grateful. Had Sally not appeared to be so rich, they could not have forgiven her this exaggerated consideration. Because she seemed so unneeding there was nothing most of them would not do for her.

In moments when she was pressed, however, any servant was a mere tool—a vehicle that was expected to go someplace with a silent horn, and get done whatever was to be done. Impatience and anger rewarded any failure then. But this passed quickly. "It's just that I can't stand things done in a sloppy way," she would explain. "Moreover, at least they ought to do what they're paid for, damn it." But none of this concerned this moment. She was tipping the two men with great cheer.

The porters smiled broadly as they left, and then action began.

Sally hurried to ring two bells, two fingers in one push, for the floor waiter to bring her a light lunch and for the maid to unpack her things. Then she phoned for the florist to send up some flowers.

With the unpacking process started in good Irish hands, Sally wiggled out of her traveling suit, her underclothes dropping like foam around her in the bedroom.

Kicking her shoes into a corner and stripping off her stockings she called to the maid through the door, "Will you run the water for a bath, please," and added with a note of warning in her voice, "I want it hot; steaming hot."

Invariably, a bath was Sally's refuge. "The best place on earth to think," she always insisted. "If I were a man and had to decide the fate of nations and, in fact, of the entire human race, great God—I'd get into a bath!"

The steaming water, and then the cold splashes with her hands, did their magic for her before the waiter rang the doorbell with her lunch. She ate it in her usual unconscious way, toying with the tips of the asparagus in the hollandaise. It could have been Chinese rice for all this handsome woman cared.

The maid helped her into a well-cut, deep blue dress she especially liked. Yet it generally made little real difference to Sally what she wore, nor, as she had long ago discovered, did it make much difference to a man.

Now it became time to do something. Action.

Sally caught Vincent Emery's friend John Bixley at the Liberty News Syndicate on the telephone just as he was leaving the office for lunch.

"This is Sally Bryce," she said, and hardly a word more was needed. She arranged to see him that same afternoon.

The ride down Fifth Avenue thrilled her. Could she have known Janet's thrill on this same street amid the greatest outpouring of pride and affection that mighty America had ever brought to the ears of homecoming sons? Much had changed since then, for the street, for Janet, for Sally, for the world.

She knew she was now near the hub of things. She was at the decisive scene of speculation and of events. Men and a great people had the future of the world in the making here. She could feel it in her spine and see it in the sunlight sparkling on the high windows in the busy canyon of the street.

The history of this nation had shown that its mere weight of numbers had not advanced it. Repeatedly, its history had displayed that the inspiration and example of determined and dedicated men upset all calculations. Who were they today? What would happen in the United States? Could it be true, could she make it come true, that she could help something—anything—to happen here?

There was no more doubt of this in Sally's mind, heaven knows, than that she was riding in that taxi, although she had not the faintest idea what this might be or the how, when or why of it.

In this strange way she saw her future, as having been settled; for she was entirely without her London consciousness of a split between her life and decisive action; that gnawing, corrosive lethargy that sapped her mind and spirit.

As in many women who have found sensual love early, and with both gaiety and intensity, the scope of her emotions was left free. She had told Charles nothing of Emery and his arrangement in America for her, for she did not want Charles pestering him about her on any account while she was away. For how long? Who knows?

Meanwhile? She never liked this word. "Meanwhile," she quoted, "is for people who find it easy to wait."

She had made every plan for her trip, at her bank, at the consulate section of the American Embassy, at the Cunard office, before informing Charles. It was only within the week before she sailed, when her packing had to be done, that she informed him that she was leaving, "hoping to do some newspaper work in the States." The scene was to come back to her again and again like the ghostly echo of London's Big Ben.

She was smiling but her plans were revolving too fast in her head to really care what she said. "Besides," she added, "I simply have to be by myself for a while, somehow. I just have to be, Charles. You know how it is with me."

Charles, who was normally a cheerful man and used to better tidings, felt depressed. But there was no one to say her nay. As he spoke his words slowed down in the slow manner of carousel horses at the end of the ride.

"What's the matter, Sally?" was the best he could muster, his fat, pink, well-washed fingers stroking his chin.

"Nothing's the matter," she answered dully. "This is just something I must do."

He was wearing a curious black frock coat known among Near East diplomats as a stambouline. They were sitting in the library where she had sat with Emery. The rain was pelting the Gothic windows in a downpour that seemed to close out the world and trap these two near-strangers in the falling twilight.

"I don't like this, Sal," he finally said. "I don't like it at all. I ask you not to go. And I don't intend to have you go—go off like this." They were the words of a man who had left dreams behind him wherever he had dragged his life, dogged and bedeviled by inertia.

Sally had foreseen approximately this reaction, but she did not like the warning tone in his voice. The running battle was beginning to have the bitterness of a perpetual draw.

"Oh now, Charles," she said. "We're not children. You know how many years it's been since I've been to America. After all, it's my home, you know."

"I just don't like this; not at all." Connubial confidence? There was none; at least so little as to mean there was none. He launched into his objections with sly eloquence and solid monologue fueled by brandy.

"I could tell you I was anxious to see Mother," Sally interrupted. "But she's way out in California, and I don't intend to go that far. I could talk about visiting friends. You know I would never cross the Atlantic, up and down on that sea, to visit friends. I'm trying to be frank with you, Charles. I just have to be over there now. I feel it. I want it. It has nothing to do with you, Charles. Things are happening there that I want to be in on. Somehow I feel like I think a woman must feel who wants a baby."

"What!"

Sally laughed. "Oh, Charles, I'm just stumbling around trying to make you see that leaving like this is just a yearning, that's all."

"You've said nothing to me. You must have done a great deal of arranging behind my back." He shook himself like a poodle.

"Not behind your back, in a sneaky sense, surely. I just didn't want to have the days string out between such a talk as this and my leaving."

"What ship are you sailing on?" Ominous, angry, but now calm, Olympian, patronizing, his tone as frigid as a dune on the rim of the cold Irish sea.

"The *Queen Mary*—Saturday. Mr. Caruthers at Cunard has been very nice about that," Sally answered in an appreciative voice.

"And I suppose Haskins at your bank has been 'nice,' too," Charles added, "and that Sir Samuel at the Washington Embassy will be 'nice' too. And will you be 'nice' enough to tell him I knew nothing about this and do not approve; do not approve at all?"

"I will, if that's what you want."

"Well, it is what I want. I gather, if you will permit me to say so, that you intend to stay away some time. This means a few explanations here; unless you have already made them. Our friends."

"I've made no explanation to anyone. I'm just a little sorry I have made so much of an explanation to you. After all, I'm not eloping, running off with the hairdresser or something, you know. I'm just going to an exciting place. In fact, I think it is very clever of me to go. Moreover, I'm a newspaper writer. The opportunity now is in America—America on the move. And my pilgrimage is for the destruction of hackism."

"How easy everything is if one is clever!"

"It may not be easy; but it's fun."

It was typical of him to quote Horace. " 'Those who cross the seas change their skies but not their nature,' " he said, with some gusto. "For a clever woman, you know precious little about what can happen in a matter like this."

"Oh, Charles, you are simply unused to anyone wanting to be himself or herself. Yet it will mean more leisure for you, more freedom, and of course more responsibility for me."

"You're to have an adventure?" he asked bluntly.

"I don't think so."

"Don't, Sally," he said, and left the room.

She left him at the boat train that Saturday still asking him to understand, but also telling him that she found his life useless, that he lacked comprehensions and convictions. Charles, who was watching her carefully, said nothing. She knew that at odd moments he would think of her affectionately, ruefully. And she had kissed him a gentle goodbye.

Bixley's office was in the Times Building, built in 1903, the era when Adolph Ochs rechristened Longacre Square as Times Square and built there the building that Stanford White patterned after Giotto's Florentine tower; the era when New York was the vibrant, poignant city of O'Henry's *Four Million,* of *Floradora,* hansom cabs, Delmonico's, Diamond Jim Brady and Maude Adams' *Peter Pan.*

"At night it's like the *Girandola,* the great fireworks in the Piazza del Popolo," Sally mused as the cab pulled up at the curb.

The Times Building was now an old building, but the Liberty News Syndicate offices were modernized in the stark, functional style of partitions and glass that had a tidiness belying the usual idea of a newspaper office. After all, it was not a newspaper office. It was the editorial center and distributing hub from which its columnists' writings were distributed to subscribing newspapers throughout the country and abroad. None of the writers worked in the office. Their copy was delivered to Bixley's desk, checked in the copy room and sent to the telegraph machines for wire dispatch or the mimeographing rooms for mail delivery. This was seldom a high-pressure operation, and the friendly, easy pace of the office showed it.

Bixley saw first Sally's hair, for she never wore a hat, her wide-apart, smiling eyes, her tanned skin, a fine waist, a slender figure and a walk that shouted vitality; the over-all impression he had was of elegance and presence.

It was the face of a woman who had seldome denied herself satisfaction; a woman with a great deal of experience, by which she had profited, her way.

That was an explanation of her appearance; every inch a guardsman of the breed that dies but does not surrender.

"How do you do, sir," she said, the "sir" catching him up with a little start. "Thank you very much for letting me come in so promptly." Butter would not have been safe in Sally's mouth, but this was only an honest reflection of her delight in being there.

A Roman type, he thought to himself, as Sally held out her delicate hand. My God, I didn't know Emery was sending me something like this.

He was a fair, tall, lanky man with short, famous curls that seemed to dance on his head like snakes: his trademark throughout the newspaper business. This meant the inevitable nickname of "Curly," of course, from nearly the day of his birth in this city. A native New Yorker.

"Bryce?" he said, sitting down in his chair and nursing his knees, as he looked squarely at the surprise that had walked through his door. "You're English, Miss Bryce? Italian?"

"No, Mr. Bixley, I'm American. I was born in Philadelphia. I'm married to an Englishman; my name is Mrs. Charles N. Benson and we live in London. Sarah Bryce is my maiden name. I write as Sally Bryce in the newspapers."

"How's Vincent?"

"Well, he's Vincent. He's fine; well; wicked and worried. Have you ever known him to change?"

Bixley laughed. If this woman writes like she talks and thinks like she looks, the fine old Liberty News Syndicate has just received some money in the bank. But he knew, of course, how Sally wrote and how she thought. Emery had sent him an abundant package of her articles. "Damn good" was the consensus in Bixley's office. These were also the words Emery had scrawled at the bottom of his letter—his final inked-in emphasis in a scrawl as indecipherable as a physician's.

"When were you last in our country, Miss Bryce?" he asked, hooking a finger in the rim of a garterless sock which hung around his ankle and tugging at it.

"Oh, many, many years ago. My husband is in the British Foreign Office, as perhaps Emery mentioned. We've been posted in Paris, Rome and London. It really hasn't been too possible to come to the United States. Mr. Bixley, I've missed it here!" Had anyone told Sally this as recently as a few months ago she would have said they were out of their minds.

"I suppose it would take you some time to get into things here," he suggested, "but perhaps you'd like to do some pieces about Britain in the meanwhile?"

"Surely you're the best judge of that, Mr. Bixley," Sally answered, although she looked somewhat puzzled. "But I'm just wondering if the papers you may solicit for my column, if you take it on, won't feel that the American wire services and feature syndicates aren't already covering England and the continent heavily."

"They are, and with more material than most of our papers want to print."

A pro, too, he thought. Where have I been all these years in the newspaper business—including England—with somebody like this floating around?

"Yes," he continued, "and I would think that if you're covering the scene here your columns should be typical from the beginning. The newspapers, of course, will want to see the samples. That's all they buy on. We can dress up a writer's samples in impressive presentation portfolios. The editor-prospect simply throws these in the wastebasket and pulls out the product: the writing. That's all his readers are going to see. Interesting them is all that interests him."

A smile crossed Sally's face. This was another hurdle jumped. Why be here writing about Britain, the continent, profiles of the people she was leaving? She nailed this down at once.

"I'm glad to hear you say this, sir. I heartily agree. I'm in America because I want to write about what's happening here—and who is making it happen. How, when, where and why. And, Mr. Bixley, I want to write for Americans. I've no interest at all in having what I write published in the U.K., unless Emery prefers. For my part, it's the readers here, just as it's America, that will mean the most to the world, and I'm going to try to write for them." She paused, looking the interested man square in the eye. "And for you, Mr. Bixley, and the Liberty News Syndicate, I hope." This did it, if anything remained to be done.

"Where are you living, Miss Bryce?"

"The St. Regis. I hope to get an apartment when I can."

Dough, he thought. Dough, besides.

But there were no terms to discuss, for the Syndicate terms were standard; fifty percent of what each newspaper paid the Syndicate for Sally's column, minus the telegraph or mimeograph costs, and one-half of the costs for promotion brochures, advertising in *Printer's Ink* or other trade journals, and any special charges.

Nevertheless, Bixley made this clear. "Our contracts are standard, you know."

"I know. Emery told me. I'm entirely satisfied. And I realize you must sell me to a great many papers to break even, too. I'm grateful, Mr. Bixley."

Sally met the lanky editor's associates in their offices. The Syndicate sales manager added his own touch. "We'll want photographs, Miss Bryce," he said, blinking at her like an incredulous owl.

In less than two hours from the time she had left her room, she was back at the St. Regis and had stopped at the desk to send a cable to Emery. "DARLING DEAR EMERY," she wrote, "IT'S DONE. BLESS YOU."

In her memory the conjunction of events that night and the days immediately thereafter did not stand out; these became merged with so many later memories. But Frank, of course, could not have been further from her thoughts had he been warming himself by a campfire on the Russian steppes. No thread had bound them—not a wisp. Her recollection of Killory and Chamonix would have been vivid down to the smallest detail had something arisen to recall it, but the long-ago incident had merely come and gone and that was all.

As an avid newspaper reader, she realized that a political newcomer
amed Killory was surprising the country in a whirlwind campaign, but even
s significance on the American political scene failed to register fully.

Then it happened. Hunched up in bed, thumbing a magazine, she saw his
ame, his picture and a reference to Braidwood. "Great God!" Sally yelled,
tting bolt upright. "Great God! Braidwood! Killory! Frank Killory!" She sat
ere staring at his picture in open-mouthed amazement. Whether this man
ould remember her, it never crossed her mind to ask herself—a useless exer-
se. All that crossed her mind was "Profile."

Sally was on her feet. Bells began ringing—for her breakfast, the maid, her
othes, some paper, the telephone. Within moments she was on the line with
hn Bixley.

"Does anyone in the office happen to know where I could locate Mr. Frank
illory?" she asked, her tone as level as tea in a cup.

"Oh, hello, Miss Bryce. Why, yes. You can probably get him through his
w firm: Allen, Van Biber, Caxton and Shaw. It's in the Whitehall Building,
owntown, I know. I haven't the number. I do know, though, that he lives out
Glen Cove. That's on Long Island, of course. Do you know Killory?"

"Yes, I know him," she said, ending the call. "But it's been so long he may
ot even remember me." This reservation was an automatic pleasantry which
mply popped out of the top of her head. The problem was not whether he
ould remember her but what to do with him when he did.

Sally nibbled at her breakfast slowly, shifting in her peignoir and stroking
e back of her heel with her feathered slipper, rereading the magazine article.
here was Frank, bending over a rostrum in Chicago, shaking hands with one
and, waving to the crowd with the other. "Well, I'll be damned!" summed up
hat Sally saw. "My Lord Braidwood; what in the name of God do you
ppose he's like now?"

With the genius women have for recalling every impression of their first
eeting with a man who later becomes important to them, this resource sprang
life.

Sally could see Frank come into the train's stuffy compartment and toss his
ggage up on the rack. She remembered how he attacked the cold duck she
ad in her basket. She even remembered what she was wearing; the wide skirt
nd open blouse. She saw him handing her the Alpine folder and saying, "I've
een looking forward to this all my life"—and how she had thought in that
oment: Nice eyes.

She saw them riding in the old carriage from the station; she even felt him.
he saw them going down the hall of the Chamonix hotel, surprised to find the
harm of bright moonlight breaking across her balcony. She remembered his
illing around, running his hands through his hair, while she started to get
ndressed for bed, obviously wondering what was to come of this. Nice hair,
e had thought. She could even revive Frank's expression as she edged him to
e door and waved goodnight. I thought him something of a dear, Sally
ecalled.

Then Sally saw them walking in the village street and remembered kissin him solidly in the little Renaissance square. She could not clearly rememb why they had not gone to bed. For a moment she pondered: Did we? N But, did we? No. And then she coupled this up with her flight from her promi to the Belgian after the evening at Maxim's, and remembered her mood going to Chamonix. She shrugged.

The article's description of Braidwood, Killory's going into the law, can to her like an echo. Already, she could see Frank standing in her St. Regis suit "Editor Bixley," she said to herself, "We're under way."

Sally glanced at the pencil note she had made. She located Allen, Va Biber, Caxton & Shaw in the Manhattan telephone book, putting her long na on the number. She asked the hotel operator to call Whitehall 4-0026. But sh stopped when the operator said: "Yes, madam."

With a "Never mind, thank you," Sally put down the phone. This was n way to start. She glanced back at the book for the office address. Then she s down at the desk and wrote Frank a note on the blue notepaper of the hotel:

Dear My Lord Braidwood—

I have just come to *our* country, greeted in the public prints by Frai Killory.

Seriously, I'm thrilled—just to think how well these years must hav passed for you. Please, please tell me everything that has happened. If you ca find in this great city a *langouste* as good as we had at Courmayeur I wish v could have it together, if you will just telephone me here.

But before she signed this Sally had an inspiration. The tiny gold cro Frank had bought her in the village store the day before they left Chamon had long since been lost, strayed or stolen. Somehow she thought of it; as Sal would.

Unable to enclose the token as a pleasant additive—her genius, again—sh drew it in very small outline under her scrawled but firm Sally Bryce. Sh added beside it: "Frank, I'll always thank you."

She sent the note by hand; proper and faster, she decided. And the de porter was utterly appalled when she told him she wanted a man from th hotel to deliver it.

"Way down to Battery Place, ma'am? Why, that's at the very tip of th island. It's very far, ma'am, in a taxi."

"Taxi or subway, I don't care which," she answered firmly. "Just so yc send a boy up here now to get it and see that he leaves right away."

"Yes, ma'am. Anything you wish, ma'am."

*Mektoub:* First fate rings; now it is written.

Mail flooded Killory's office these days, of course, and Sam Welsh receiv the note from the hands of the hotel's messenger. Had it not been delivered th way—boldly marked "By Hand," with the angular word "Personal"—Sa

uld have opened it. Instead, he gave it to Mary-Louise to put on Frank's
sk with some other papers.

Walter Karnes was just leaving and Archibald Scriver followed on Mary-
uise's heels as she went into the inner office. It was the kind of thing he did.
is mercurial creature in the realm of political magic gave the cough of a seal
a hemp bed and then began: "Just a hello, Frank . . . only a minute . . . must
along . . . Never saw you looking better . . . everybody's still rooting like hell
r the Chicago speech . . ." Frank nodded absently, trying to locate something
his pockets, as Scriver waved himself back out of the door. The day's unre-
tting contact for Archibald Scriver.

Frank was talking on the telephone when his fingers fell on the note. He
ummed with it a few minutes until he finished, and then cut the top with a
ıg silver opener.

The world of fan mail is a weird place. Frank glanced at all of this
anger's note before he realized what he was reading. His eye fell back to the
lutation, which he had missed completely. "My Lord Braidwood—"

The inked words sprang up at him now. "My God," he said, "and that
tle gold cross!" Then the human mind entered its predictable groove: "Sally.
lly Bryce. What on earth do you suppose she's like now?"

"Mary-Louise," he asked. "Will you get me the St. Regis, please, and
nnect me with Miss Sally Bryce."

In a moment or so the secretary told him Miss Bryce was not in. "I left a
ssage that you had called."

"You gave the number?"

"Yes."

But before he left the office he called again. This time the phone was
ıging as she had her key in the door.

"Oh, Frank, dear Frank. I've just come in this moment, this very moment.
you got my note all right?"

She laughed with him on the other end of the line, holding the receiver
ıile she lit a cigarette; and then confessed that, no, she did not have the tiny
ɔss, a horrid fact, she was furious when she lost it. She was sorry he had
thing like it by which to remember her. Sally was chatting as if all this were
ly yesterday. And, of course, Frank would drop by at the St. Regis on his way
town.

"As a matter of fact," he told her, "I often stay there. Our firm has had an
artment at the St. Regis for years, I don't know how many years. Some of the
rtners use it after working late or when they have to be in the city too early
go home—the partners who commute, that is, like me."

So, there he stood now in Sally's suite.

Shakespeare has Cleopatra playing billiards while she waited for Antony.
ıoch Arden's wife was otherwise occupied in her vigil. Few poets have failed
sing of long separations. Some have made waiting famous. Waiting, waiting,
ıiting; the waiting years.

Sally, of course, had been waiting for nothing; and especially not for

Frank. Frank had been waiting for nothing; and certainly not for Sally. The surprise in one about how the other looked was entirely on Frank's side, as she called "Come in" and flung open the door. For Sally, the man in front of her had merely emerged, full blown, from the magazine photographs: a little like seeing a clear aerial reconnaissance photo and then inspecting the site close up Not a detail missing.

"Why, Frank," she said, a murmur of excitement in her voice, "I would know you anywhere! Absolutely anywhere!" She really meant it.

Then Sally moved toward him in the friendly, easy way that was her own and, taking Frank's face between the palms of her two hands, paying no more attention to the open door than she had to the crowd in the little Renaissance square, she kissed him solidly on the mouth.

Frank laughed gaily, holding her in front of him by her elbows and staring into her brown eyes. "Sally. Why, Sally," he said, "if this isn't the damnedest thing. For heaven's sake, what's been going on all these years? What are you doing here? Tell me all about it." They were walking toward the settee. "I want to hear everything, Sally. My, you look wonderful." He seemed as joyous as youth on a hayride. But his joyousness was also definitely spiced with awe.

Out came their cigarettes as they sat down, her hand over his in a natural, delicate intimacy, her long legs stretched out in repose.

Sally had no more interest in telling her life story than she had in flying out the window, and she came—by instinct—smack to the present. All else would be a filler, anyway, from her viewpoint. Things were happening now and the present was the interesting thing.

She told him she had come over to work for the American newspapers, the Liberty News Syndicate, told him of her meeting with John Bixley—"I think he knows you"—told of her joy in being here, what it meant to her to find herself in America. "Oh, Frank, it's so thrilling," she said. Here was a steaming libido, leaping, grasping vibrancy that showed in the restless eyes of a woman with great thirst for life.

"The newpaper business?" He looked somewhat puzzled.

"Yes," she smiled, "I worked on the London papers. Why, that's my life. My editor, Vincent Emery—dear soul, you would adore him—arranged every thing here. Cynics say so many newspaper readers are stupid. They say many stupid things are printed; that stupid people read the stupid things; that's why you get a stupid world. And that when the stupid read the stupid newspaper they feel clever and think they know everything. Well, I want to do a better job than that. And, my Lord Braidwood, this is why I'm here."

"More power to you, Sally. I think it's wonderful." Frank all but applauded.

"My sweet oaf," Sally smiled, "what I want to know about is you. You could have knocked me over with a feather when I picked up that magazine and thought to myself—"

"It's a long, roundabout story."

"But what happened to Braidwood?"

"It's still there—"

And on and on and on, until Frank glanced at the clock on the small mantel and made their date for dinner the next night, when he would be staying in town.

"*Langouste!*" he said at the door.

"*Langouste.* Forever *langouste*," she answered, her musical laugh sounding in the corridor. "Goodbye."

# 11

THAT NEXT NIGHT Frank stayed at the St. Regis, and he stayed with Sally. The *langouste* was served in her room, for he came there a very tired man.

At lunch Scriver had brought up the subject of money. Until then no one in the amorphous group had discussed this within the group or said anything to Frank about the money side; each merely paid his own expenses, including Frank, for whatever he did. But money makes the mare go, and this political mare would soon need a good deal of it.

"Frank," Scriver said, "you'll need a whale of a lot of money between now and July. I think I'd better begin tending to it. Don't worry. Just forget it."

"Don't worry?" Frank answered uncomfortably. "Why, Arch, I really haven't been thinking too much about it . . ."

"I know, I know," Scriver interrupted. "But it's never too early to get moving about money. I think I'd better pass the hat around—and the sooner the better. Then I'll work out some plans when all this gets more and more expensive."

Frank began drawing lines on the tablecloth with the points of his fork and he could not keep a frown from his face. "Arch," he said with a touch of embarrassment, "I never had anyone raise money for me to do anything. It's an odd feeling."

Scriver cleared his throat in a professional way. "Nonsense," he coughed. "There will be a high cost for facilities, reception halls, staff workers, the publicity departments and people, telephone and telegraph, and all the rest, plus the big lump in July at the convention. But people like to spend for causes, Frank, so long as they feel that it is a cause and they feel it's for 'their boy.' This is one of their satisfactions, I guess. Anyway, they do."

"It's still odd to feel you are a 'cause.' And, Arch, when you talk abo
other people spending money for 'their boy,' I just don't think about myself
anybody's anything." Frank stopped his hand as it carried some vegetables
his mouth. "I don't know just what to say about it."

Nothing more was said about it. Frank grabbed at a chance to change th
subject. He had called for no details, nor thought to issue any warning
Scriver, marveling at the ease with which he had made himself the Killo
money-raiser, with the future advantages to him that this could imply, slapp
his knees and stood up.

"Well," he groaned, "another five pounds around the belly. God, I'm ge
ting fat." He stood with his legs apart and his feet planted, balancing h
weight like a doll that rolls on a round bottom of lead.

Within half an hour Scriver peered through the door of Sam Welsh's sma
office. He jerked his head toward Mary-Louise, indicating he wanted to spe
to Sam confidentially. Feigning a conspiratorial tone, never too busy to strike
pose, he sat down, pursed his lips, and spoke with a dry tongue, close to Sam
ear.

"Mr. Killory is very anxious to have me raise some money for all th
Sam," he said. "It has worried him a good deal, having no solution, so th
worries me." Sam, flushed and stimulated by such intimacy from Archibald A
Scriver, turned to him. "Yes, sir," he said.

"We want you to open an account in your name in the bank downstair
Sam, so that you can sign the checks."

"Yes, sir."

"I'll bring you the money," Scriver continued in a muffled voice. "You kee
the records of the deposits. If any of the money is in cash, just put it in a sa
deposit box. You tend to everything, Sam."

"Well—"

Scriver barely hesitated before plunging further into the narrative. "B
tween us we'll manage everything in good shape. The main point is not
bother Mr. Killory about money. That's the thing. That's the least we can do f
him, Sam, you and I. The very least.

"All this is going to be very expensive and a man in his position who h
never been in politics before needs a lot of protection, Sam, my boy, in this so
of thing: confidential things, some of them, because everybody isn't anxio
to have it known they're giving money in a political affair, you know, althoug
they're anxious to help."

"Oh, I understand, Mr. Scriver." He was talking to himself rather than
Arch.

Scriver took a pen from his pocket and wrote out a check for sever
thousand dollars and said, as he handed it to Sam: "Just so Mr. Killory doesr
have to worry about money."

As Sam read the amount with widening eyes, Scriver laid a hand on h
shoulder. "Take that downstairs, Sam," he said. "Nothing is done till it's don
You will be a very valuable man for all of us in this confidential capacity."

"You know I'll do anything I can, Mr. Scriver."

"Keep the records in apple-pie order, Sam," he continued in a voice so low
t Mary-Louise could not hear him, "but keep them for you and me. Just us.
nfidential, Sam, confidential."

"Right," was Sam's barely audible reply, not knowing that he was looking
o the soul of a well-fed bagman.

Frank's session with Scriver about money lingered in Frank's mind, how-
er, and this had been followed by another of the sessions which he found
er drudgery: the long discussions covering practical political problems with
lter Karnes. Even as presented by this veteran, the haunting realities were
sive and frustrating to Frank.

Faced by the demands on his time now that the tactics were being
nned, as well as by the irregular hours of politicians, Frank could not have
ctioned as a nightly commuter to Glen Cove. More and more often, as in the
g periods of the coal strike suit, he stayed in town overnight rather than
ak away for the Glen Cove trip, only to return on an early morning train.

It is also doubtful if, by now, he could have functioned without Sally.

The nighttime was Sally's time. There would be political meetings in the
en, Van Biber, Caxton & Shaw suite, which Frank now entirely possessed.
en with cigar butts and scribbled notes to show as the result of the confer-
ce, late and weary, as on that first night, Frank would come to Sally: a small
e to eat at her elbow, a slow undressing to the drone of his problems of the
v, and the outlook for the campaign, and then to bed.

Men give themselves to women who know what it is to dare. If there was a
re fascinating and detached woman on earth he could not imagine her. He
d never seen anyone like her before, so amusingly prejudiced and intolerant,
sure of her independence and yet, underneath, a lustiness that (wrapped in
r beautiful body) gave Sally a force utterly foreign to anything he had ever
t or seen.

His appearance, which revealed him fairly well, suggested his passionate
ture, his distrust of regrets, his rejection of half measures. Depriving other
n of their expectations, and even taking some pleasure in doing so, Sally
ved to herself through Frank—as through Alberto in Rome—that what many
n wanted from her and she had refused them was, in fact, valid. No man
s wrong who wished to go to bed with her. And it added to her passion with
ank to realize that no man was wrong who had tried.

Her long legs, her breasts, her thin waist, her thighs, were made for this.
r clothes, her perfumes, her coiffure, were made for this; her lips, her wide-
eyes, her infectious laugh, were made for this. It was intensely satisfying
thin her—incredibly satisfying—to show herself that she was not a fraud.
d so it had always been, without change.

She could be quiet, and even tired, when she was naked and Frank
iched her. Small explosions would start that grew into convulsions as if this
od and the desire were a thing apart from all weariness and anxiety, and
en apart from herself.

Her urge to be satisfied, even satiated, remained a fierce compulsion.

Moreover, she had still never offered any explanation to herself for its intensi Was the impelling source, at bottom, the curse—or fear—of loneliness that h been on her as far back as Sally could remember? She could not say. Or, "Wl is the real source of anything?" she would have replied.

Long after he thought she had fallen asleep she would often lie awa nursing the peculiar, calm sense of triumph that had always puzzled her, wc dering why the smell of the room, and the bed and the silence were so utte: alien. She would glance at him with a faint smile of satisfaction. His he would be buried in the pillow and she would brush her lips against his hair let them cling lightly to his shoulder. A little chill would go up her spine a she would place his hand back on her, almost demurely.

The first soft glow of summer light comes early in the high windows this Fifth Avenue hotel and with it, or in the spreading dawn, Sally would s Frank gently and draw his eyes to her by stretching out with luxurious inc lence, waiting for some little move that would show her that she would th have him again, and her breasts and flat belly would grow moist in anti pation.

To Frank, in turn, there was something in her passions which tapped area within him that he had never known. The physical force was there, t lovely curves of Sally's body, the exciting grace of her legs and lovely boso her shoulders and arms that folded him in her soft embrace. But with tl softness, and so in contrast to it, the intensity, the ecstasy, the low cries complete and shattering release and the seemingly incredible pleasure that gave her was a personal justification that he had never experienced: it four him totally possessed.

The astonishing thing about all this was that Frank promptly consider Sally devoted to him, the full possessor of her heart; misreading her physic intensity. Yet her physical loyalty to him had no more to do with Sall broader philosophy than her proficiency in Alberto's Italian language had to with Alberto or with her not being Italian.

Nevertheless, knowing this within herself, Sally was sometimes caught ir pang of remorse afer she had responded to Frank's instinctive kindnesses a devotions with perhaps a touch of cruelty, or selfishness. Sometimes wh everything outside was quiet and only a few tiny stars were visible over Cent Park, like holes in a dark curtain, and they were quietly in each other's ar she felt that a confession was hanging over her like a storm that would r break.

Within moments the feeling would pass, the question would simplify its through the medium of her body, and Sally would devour this man agai There was no such thing as a simple moral problem to her. "If it's simple," s would say, "there's no problem. If it's complicated, who knows the answer?"

There had been no "profile." "That's silly; everybody knows you, Fran she said, "and it's already been done to death."

John Bixley agreed. "In this business a writer has to specialize to ga public credence," the editor emphasized. "Don't be a writer who covers ever

ng and feels nothing. Your specialty right now is Killory; the human, de-
loping, suspenseful story of a man on the up, up, up in America who may
rprise us by controlling our destiny and even the peace of the world. What
u have hold of here is a thousand times better than Horatio Alger. This is
cause it affects a million times more people.

"Stick with it, Sally," he had said, "and you'll be way out ahead by this."

Accordingly, from the first, Sally's coverage had been news—straight news.
e attracted her following with readers through the Killory campaign; the
side operations, the gains, enthusiasms, the successes and the remarkable
omentum that was catching the nation's imagination.

Predictions about what would happen next to this interesting man and his
usade leapt from Sally's typewriter with increasing fascination and force. Her
edictions, accurately made and far ahead of the competing pack, delighted
d impressed Bixley's subscribers. The major papers across the country bought
lly's writings hand over fist. "A triumph for the Syndicate," even the sales
anager said; and he said this even to Sally. And with each new outlet she was
fluencing a new and wider audience. Oh, yes, Sally was becoming a factor
here things were happening.

What is good journalism? Obviously it is rooted in who, what, when,
here, how and why—as copybooks proclaim. But all writers who challenge
e competition with the same twenty-six letters of the alphabet know that it
ly begins with these. Find it where you please, define it as you will, you
nnot separate good journalism from imagination's creative power. Sally had
is. And she was writing now like the musician who cannot strike a false note
 draw a wrong tone from his instrument.

The writing came hard—the elimination of the scaffolding that every
riter has to knock away. But the inside angles and predictions, of course, did
ot. Sally had never set foot in the Killory headquarters, then or later. But if it
 true that, among intelligent people, passion's source is in the mind and runs
om there to the body, that source served her will in a dual and satisfying way.

Again and again Sally would wake up in the middle of their sleep, lie
wake and then move restlessly. Soon she would flick on the bedside light,
ach for her mules, struggle into something and hunch herself for hours in the
tting room writing with a sharp pencil or pounding on her machine.

Frank would stir and she would motion him to be quiet and sleep. Inspira-
on, if that is what it was, came to her consciousness like that. "Next to the
athtub," she once told Frank, "the best place for me to think is just before
m going off to sleep or just as—somehow—I wake up. That's the time."

So they always left some fruit or perhaps a few sandwiches in the sitting
oom in the event of a late session there by Sally. The way she would begin to
ir and then steal out of bed amused him. Without make-up her face actually
ooked younger. There would be a glass full of her sharp-pointed pencils at the
esk, along with her typewriter and several half-empty packs of cigarettes. At
ne side, books were piled in disorder. It was often daylight before she fin-
hed. One night he was surprised to find her singing softly. She had a pleasant

low-pitched voice and seemed to be happy in the words of some small Frer
song.

Working her shoulders, stretching her legs to get out the kinks, massagi
her thighs and breasts, Sally would tiptoe back and snap off the light. S
would bury her head in the pillow, her body and legs along his, and kiss h
gently on the shoulder. Then this high-strung woman would perform her li
long miracle. She would instantly slip into the world of sleep, easily as a chi

Sally would set the clock to wake them early and Frank would go back
the firm's suite to bathe, to change, to be ready for the next day.

Yes, Sally had arrived in the field that had beckoned her to America, a
she was enjoying it with all the reticence of a gold miner fresh out of the Arc
wastes.

Through addressing local gatherings and by interviews Frank had s
tained the public interest well since the Chicago beginning. But Karnes was,
course, casting around for the most strategically valuable place to take 1
second major step after the Chicago affair and repeat the nation-wide tie-ins.

Friends pressed Frank hard to speak in New York. But Karnes ruled th
New York was out of the question for the Chicago follow-through.

"The first time you speak here," he advised, "it should be to a big crov
and in a very, very big way. It ought to be at the Madison Square Garden lev
New York is much too big, Frank. The affair would still be drowned.

"Further, we need to shake off all we can of the New York atmosphere tl
surrounds you, and the label. People across the country just don't trust Ni
York too much, in principle, which is a part of the importance of getting t
Illinois base at the nominating convention.

"No, I would say you should stage the major affairs and make the imp
tant speeches away from New York until the very end. We'll wait for that ur
we're at the absolute top of the drive."

An invitation came to address the large convention of the National G
cery Manufacturers in Philadelphia. Such opportunities now meant more c
batable considerations and longer sessions as the ramifications widened. Tl
one involved Senator Means' home state.

Was Frank now strong enough to accept the invitation—productivel
Even though the veteran Senator did not yet recognize Killory as a factor, a
surely not as a threat, in the coming convention, nothing might more sur
antagonize and dismay this opponent and his powerful group than to grat
tously invade Pennsylvania at the very start of Frank's drive.

Karnes emphasized this and, as in the case of New York City, dismiss
Philadelphia. "Or Pittsburgh," he added, with a wave of his hand. "Not unl
you want to spit in Arthur Means' eye, and anybody who spits in Arthur Mea
eye better watch his step. My guess is that Means isn't taking you seriously y
as a threat in Kansas City, but he will sometime in the future. When he does
won't forget either your bad manners or your political stupidity in heading f
his home base of Pennsylvania right off the bat.

"Moreover," Karnes added, "those in the regular party organization cou

ke that local Pennsylvania climate mighty frosty for you, and would. I don't
nk they'll change that freeze much, and don't see why they should. But we
tainly don't want to dramatize any cleavage with the party regulars if we
help it, and surely not while we're not even up off the ground."

Usher and Putnam agreed. They also agreed that the same veto was wise
inst going so soon to the Pacific Coast, the California domain of Senator
ant Willis.

The South—with invitations in hand from New Orleans, Richmond, At-
ta—was too special for the important follow-up talk, with too many sec-
nal issues demanding attention and reference. Means had long been the
ath's best friend and champion in both the Senate and the party as a whole.
ans would go into the convention with the reliable support of most southern
legations. Means had his powerful Pennsylvania base and the attachment of
East to him in many places as something of a favorite son, plus the South.
ong sentiment bound him to much of the big urban vote on the Atlantic
board and in the newly industrialized southern centers, and finally, he had
better support from the trade unions—such as it was—than Willis.

The core of Willis' strength would be his powerful California base, the rest
the Pacific Coast, most mountain states and the majority of the plains states.
was strong and favored in the Mississippi Valley and through its farm belt.
e Kansas City location of the convention would not help Willis, for in the
dwest there was a distinct inclination to go for Means.

The Midwest was tempting as the locale for the second speech. The de-
ion crystallized when Morton's Omaha representative conjured up an invita-
n to speak at a large meeting of the Livestock Breeders' Association there.

"It's only been six weeks since our opener in Chicago," Karnes insisted
en Scriver pressed carefully for its acceptance. "Turn it down, Frank, for the
ne being."

"Postpone it?" Frank asked.

"Yes, just postpone it. Surely some other organization will be convening in
naha when we want to go there at the right time. I hope. But not now."

The breakup of the session left the locale for the follow-up attack still in
e air. It was Sally who pulled it down when Frank carried the problem back
the St. Regis with him that night.

"What's the matter with Boston?" she asked. "You're a big switch from
at Boston is used to, Braidwood, and it seems to me you'd create quite a stir
there."

"Sal," he said, "why not Boston?" He told her no one in Boston had shown
y interest in having him come.

"Wouldn't you know," she said, with a light laugh and a wiggle of her
gerish little nose. "Everybody wants you where you don't want to go and
body wants you where I hope you'll go. To hell with Boston. But you have a
t to tell them up there just the same."

Frank turned serious. In moments of candor when he made a quiet report

to himself he knew that during most of his public appearances and interviev
now there was not much wheat in the eloquent straw that he was threshing.
mass of uneasy doubts burst in. Was he to be like a book or a man who ow
being a celebrity to a trick of time rather than to intrinsic excellence?

Sally was at the dressing table, tired after a long meeting that afternoc
with John Bixley, but relaxed, and smiling back at Frank in the mirror, her lo
delicate fingers making deft movements around the corners of her mouth ar
eyes. She was doing her little ritual touches, idling her hands over her smoo
thighs, or running them lazily through her hair, or probing them into h
stockings to detect a snag.

"Sal," he said, moving closer, "I'm running around talking a good deal
emotionalism, you know. But I am also running for a nomination for tl
Presidency. If it all works out, a President cannot just talk emotionalism. He
a man who has responsibility—*the* responsibility.

"I'm not being equivocal about what I stand for, exactly; and I guess
don't sound equivocal to the public. But, honestly, Sal, I really don't say muc
either. Sometimes it makes me feel just a little bit like a phony."

Sally laid down a nail file. She took a cigarette and lit it slowly. She blew
long puff to the ceiling and then settled her elbows on the narrow dressir
table.

He talked into her mirrored eyes and she looked at both their reflections
the mirror, veiled in the smoke of her cigarette.

"Why, the gate is wide open for the phony. Putting aside all the machiner
of politics," Frank continued quietly, "the primaries, nominating convention
in-fighting, and everything, think a minute, darling, how much ignorance the
is that a man can appeal to in our country.

"Education and educated people? Sure. Yet, a *New York Times* surve
even a college survey, discovered in answer to its questions that thousands
college freshmen actually thought Thomas Jefferson founded *The Saturd
Evening Post,* that Alexander Hamilton invented the telephone, that Wa
Whitman was a dance-band leader—confusing with Paul Whiteman.

"Twenty-five percent didn't know Abraham Lincoln was President durir
the Civil War. More than thirty percent didn't know who was President durir
the World War. My God!" He shook his head. "I feel ashamed sometimes t
realize how easy it could be to trifle with the good faith of ordinary folks acro
our country."

Here was the part of Frank that Sally always enjoyed most; when he wa
conversational without being clever, reliable and full of common sense withou
being brilliant. In short, the easy naturalness and the heart-warming glow tha
was lit by underneath qualities—solidity, humility, knowledge of one's self-
that she herself needed at certain times. They gave him dignity, gave a fidelit
to his roots. She could not help wondering how it was that she had ever com
to share either his bed or his secrets.

"Well, Braidwood," she said, nodding, "Vincent Emery told me what ha pened in England. When Anthony Eden was visiting America the London *Daily Herald*—Old Sir Ronald—polled a large cross-section of a typical industrial city in the States—Bridgeport, Connecticut.

"Less than thirty percent correctly identified Eden. Others reported to the *Herald's* poll takers that he was: a United States senator; an ambassador; a movie star. One confused Eden with Tommy Manville, Jr., and said Eden was the marriage champion, and a woman told the *Herald* that she listens to Eden every week on the radio in Bridgeport because he is her favorite comedian. You say, 'My God.' I say, 'My God,' too. But nobody is forced to cash in on the ignorance who doesn't want to: and you're not cashing in on it."

Sally found a glass and poured some water in it from the Thermos, offering it to him, but he shook his head. She drank slowly, pensively. Suddenly she leaned over and kissed him.

"Don't worry, Braidwood," she said, "and as for emotionalism, it all depends, doesn't it, on whether you're honest? Is it honest emotionalism? I say 'yes,' with you."

He turned to the bed and sagged onto it. Sally's fingers tightened on his hand. She was seized suddenly by the thought that she was not answering his anxieties very well after all. "The only thing you can possibly do, it seems to me," she continued, "is rely on the admonition: 'For if the trumpets give an uncertain sound, who shall prepare himself for the battle?' Generals can lose battles by themselves, certainly. But the greatest general in the world cannot win a battle alone. He must have troops and they must have faith in him.

"No, you're not a phony," she continued, tossing her hair over her shoulders, "you're a campaigner for the nomination; a campaigner for the nomination with some advantages, but many specific disadvantages—like not a single state behind you—and you have to play the cards dealt you."

Sally spoke with the compassion of a worldly woman who knows that it is a man's strengths and weaknesses, his lapses and his recoveries, that make him a man of flesh and blood, but that certain errors are decisive in his own self-respect.

She took both his hands and held them closely in hers. "But there's one thing you can't do, Frank," she said, with an emphasis that showed in her searching eyes. "You can't fool around with this opportunity—this responsibility. By God, I've seen enough of that everywhere. False promises, unattainable promises, broken promises. These three things are the curse of men and nations. The windbags who come to mean not a damn thing they say make me so sick I could vomit.

"You don't have to be President of the United States, you know. You didn't make America. America made you. Look at it as if you were paying back a debt. I think you are."

The next morning Frank telephoned Chicago and had a long talk with Jacob Morton about a Boston possibility.

"Mid-Continental doesn't have anybody in Boston," Jake moaned in his husky voice. "We don't even have an office there. No, Frank, I can't help in

Boston. Boston is Boston, beyond which there's the rest of America. Nobod
can help you except a Bostonian, that's for sure."

But Scriver knew the owner of a large Bay City department store, Clar
ence Fenton, a citizen of many parts, prominent in Boston civic affairs and th
Boston music world, although not in politics.

Scriver left for Boston. When he returned, Frank had won an invitation t
address the National Association of Shoe Dealers, in which Fenton was a
important factor. Fenton, in turn, arranged to have Frank's old client of hi
Braidwood days, the Excelsior Shoe Company, endorse the Fenton sponsor
ship. The Killory attack on Massachusetts was under way.

The banquet would be in the large ballroom of the Copley-Plaza. A tie-i
with all the nation's news media was assured. Fenton's advertising agency—h
store its principal client—offered its services to the banquet committee an
would ride herd on the publicity.

Elation ignited the Killory group and Scriver basked in the bright light
this moment like an aging beach boy at Cannes. Moreover, he returned with
check from Fenton for one thousand dollars, the first outside money raised
the group. "Put this in the bank," he said to Sam in his conspiratorial tone as h
handed him the check, made out to Samuel Welsh. "Just a little early cream fo
the kitty."

Sam smiled reverently. "Yes, sir." He hurried downstairs to execute h
private mission, now a regular fixture in the world of confidential operatior
and discreet performance. Scriver laughed briefly as Sam disappeared, the
shook his head, answering Mary-Louise's inquiring glance.

Although she gave no sign, Scriver nevertheless experienced the stro
sensation that he was unwelcome to Mary-Louise in this office and his aut
matic reflex was to win her; his normal habit among the lowly surrounding
sovereign.

"Well, Mary-Louise," he said, smiling through his mustachios like an ami
ble tiger, "Mr. Killory has a great helper in you, all right, and Sam, too. A luc
man, especially coming here a stranger to the firm and the city and you kno
ing all the ropes. A good secretary can make or break a man, I always say. B
try to find one. Just try to find one."

Mary-Louise made a shy, disclaiming gesture. "Thank you, Mr. Scrive
she said, coldly, as she went out the door. "Mr. Killory is not as lucky as I a
Left alone by the window viewing the sea, Scriver was the victim of a sudd
silence. Glancing at his watch, he went next into Frank's office to take up a vi
until Killory returned for their appointment.

"I think I'd better go up to Boston a few days ahead and nurse t
arrangements through with Fenton," he said. "This kind of thing is all new
him. He really joined up on that condition. I told him I would take over wi
him in Boston as far ahead of time as I could. And, by the way, Frank, you'll
glad to hear Fenton also gave us a thousand dollars."

"No? Well, that's—"

"Yes, he did. I really don't think Fenton would refuse me anything if
could do it. Fenton's not a big man, not your caliber; I don't think you'd fi

oo much in common with him, as a matter of fact. He's limited and somewhat old-womanish. But by my second day up there he'd come around. Yes, he had, and—what the hell?—he should, for the man who is going to be the next President of the United States."

Frank was listening with the look of youthfulness that often made you forget his years, his eyes alight with good fellowship.

"Fenton has about the best store in New England, hasn't he?" Frank asked. "I'm anxious to meet him and thank him."

"But not for the money, Frank," Scriver interposed. "That's just between us girls." Glancing at his watch again, he discovered it to be ten minutes past the hour. He rose precipitately. "See you in Boston," he said. "Tell Janet that Grace will be along. Grace will take good care of her. Knows a lot of people in Boston—went to Radcliffe, you know. Tell Janet not to worry. Goodbye, Frank, and happy landings."

"Goodbye, Arch," he answered, getting up from his chair, "and Arch, I simply don't know how to thank you."

"Bosh. Why, Frank, we haven't even started yet." And away he went with farewell wave to Mary-Louise, unreturned.

# 12

ARNES HAD URGED Janet to make the Boston trip. "And bring the girls," he suggested. "It's a short, comfortable trip. Just up one afternoon and back the next morning."

Margaret stayed home because of an engagement with some friends, but Frank packed Janet and Jan off with him on the day of the dinner. Scriver and Grace had the Killory rooms ready at the Copley-Plaza.

Putnam was on hand, waiting. Usher arrived, bringing one of the two men his organization that he had volunteered to deliver to Frank. He was statistician John Gibbons, chief of the magazines' economic research department, a man who would have all the figures and be able to produce facts, or find someone who could.

"John is the best in the country at making statistics meaningful and giving them the human touch, the human urge," Usher told Frank at the hotel, "and you'll need him for your economic research material. We've given John a leave

of absence. He's tickled pink, although, in fact, he once served three years
digging out material and putting it into shape for the President you'll be
running against."

"Did they have a break?" Frank asked, walking across the room and
stretching out on a sofa.

"Oh, no. Not at all. Gibbons merely quit the White House when our offer
came along. He was there only professionally. He went to work for us. Now
John's working for you."

Frank met his helper a few minutes later; a stout man with a bald head
although Gibbons was really not so stout as he was pouchy. And under the
rather small eyes, set too near each other and in thick, whitish skin, were gray
pouches as well. There was a certain sexlessness about the statistician, as if
whatever masculinity there had been in him was muted.

"Welcome to the cyclone, Mr. Gibbons," Frank said, sticking out his hand
"or to the cyclone cellar, we don't know which." Gibbons said he was glad to
help in any way. He would listen to the speech this evening and travel back to
New York with Frank and the group the following day.

Frank ordered cocktails for Usher and Gibbons, then excused himself and
put a call through from another room to Sally in New York, telling her Usher
had produced Gibbons and that he was with him now. She had never heard of
Gibbons and was, in fact, in something of a hurry to rush out. "Work him hard
Braidwood," she said, "and hurry back."

But her interest, clearly, was concentrated on a struggle with her pinching
shoes. "What I'd like to know," she said, only half into the phone, "is how
happens that nature, so wonderful in other ways, didn't design women with
feet to fit their shoes?" He had expected, and wanted, a longer conversation
and it unsettled him a little to hear her "I'll be listening tonight" and her
cheerful goodbye so quickly. At moments there was a strange undergraduate
quality about him and at this moment he felt sadly disappointed.

The Scrivers had arranged a tea for Janet and Jan and they brought Mr
and Mrs. Fenton back with them to meet "the candidate," as Scriver so prema-
turely insisted on referring to Frank. The gratuitous implication hurdled a
barriers to the nomination and catapulted Frank directly into the joust with
the incumbent President. In fact, sometimes after a highball or two, Scriver
would tilt his glass and address Frank as "the next President of the United
States," an assumption of substantial size when applied a man whom the Gallup
poll accorded only a sudden fifteen percent chance of even the nomination, and
this solely as a reflection of the vulnerable Chicago enthusiasm.

Mrs. Fenton was a little woman. Her narrow forehead and sharp nose
gave her a bird-like appearance. She had bright copper-colored hair and a shrill
voice that hardly fitted her actual rank as a Beacon Street dowager. Fenton
was George Apley in the flesh, except that he was as small as his wife and
seemed lost behind the bulk of Scriver, who rolled along in front of him when
they arrived.

"Mr. Killory," he said, with an engaging sincerity, "we're honored to have

u in Boston. The Excelsior Shoe Company in Braidwood really gave you a
onderful endorsement. The Shoe Association is looking forward to great
ings tonight."

"We feel it was very kind of Frank to come," Grace purred, casting a dry
ile at Janet, "and very kind of your Boston friends to make all these helpful
rangements."

"Nonsense," Fenton replied, "a good speaker is harder to find then hen's
eth; most of them talk too long, too long, and say nothing. Mrs. Fenton and I
ard your Chicago speech, Mr. Killory, and we were deeply impressed.
ere's also a lot in our papers up here about what's happening to you. Wel-
me, welcome."

"Oh, yes, we were and are impressed," Mrs. Fenton chirped, grasping his
nd and blushing with pleasure. "From the moment we heard you from
icago I've wanted to meet you, Mr. Killory. I never wrote a fan letter in my
e but the closest I ever came to it was after that speech. I've been telling Mrs.
lory all afternoon that you have been the main topic at our women's club for
ys, ever since the ladies have known you were coming. The waitresses,
erybody. It's not just us that like you, Mr. Killory."

Young Jan sighed and asked boldly, "Do you think the women of Boston
uld vote for my Pa?"

Frank did not hear this but Janet felt a lump in her stomach and Mrs.
nton gave an embarrassed little laugh, as did her husband. "My dear, they
uld," she ventured. "I really think they should." But more than this seemed
yond easy statement and was lost in murmurs and a quick look of dis-
proval.

The dinner committee had orchids for Grace, Jan and Janet—it all seemed
ite a strain to Janet—and, suitably identified as honored guests, they went
wnstairs to join Mrs. Fenton at a table in front of the podium. Frank and
ch hurried to the reception room for honored guests who were to sit at the
eakers' table. Fenton's small face beamed a welcome in the doorway.

"There they go," Janet whispered hurriedly.

All applauded when the tuxedo parade of association leaders came in—the
hts out and the spotlight playing on the flag—and the music broke into "The
ar-Spangled Banner" as soon as they reached their places. The room was
cked and Janet, Jan and Grace smiled up at Frank, seated on the right of the
astmaster. The timing of the dinner courses was controlled by the air time
ast-to-coast, and a few minutes before nine o'clock the serving of the iced
ssert was cut short and the toastmaster asked for quiet.

As the silent interval dragged by until a control man gave the signal that
e proceedings were on the air, Frank fumbled with a lump of sugar, dropped
 into his coffee and studied the small froth it made on the surface. He
ought: There are an awful lot of people out there listening clear across our
untry; many more, even, than from Chicago, for this is prime evening time
stead of early afternoon. What an immense unseen crowd, what a vast unseen
dience.

The distracting thought was a blunder, leading as it did to the inner idea that he was now speaking to a vast assembly and thereby unconsciously givi his manner and the talk the impact of a detached oration.

He had forgotten how startling, and even frightening, it would be if som one stepped suddenly into a living room, kitchen or bedroom and began ma ing an oration. There was no vast audience. His audience consisted, on t average, of two to three people, sitting at home, or standing at a bar, nearly of them doing something besides listening; putting the children to bed, was ing the dishes, or busy with the various timely occupations and distractions the four differing times of the day or evening in the East, Midwest, Mounta States and on the West Coast.

Moreover, the content of the speech itself was a disappointment. As Chicago, Frank spoke extemporaneously. "I can't feel natural, I can't be myse reading something," he had insisted to Karnes and the others. But Frank h plunged into a sea of platitudes with the powerful breast strokes of a chanr swimmer and made his confident way to the White Cliffs of the obviou Somehow, it just did not go over. Frank felt this while speaking, as Janet d sitting at her table. There were only two brief interruptions for applause, a even some coughing in the room that gave its own unintended signal of re lessness.

"What happened, honey?" Frank asked Janet when they got upstairs and slightly embarrassed Mr. and Mrs. Fenton had gone. "I guess I pressed t hard."

She could feel the rush of blood to her cheeks. A sigh escaped her, but s smiled.

"Frank, dear," Janet said, her eyes appealing for help, "this is a differe part of the country up here. They think differently in New England, you kno you've always said that. It was really a wonderful speech. You wait and s what Walter and the others have to say about it. Jan and I thought it w wonderful and Sam telephoned from New York to congratulate you."

But Karnes, Usher, Putnam and Gibbons, reviewing it with Frank, did r think it was wonderful and neither did anyone else.

"It had sudden flares of beauty and bromides," said Usher in an aside Gibbons, "and that was all there was to it." Gibbons laughed. The laugh w not really mirthful, however, and it made this moment of jovialness somewl grating. Gibbons now saw his new assignment as a first-class problem if Killc turned out to be a stubborn man.

Usher summed up the situation. "Anyway, Killory," he said, "you launched and last night unlaunches nothing. The next speech will be better."

"It better be better," Frank answered. "What I threw tonight was a lea beanbag. I'd made up my mind to take a good, solid crack at the outlook peace and how we're building our policies on quicksand. I intended to say tl the President builds a Taj Mahal around his own thoughts, and so forth. The didn't do that at all," he muttered, tapping the edge of the table with fingers.

Frank was co-operating in a project and, wisely, was not interested in se alibis. Yet an odd thing happened shortly thereafter. The nationwide roar of approval when Frank threw his hat in the ring at Chicago had sent him zooming upward in the Gallup poll, straight as an arrow into the blue. From a few percent he had jumped to fifteen. Boston touched off a bad tumble.

Putnam's newspapers, as poll subscribers, recieved Gallup's releases the day before publication. Marshall showed Frank the down-dip.

He was bringing him to India House to meet some publishers and stopped as they approached the dining room.

"I've a little bad news for you, my friend," Putnam said as he pulled Gallup's mimeographed sheet from his inside pocket.

Frank took it quickly in his hand. Curiously, he dropped it, and then when he picked it up and his eyes ran along the figures Putnam saw his expression of surprise harden a little. There it was, the minus sign, bold-black and sharp as a razor; plain, uncompromising and substantial: the first decline.

Frank hesitated, as if to help make up his mind. Then he looked up stonily, turning Putnam toward him with a hard hold on his arm, and said, "Marshall, what do you think George Gallup has got against me?"

The amazed publisher was completely at a loss. "Why, Frank!" he exclaimed. "For heaven's sake, Gallup hasn't anything against you. How could you get such a preposterous idea? He's running a difficult business. His sampling may prove correct, and is usually very close. Or, he may be off some. But all on earth he's trying to do is hit as close as possible. Preposterous! Against you!"

"You know George Gallup?" Frank persisted.

"Why, yes, I do."

"Why don't you bring us together at lunch sometime?"

Very odd, the puzzled Putnam always thought afterwards. But he never repeated Frank's question, nor did Frank renew the idea about lunch when the poll began to turn upward again. Nevertheless, something did have to be done to improve the radio projection.

This weakness was a private mystery. Frank had spent his life talking intimately and persuasively to jurors and pleading quietly and effectively to judges sitting only a few feet away. He projected with extraordinary effectiveness in small gatherings of people who could observe his sincerity and personal conviction. But the "vast audience" complex, so damaging in Boston, had become a pistol at his head.

Bill Westley, the leading news commentator, who knew and liked him, felt that the waste in effectiveness could be overcome. He began giving Frank pointers immediately after the Boston talk. So did Sally, as a guinea pig, for she had urged him to adopt rehearsals.

"Now you've got it," she would say, sitting across the room, her legs crossed under her, yogi-fashion, her eyes and ears all attention, "that's just fine. Just be yourself, Frank. Forget that vast 'unseen audience' that doesn't exist, exactly as Westley told you. Think that you're talking only to me."

She would flutter her eyes and smile, mimicking a schoolgirl, hand on heart. And when he came to some point he thought was his best she would give him a big open, delighted "Darling!" with handclaps and all, or pound her mules' heels on the floor, or shout "Bravo!" "Bravissimo!" like a gallery fan at La Scala. This was the animal zest that locked her so close to Frank, ready to be spent soon in Sally's own devouring way.

Sally felt that while the Boston meeting was a setback, as the Gallup poll had shown, it had done no real damage and was saying this in her articles with refreshing confidence.

"Listen to him the next time, Bixley, he'll be better," she told the lank editor. "My God, what do you expect from a horse in the Grand National the first time out."

Then, in the strange way in which bad moments are sometimes relieved by what may seem at first to be a small event, the Boston fiasco brought an important result—at least this was the timing of what happened.

A telephone call came for Killory from Ithaca, New York. Sam took it and as was often the case these days, found himself talking with a stranger. The man promptly stated that he did not know Mr. Killory but would like to speak with him. This fact once established, Sam's system went into gear. Mr. Killory would be delighted to speak to him, if he were available. But he was not. The was Mr. Samuel Welsh, Mr. Killory's assistant. If the speaker would be kind enough, instead, to write Mr. Killory a letter he would see to it that Mr. Killory received it at once. The words came hard to Sam, staring as he was at the adjoining file room loaded with unanswered letters, but come they did and with a cheerfulness as unfailing as the moonlight in ballads.

The letter arrived the following Monday morning.

A young scientist on the Cornell faculty wrote that he was due for sabbatical and wanted to volunteer to work for Killory's nomination. He stated that although he had no experience in politics he felt that he could organize Killory Clubs in the grass roots across the country in the way that he organized one in Ithaca. "I am an independent," he said, "and I am convinced that the organization and enthusiastic support of the independents represent the key your nomination and your election." Frank lifted his eyebrows when he read this. And when he had finished the letter and put it aside he asked Sam reach a Mr. Benjamin Watson at Rockefeller Hall in Ithaca. At Frank's invitation, Watson came to New York the next day.

He refused any offset of his expenses and moved into a midtown office where a relative allowed him enough space to go to work. Watson said would recruit his own helpers.

Meanwhile, Sam sent young Watson all letters Frank had received since the opening talk in Chicago—the answered and unanswered alike. Ben Watson used these as a nucleus to build his Killory Clubs from one end of the country to the other.

Karnes looked on, hardly believing, as the mail poured in. "To hell with the Boston people," he said, with joy. "If this isn't a natural groundswell even that speech couldn't kill off, I'll eat it.

"I want to bring Jacob Morton on here to meet you," he told Ben. "A lot of
t mail would never have showed up, you know, if it hadn't been for Jake
l his whoopla in the twenty-eight cities."

Ben merely smiled matter-of-factly and came up with an improvement on
suggestion. The others soon recognized that to be his custom.

"Don't you think I could get nearer to what he has done and is going to
with all his Mid-Continental people, if I went out to Chicago?"

Ben spent the next two weeks with the Mid-Continental crowd in Chicago.
worked out an arrangement by which Morton would develop the Killory
ibs in the Central States; and Jake, in turn, went on to San Francisco to put
nry Jennings of Mid-Continental's Bay Area office to work for the Pacific
ast. "Take every man we've got to help you as best they can," Jake had told
n. "Just get them back into the life insurance business after the nomination,
t's all."

Ben telephoned Sam to line up more space in another midtown building.
n dipped into the till for the first time and drew a check on the account
wnstairs. The building needed tenants, the rent was a bargain, and Sam took
hole floor. Karnes told him that surely this much space would be needed, the
y Ben's operation was growing. Sam tended to the door lettering himself
l saw the building man paint it on. THE KILLORY CLUBS OF AMERICA, it said,
l this was the legend which welcomed Ben back to New York—bringing in
y four of Morton's men from Mid-Continental's New York office. In less
n six weeks the enrollment in the Killory Clubs had passed its first million.

"Now I guess it'll level off," Frank told Sally when this mark was passed.
t it didn't, and Sally wrote about the phenomenon with the rich, possessive
asure of a discoverer—a discoverer of the American people.

She expressed this more simply to Frank. "My Lord Braidwood," she said
oyantly, "it looks to me as if an awful lot of people want you to get that
nination. They want you to win, just as I want you to win."

"And an awful lot of people don't," he replied.

They were playing some two-handed game; Sally going about it in her
ical, no-nonsense, straightforward way. But Frank was thinking more of her
n of the cards. Her remark had given him the usual tang of pleasure and
ught to his lips a passing smile of tenderness.

He wondered—and supposed that he would always wonder—how a
man could be so many things and, of course, construed that he was in love
h her. For love has as many meanings as there are people. But Sally per-
ted in not using the word. She had never exchanged it with him.

"It's a scruple, a principle, with me," she would say. "I told you in Cha-
nix that I'm superstitious. Somehow, I am superstitious about the word
ve'. You're a romantic, Frank. And romantics are dangerous animals, it's been
d, to themselves and to others.

"Take me as you feel me to be," she insisted. "Feel me, and make up your
n mind about the rest. No, although I really don't know quite why, I just
n't like talking about love, or your talking about it either."

Up would come her delicate hands in a quiet gesture that implied "Say
more," the constraining subject would be changed, and within moments s
would be looking at him with all the serenity of a house filled with sunlight a
music.

Frank could not follow her in such very rare moments when Sally spoke
her inner nature and he told her so in the thwarted spirit not unlike t
poignant, perplexed letters a soldier may write when he is trying to und
stand the war that has him.

In Sally, a prickling thought of Frank's home life, and of Janet's existen
was undoubtedly diminished by the meaninglessness of her own life w
Charles. Existences beyond her vision, her responsibility or contact, can
nebulous in a worldly woman. Concern, in any area of life, unless it is requir
depends somewhat on one's desire to be concerned. And in any case, for Sal
with the requirement missing, the concern seemed missing; that much w
clear. Moreover, the importance, variety and success of the activities arou
her, and the stimulation, were constantly increasing.

What was Killory's progress by now, his status? Senators Arthur Mea
and Grant Willis wondered.

These two met nearly every day at the Capitol. Today the Senators we
the Metropolitan Club, however, and they drifted to a corner of the library.

Means' forthrightness was legendary and with this he combined an in
pendence of mind that was honored in a thousand Senate debates and
political platforms alike. He led in the Senate by persuasion, but also by for
for his arguments were solid and to the point. He was a hard opponent to dr
off the main road and never even bothered to knock down a blow if he thou
it would be knocked down in the general discussion.

Means knew the government, knew the Senate, knew the party and kn
the State of Pennyslvania like the palm of his hand. Only three men had be
in the Senate longer, and this resulted in his position as chairman of the m
important committees when his party was in power and, always, as the oppo
tion leader in the committees when his party was not. Means loved politics. F
even his most staunch opponents agreed that he loved his country far more a
that the nation was deeply in his debt.

"You always know where you stand with Arthur," they would admit. "1
doesn't compromise much, and can be stubborn as a mule, but he's straig
He's honest and he knows what he's talking about. The trouble with argui
with Arthur is that you find he has done his homework or he wouldn't
talking at all."

This, of course, was the principal liability he faced for the nominati
Few felt casually about him, for through the years opinions had crystalliz
one way or the other. Yet he had a deep awareness of the bonds of our natio
clan. This public man's principles were safe inside him. And in the campai
for the Presidential nomination, at his age, he was listening to the last cann
shot he would hear in all his life.

Grant Willis, ten years younger, was nearly as legendary for his frankn it also for his adroitness and for his bawdy humor. There was the breeze of ilifornia and the ocean about him, and a touch of satire in debate. But Willis as an intellectual and ideas burst from him in all directions.

Thus the hail-fellow atmosphere which sometimes surrounded him was isleading. His insightful intelligence was calm and practical, and he had the ipe which maturity lays on the shoulders of an adult—the mark of the periences which age one.

Willis was an aristocrat, and this was evident in his appearance. He had a ng, pale, spoiled face, set off by a splendid head of silver hair, which was a idemark. But it was not a lackey's countenance and his bearing radiated thority. It helped to make him the undisputed leader of one wing of his rty, although the support on which this rested was less firm than his rival's.

For contradictions often came together in Willis, like a backwash from the each comes with the waves. In the minds of many his eloquence did not rmount these elusive contradictions. In fact, Willis was almost too well own for his eloquence. There were those who said that, like the High Priest Eleusis, he had a different incense for each divinity. Means was one who felt . And this was the cleavage between them.

Theirs was a comparison in which each man, viewed alone, was an out- inding example of an exceedingly able public servant. But when viewed in mpetition with each other, each provoked comparisons with the other and th suffered a diminution.

This was so needless that it was a pity the comparison ever arose. For mocracy is difficult to maintain because it requires the active participation of le, experienced and selfless public servants, and there are seldom enough for e task. Anything which detracted from the effectiveness of either Means or illis was a step backward in the very area where good government needed to p forward. Neither had an enmity-motif. Neither had any personal bitterness their rivalry. But many of each man's supporters were bitter. And as for eans supporting Willis or Willis supporting Means, each had only a single ird to say: the hard word "No."

They sat by a window, while the rain poured rivulets down the pane, and ch ordered a drink. Willis stretched his long frame in comfort, noted the uch of brightness which a vase of wild flowers gave the mantelpiece, and ilized that if this meeting was premature it might result in an undesirable arrel. But he experienced a strong sensation of relief when he sensed that eans, too, felt that a little talk at this juncture could be very clarifying.

"Artie," he said, "what do you think of Killory and what he's doing?"

The older man raised his eyes to the ceiling and was silent, his brows ntracted in thought. Then he said, slowly, "There is some eel under that rock, hough I don't quite know what it is."

"Do you think he really imagines he's going any place?"

"Why sure I do, Grant; did you ever see anybody in politics who doesn't ow the difference between getting back-slaps and getting votes who didn't ink he was going someplace? Through the years, couldn't you give me a

hundred cases in California? I could in Pennsylvania. And how many outsi
candidates for the Presidential nomination are there at every conventio
There were six at the last convention, in addition to all the favorite sor
weren't there?"

"But I think this Killory thing is a little different."

"So do I. First, Killory is different. Next, the convention situation is diffe
ent. Killory is trying to bounce himself off both your back and mine. We'
supposed to be the patsies, the fall guys—or even the villains—both of us,
course."

Willis laughed. It was obvous to him that his rival for the nomination w
ready to call a spade a spade.

"He and his crowd are raising a lot of money," Willis volunteered.

"How much?"

"Well, in addition to staging that Boston thing, I know that Mr. Fenton
Fenton's up there gave Killory ten thousand dollars for the kitty."

"How do you know that, Grant?"

"Well, Arch and Grace Scriver had dinner with Mary and me here t]
other night and Arch told me."

"Arch said Fenton gave Killory ten thousand dollars?"

"Yes, before the Boston meeting. Scriver specifically stated ten thousan
he said he brought Fenton's check for ten thousand back from Boston when ]
arranged that affair. And if Fenton in New England is laying out that kind
money for an outside candidate a good many other substantial people arour
the country must be taking Killory's chances seriously."

"Did Scriver say anything else?"

"Well, I guess he is the closest man to Killory, all right. One of the earli
to whoop it up for him, he says. Scriver is the kingmaker in there, I gathe
He's that close, Artie."

"How about Walter Karnes? I think Walter and Arch are the only tv
members of the National Committee who are interested. What do you think?"

"Only those two, so far as I know. If you or I want some contact wi
Killory I think we had better work through Arch."

"I don't want any contact with him," Means insisted, with vigor. "I ju
wonder what's coming out of all this activity by the Killory Clubs. There a
quite a few in Pennsylvania now, and they're spreading."

"And in California."

"Where I live these mushroom organizations are getting in the hair of t
regular party clubhouses and party organizations. These independents, at le;
some of them, seem to think that the way to show that Killory is a good man
to show that he has nothing to do with the regular organization and is r
backed by it."

"Well, where I live," Willis replied, "that's happening in some places, li
Los Angeles, and not in others, like the Valley. There these clubs seem to be c
operating with the regular organization. The California head of the Killc
outfit is a San Francisco man representing a Chicago insurance company,
outstanding man in the community named Jennings. He's been to see 1

;ular organization people a dozen times. But it's obvious Jennings can't con-
l his own mushroom groups scattered around the state. And if these don't
p lambasting the regular organization as if we were dirty deuces in a wet
ck they're going to make it hard for anybody in our party to win the election,
matter who is nominated."

"Why, sure. And Killory must know that. I get the feeling he doesn't care
ich what happens to the party just so he wins in Kansas City. But if he uses
ɛ party as a whipping boy, where is his vehicle for the election—or anybody
ɛ's vehicle either?"

"Oh, Artie, it isn't that serious. They have a lot of amateurs running around
d spending lots of money; I know all that. But if this crowd can damage our
rty as much as that, then the party is so weak it has no more chance than a
owball in hell of electing anybody. But that's not the case."

"Of course, of course."

"Moreover, Killory has no political base."

"Now you hit it, Grant, exactly. That's what I've been telling my people.
et's see his political base for the convention,' I've said. And he hasn't one.
hat delegation is going to be his rock? None. When you stand off and look at
is thing, Grant, it's downright silly. With radio, with good newspaper and
ıgazine backing like Putnam and Usher—"

"I wish I had them both," Willis mused.

"And so do I. Well, with this powerful whoopla and plenty of money
cked up by a good personality—my God, you can do a lot. Mass communica-
ns have helped all these fellows like hell, we have to remember that."

"I don't think Killory is as well known in the country, obviously, as either
us."

"Well, neither do I. But he is moving toward a blitz. The newspapers like
ıtnam's and the rest have picked him up as a political force and so have
itorial writers. He multiplies the effect very nicely, I think," Means brooded.
's the whole package put together that does it."

"What worries me is Mary, Artie."

"Mary? For heaven's sake why Mary?"

"Yes, Mary. Mary really likes this man Killory. I tell you my wife thinks
illory's really something. Never met him in her life, but she pumped Grace
river to know all about him the minute she knew they were friends. Mary
esn't go overboard, you know that. Men are not the real spark under this. It's
e women, Artie, that are putting the real umph in this thing. Somehow, a lot
them in the grass roots just want this fellow."

Means smiled and then began to laugh in his forthright manner, his broad,
ain, honest face lighting up in the appealing way which, had it shown more
ten, would have meant much to his political pulling power. Unfortunately,
is congenial look was rare.

"Grant," he said, "here you are with a toehold on the women in our party
-e never been able to get and will never get. I have to work against this lack
appeal as if I were a hunchback and you're Cary Grant instead of Grant
illis and you talk about Killory running off with the women's vote. If any-

body is going to hold 'em for this party, Grant, it's going to be you. And, f
God's sake, my boy, don't let 'em go. That's your department—the ladie
young and old. They're not going to vote for me unless, or until, they get re
old. Also, they're not going to vote for Killory because they're not going to get
chance to. Grace Scriver gives me a pain anyway, if you must know the trut
and so does Arch, for that matter. I've never liked him, and I know he car
stand my guts. But he keeps fawning around anyway.

"I'll bet you a hundred dollars that before this campaign is over Arc
Scriver comes to me with some dirty little thing about you. I'll bet you anoth
hundred he comes to you with some dirty little thing about me. If he's th
close to Killory, and I don't doubt it for a minute, then Killory's a dope ar
doesn't know any better. Maybe Killory is just on the make and giving h
confidence to anybody who's been in this business a long time. But, Grant,
you mix with the pigs you get your hands dirty, you know."

"Artie, you're too hard on Scriver," Willis demurred. "And, anyway, wh
on earth can Arch Scriver do to influence any delegates?"

"Nothing. But Walter Karnes can," Means said.

Willis took a slow swallow of his drink while Means pulled out a cigar ar
lit up. "It all still comes back to the fact," he said, "that Killory has no state a
his delegation base. And I simply don't see how he can get one."

Means grinned. "Well, of course, that's right, Grant. But in making h
pitch the fellow is fouling up the whole nest. And for what? As you say, l
hasn't the delegates. He won't get the delegates. He's banking on a deadloc
naturally. But who says there's going to be a deadlock? Now, Grant, let me a
you something. Of course Killory's bet on a deadlock is the key to the who
thing. You and I have been in this business a long, long time. Let me ask yo
Do you think there is going to be a deadlock?"

Willis raised his eyes and looked at the older man gravely. They had bo
done well, he reflected with an inward thrill, to be able to talk like this after a
their supporters' tale-bearing and back-biting that could have harmed the
mutual confidence beyond repair.

"Do I think there is going to be a deadlock?" Willis repeated. "No, I d
not. Do you?"

"No, I do not," Means answered, deeply sober. This was the privat
considered and confidential judgment of the two best-informed men in th
United States on the issue in question.

Willis pondered. "Suppose with all this public commotion Killory come
way up in the Gallup poll?" he said.

"Well, he may climb a few points more between now and mid-July, u
doubtedly will. But can you imagine those nine hundred delegates sayin;
'Well, I'll tell you what we're going to do at this convention. We're going to d
something real smart this time. We're not going to nominate Senator Mean
who is about forty points in nation-wide popularity in the polls and has bee
carrying our party's standard through thick and thin all these years. Oh, n

id we're certainly not going to nominate Senator Willis, who is about forty
ints in the polls. We're going to nominate, instead, Mr. Frank Killory, who is
out twenty points in the polls and battle him against the President of the
nited States, who is in office. We're going to win the election with Killory
en though, in addition, he never ran for public office in his life . . . and so on.
ant, that's nothing but the 'silly season' in politics. No, there won't be any
adlock. You're going to get that Kansas City nomination, or I am.

"Grant, it's you or me. And for either of us that gets it, winning the
ection in November is going to be one hell of a job. That's the way I see it,
yway."

There was a sharp silence. Each man had had a full, rich, rewarding life
d not, of course, an easy one. For one of them this year would mean the
lfillment of his proper ambitions, hopes and dreams in the field in which he
d labored for a lifetime against all turns of events, good times and bad, in
ir and in peace. The other would fail.

The self-education of a scrupulous and deserving political leader is severe.
ie rules of political morality are less agreed upon than any applied to the
es of men; some would have the principles of private life carried whole into
litics, while others make exceptions for necessity. But the public men who
opt the more rigid creed may get their consciences broken down in an
iavailing struggle, while those who deny the applicability to political life of
e principles of private morality are often unable to find footing for any
inciples whatever.

A deserving man answered a deserving man. "Artie," Willis said, rising to
, "that's the way I see it too."

# 13

tank found the crowds exhilarating, but the long sessions about political
alities were tiring and affected him like the man in the myth who kept rolling
e stone up the hill only to have it roll back on him.

Able professionals like Karnes spoke a language of political personalities,
litical facts, political truisms so unfamiliar to Frank that Walter, for one,
owed true patience in grinding out the indispensable education.

Politics is not simple; it is devilishly complex. And why not? The human mind, the public mind, is not simple. The human heart certainly isn't.

Impressions that influence millions and cause them to approve or disap prove of a man in politics differ a great deal. Moreover, like a stream, th public mind is permanent—but with a constantly changing content.

The problem is to associate oneself with a whole people; to see people they see themselves, to find and ally oneself with their inner aspirations.

This is an art. And it is made harder because the ordinary man thinks little about political affairs as he can. Thus, no politician wants to convey an impression that the business he is in is complicated. It makes him a strange Moreover, nearly anything well done looks easy. The true masters of politi make it look easy. But the underpinnings in the art depend on a comple understanding of political realities and the currently available political m chinery.

"Frank, you've two absolutely separate situations," Karnes would plead confronting Frank with the earthy realities. "The first involves problems th must be solved to win the nomination, of course, not the election. What worri me is that you may be getting the cart before the horse.

"That's why your enthusiasm about the public and about issues compar to your fixation about politicians can be so dangerous in all this."

"I have no fixation about politicians," Frank would protest, honestly a noyed.

"Well, if not, all right. But let me say I think your emphasis and, yes, yo urges are badly out of balance. Just now, politically minded people from eve state mean your success or failure. You have to think in terms of that reali beyond all else: who will do what for you at the convention, and why? If y fail in that part of it you're through. The second, and very different, situatior your election afterwards—doesn't even arise."

"Naturally. I realize that, of course." Frank found it hard to hold hims in during such sessions.

"But again and again, I get the feeling, Frank, that you are running for th nomination as if it were the election. You can't do that. You're asking a girl marry you. That girl is the convention. Your general popularity is a favori factor in the girl's eyes, of course, but it isn't decisive. Too many other factor as with any girl—are involved, as she sees it. No, your general populari cannot be decisive until you win the girl and *then* run for the election. O Frank, it's so much more complicated than it looks."

Yet Frank listened little to such objections and more and more put the fu weight on his own opinions, most of which were merely desires, apparent hardly conscious that he was thus challenging the political instinct and comp tence of such a veteran as Karnes.

Grant Frank his premises, and his conclusions were usually sound enoug But he often argued hard against reality and disputed the premises vetera tried to teach him, replying: "Well, if that's true, it shouldn't be like that." T

bit of not admitting things to himself was becoming a confirmed one with
n. Exasperation and frustration were beginning to grip him when confronted
such advisers, especially when the Gallup poll turned upward again after
Boston decline.

In fact, when Putnam showed Frank the advance information on this, the
art bounce back like a sky-borne arrow again, Frank had the flicker of revolt
his eye.

"My friend," Karnes protested, "I'm still not talking about your popularity.
d I know you don't mean what you said to me about my 'revising my
litical thinking'—at least, I hope I don't. But be careful when you talk like
at. Few people in the political ranks are as interested in you as I am and,
th any crack about their 'living in the past' or that they 'should wake up,' or
at not, they'd have a mighty good excuse to throw Frank Killory overboard
norrow morning."

"Oh, Walter," Frank answered, "you know I'm just blowing off steam." But
voice had gone flat, as if he were trying to convince himself rather than
rnes that this was all there was to it. For somehow Frank's fixation grew that
own judgment was superior in politics. Never evident except when this was
allenged, that highly personalized dream baffled Karnes and failed to square
th the common sense that had been Frank's Braidwood hallmark.

Walter's remark to Mrs. Karnes one evening was the tip-off. "I'm just a
tle afraid our Frank has been reading his fan mail," he said. She was listening
the first line of a lament that would be tossed from echo to echo for a long,
ng time.

In addition, apparently Frank was now fully fertile for the compounding
this lament.

Along with statistician Gibbons, Usher's other contribution was Edward
lt, a lean man of that greyhound type not uncommon in England. In fact,
her had summoned Holt back from a London visit to serve Killory in his
eat political try.

Frank knew him by reputation as a writer capable of flashing lightning
m his brow. Holt's reserved manner belied this, however, just as it belied his
timate capacity for vindictive and specious logic.

His true home was the world of bright younger men with their whistling,
refree confidence, smacking of crew-cuts, image-making and "Oh, yeah?" to
eir elders.

At their first meeting Frank found Holt rather glum. Was it icy insouciance
simply cold fish? Moreover, Holt's eyes had a fixedness, accentuated by
usually large glasses, that seemed to mark him as a man of sharp impulse.
is manner did not relieve this, for he had an arrogance which was made up of
aring at you, measuring your value, and deciding you weren't there. It gave
m the proud-over-nothing expression of a spoiled man. In truth, he cared no
ore for the ordinary man than the big Indian cares for the little Indian in
dia.

But Usher knew Holt very well—which is not quite the same thing understanding him—and his dank personaltiy made no odds to the publisher.

Holt put out his elongated, skeletal, meatless hand. "How do you do, M Killory," he said. That was all.

In Frank's increasing glory and his own relative obscurity, Holt welcom this assignment with inner intensity, another fact that his attitude belied.

He was an oppositionist at heart, to people and to the world. He had nev liked movement and people, not because he ever took part in the one or ha much contact with the other, but because he took pleasure in what he alwa termed the folly of humanity. It was his nature to conduct a vendetta agair most of the world. He seemed to have a drive which must conquer definite whatever it casually touches. He came to hide this intention behind a wall statistics and political jargon. Gradually this facility had taken over. There w a time when almost everything he wrote was good. Now almost everything wrote was praised.

In the long curve of years between that point and this moment Holt ha become a wily coercer. He seemed deeply suspicious of all whose manner w less reticent than his own. But he responded to Frank immediately and cor pletely, even though he did not show it. He was amazed to find that he lik Killory on sight.

In perhaps some self-justification for his reaction to his fellow men, came to concentrate such approval as he had of the world into an exaggerate —even fierce—approval of one man. That man was Frank.

Holt was to begin working on speeches at once and had already staked o some space on an upper floor in Ben Watson's building, along with Usher statistician.

"You and Mr. Gibbons will be good neighbors there," Frank enthuse "and, believe me, I'll need you. I'm mighty glad and mighty reassured that yo two are helping."

Frank praised Holt unabashedly in Usher's presence. "I've read everythi Edward Holt has written in your magazines," he said, "and here's a first-cla man. You get the feeling this man knows what he's talking about; then writes it so beautifully, so beautifully. I think his 'This New Nation in the Ne World' is as splendid as anything I've ever read."

Holt appeared as oblivious of these generous words as if he had not hea them. He merely reached in his side pocket, slowly unfurled a long tobac pouch, and began stuffing a short, black pipe, as remote from the scene as if were back alone in Usher's tower.

"It's the best thing we ever published," Usher announced, a note of pri in his deep voice, "by all odds the clearest statement of national objectives, think, that has been given. I can't say I always agree with Ed, and I do expect you to."

"Oh, I don't agree with you too often, Mr. Holt," Frank replied, smili broadly. "In fact, I disagree with you a lot." He turned to Usher. "But when comes to expressing an idea I think Holt is absolutely tops."

"They will be your ideas, Mr. Killory," Holt said, quietly.

"You're damn right they will be," Frank laughed.

Theory meant much to Edward Holt. Words meant even more. His keen
ind fell to phrases the way an instinctive musician's fingers fall to the keys of
piano. And he could write sentences that set you dreaming.

He was a studious man, too studious for the good of his health, really. In
ct, he had become a specialist in breakdowns. He saw these coming and
ught against them with true bravery, for there was courage in him, and a
rtain flintiness of character. But he was never able to rest his mind, free from
guments, and he loved books with the passion of a dedicated scholar.

He suffered, at the same time, from a strange willingness to confuse terms.
nd whatever other admirable intellectual qualities Holt may have had practi-
lity was not his forte.

Practicality, along with the facts and the cold breath of mankind's experi-
ce, became lost in Holt's eloquence about human objectives. So did con-
stency.

At first Frank did not feel so sure of Edward Holt as a companion in
ought and verbiage. But slowly, in due course, his brain opened to Holt like a
neycomb. The world of mere eloquence became more and more impelling.

Certainly he was hardly conscious that he was walking a tightrope that
angled between sound and substance. Almost imperceptibly, in the hard,
spenseful daily effort of doing his part, and doing it well, the gulf between
rank's words and his convictions grew in the same man who said to Janet not
ng ago: "Convictions may be right. They may be wrong. But they must be
nvictions."

How fatal an error to give one's confidence to the wrong person; there is
mply a small chewing noise as when a cat reaches the backbone of a mouse.
ut Frank decided to give Holt a wide range.

He joined Holt in a walk on the flowery carpet of unsubstantial eloquence
at concealed from Frank the abyss.

Holt having moved in after the Boston fiasco, his first contribution toward
hat to say and how to say it was a Detroit speech. This came off much better;
e whole affair was a resounding success.

Frank spoke from a prepared text. And he spoke in a liberal, fighting way
at makes its name synonymous with justice. But there can be no doubt, in the
terlight, that that speech also contained a beacon; only a flicker, but there,
evertheless. It marked the first publicly expressed harbinger of a deterioration
 Frank's attitude toward his objective and in his generous mentality. He took
 gratuitous, unprovoked slap at both candidates in his own party.

Frank recalled Frederick the Great, "who once answered a request to
romote an officer merely bacause of his long service by pointing to a pack
ule and saying, 'That mule has carried that pack loyally and effectively for
any years. But he's still a mule.' Well, Senator Arthur Means is still a mule.
nd as for Grant Willis, why not go the whole distance and nominate Cary
rant?"

Holt had written this, but Frank had delivered it.

How far out of character this was for him, and its significance, was mos
surely lost on the public, and probably in the Means' and Willis' camp as well
but eyebrows went up on the foreheads of Walter Karnes and Jacob Morton.

The tiny shadow of suspicion about Frank himself that this dialogue
stirred in them, however, was fleeting as a ghost in the night. Jake even turned
it into a joke, telling Walter, "An Oak Park high-school football player named
Alex Jones knocked himself out crashing head first into a steel goal post. Later
he groggily explained to my daughter: 'I run faster with my eyes shut.' Our
Frank just pulled a Jones."

An important signal about what was stirring within himself? Killory would
have met the suggestion with honest incredulity. When he saw in the first draft
some phrases and ideas he might have changed he decided to leave them as
they were to encourage the writer. His own changes and additions were minor

The preparation of his speech by another mind, although Frank was to
deliver it, was not too far from his exercises in court since he had come to New
York—presenting cases essentially prepared by the assembly in Allen's firm—
although the parallel did not occur to him.

He found, however, that Sally had her views on this and was prancing
with impatience to give them.

Frank defended ghost-writing as a practical matter, adding that "with all
the demands and the pressure of time you cannot just get up there and do it all
yourself. The real test in this matter is the ideas. After all, they were my own
ideas, as well you know."

"Surely I know it," she said, opening the bedroom windows on the
drenched stillness after an early spring downpour, "but there's something in
herently and fundamentally dangerous in the whole ghost-writer, or too-much
helper concept. Oratory has us trapped today. Greece died in an age of oratory
So did Rome. And when Cicero was assassinated the burly folk nailed him to
the rostrum from which his rhetoric so often flowed, and Marc Antony's
wife—"

"Fulvia."

"Fulvia, so the story goes, thrust a giant needle through his eloquen
tongue."

"That's a hell of a thing to do," Frank chuckled.

She had unfastened her dress, put on a dressing gown, ruffled her hair and
was sitting at the dressing table.

"It was a hell of a thing to do," she continued, "but, damn it, it doesn'
follow, either, that all our political orators should escape scot-free.

"I think the pure food laws here in America are wonderful," Sally said
"the way manufacturers must print their name, address, net weight, and an
adulterations. Well, if it's essential to know what goes into our stomachs, Braid
wood, how about what goes into our brains?

"Unless the politicians, including you, Frank, announce who wrote the

peech we assume he is speaking his own intelligence and capacity. Well, this
assumption nowadays is a worse bet than the Irish sweepstakes."

Frank dropped a pile of newpapers on the floor beside the bed and
reached to turn out the light as she approached.

Lighting a cigarette in the dark, she was up on one elbow now and talking
playfully but earnestly. "If the speaker did not write it himself he should tell us
who did."

"That'll be the day!" Frank laughed. "It's a very good idea and I congratu-
ate you on it."

"Oh, you think it's funny, do you?" Sally chided, poking him with an
elbow. She kissed him also. "Well," she announced, "I realize that offering this
valuable suggestion to politicians is ridiculous, because it would put most of
them out of business as fast as hara-kiri."

Sally's loquaciousness at an hour as late as this was a very exhausting
feminine characteristic. To his surprise she remained calm. Frank looked at her
with an expression of enigmatic gentleness, lying flat on her belly, her head
turned toward him, tight to her shoulder, framed in her loose hair on the
pillow. He knew she would go on until she was finished. She did.

"Some day somebody ought to squeeze the innocent atmosphere out of this
malpractice, like a damn lemon. There's nothing innocent, nothing innocuous,
about it, Frank. You know that as well as I do. And, my God, it's important in
this age. I doubt if we'll ever again elect a President of the United States who
isn't a good gabber on the air. What a test!"

"I think you're right, Sal," Frank agreed, drowsily.

"The ghost-writer–ghost-reader combination is misrepresentation of a self-
serving nature, hypocrisy of a deliberate kind, insincerity willingly commercialized, and intellectual dishonesty employed for reward."

"Sally, oh Sally," he said, as she went on rumbling in a good-humored but
determined way, her hair streaming over her breast.

"Often we're listening only to the horn," she said. "The substance is coming from somebody like Edward Holt; men never seen, never challenged, seldom known. The system, so far as the speaker is concerned, is a fraud."

Sally crushed out the cigarette and fixed her pillow lower. She ran her
hands slowly along his back and shoulders and on the muscles of his arms. She
turned on her side and brought her legs and body close to him, voraciously; lips
open, eyes wide, swearing tender words. He felt her quiver softly and then
relax. The change was like that which comes over an animal that finds itself
suddenly safe and hidden in its own dark refuge. Her arm came across him and
her long fingers reached to find and hold his hand, whispering, smiling secretly.

"To put it in a fancy way, Braidwood, my sweet," she said, "words can be
the marijuana of man. You and Holt had better watch what you smoke. Such
goings-on have often taken men far and then cost them fortunes and thrones."

He felt a strange melancholy settle over him. And suddenly he felt how
profoundly wonderful it might be to be a person of no importance, no ambi-

tions and no hunger for anything, and no need to vindicate oneself either to oneself or anybody or to the world. It was a curious, mystical feeling, a boyhood-like feeling, that slowly transported him to the first time he had gone underground in a Braidwood coal mine.

It was a radiant day in early winter and cheery snowball fights were going on, but Mr. Mayo had taken the boy to a new mine. Only the shaft and the main entry were finished. The elevator, called the cage, had not been installed. The hoisting engine lifted the workers up and down in a large, steel-belted wooden barrel. Dropping fast, it swayed and twisted in the slimy shaft, banging from one side to the other all the way down.

Tall Mr. Mayo climbed into the barrel first. He reached over and lifted the little boy in. The cable swung the barrel out over the center of the dark shaft, twisting the man and the boy round and round as it dangled there. All Frank could see was a tiny light at the bottom. The engine man threw his level.

They started to drop. In an instant the white-blue of the sky, every sight, was gone. The twisting barrel was sucked into the darkness below. Mayo held Frank tight in his arms. His little world of time and space and things he knew and could see had suddenly been whisked away, as though some giant hand had snatched it from him.

But the tall, kind man was there. He felt him in the darkness. They were dropping very fast in the rush of air. As the cage shot down in the darkness, banging hard against the wet, black walls, the boy could hardly catch his breath.

"Don't be afraid, son," Mayo said holding his little friend strongly.

The speed of the cage diminished. A pressure came in his ears and he swallowed hard. A second later the black wall of the shaft before him suddenly gave way and they came to a stop at the bottom of the mine. He was as bewildered as a boy could be; just stood there in his copper-toed boots, clinging to the good man's hand, and wondering what could possibly happen next. Mayo took a better grip and told him to follow.

Then he saw little lights that bobbed in the distance; bobbed closer, grew larger. Suddenly he heard a voice, a flat eerie sound in the heavy, echoless mine air: "H-e-l-l-o. H-e-l-l-o." Below the lights he could see the figure of a man, stripped to the waist, a black coating of dust that was moist with gleaming streaks of sweat. The other light was on the head of an animal. The man was leading a mule.

"Look out for gas," the miner said to Mayo, not even seeing the boy behind him in the darkness. "There's a bit here up high."

He lifted his cap-lamp slowly to the jagged roof. A quick, blue flame suddenly extended from the lamp and puffed gently at him as he took his hand away. Frank was so astonished he could not speak.

"Don't be afraid," Mayo said again, as the boy gripped the tall man's hand as tight as he could. "Never be afraid. Just don't be afraid."

And now Frank fell off to sleep with thoughts of old man Mayo, good, ind, old man Mayo, old man Mayo, as if he seemed to hear the tolling of a bell whose old tower is lost from sight.

But Sally's feeling about Holt's Detroit success in combination with Frank was not shared by Arch Scriver. To Arch, of course, Holt clearly became a man to cultivate. The next morning after the Michigan affair Scriver had come first to Holt's office, cluttered with steel filing cabinets, wall charts, and leaning stacks of reference books.

"Holt," he said, "I'm hearing from all over the country the best of good tidings, the very best, about how well the Detroit speech went. Congratulations, my boy. Congratulations and *salute*."

He had—without apology—interrupted Holt at his typewriter. But Arch settled into a chair, ready to stay as long as he wished; smooth, well-dressed, well-mannered, prosperous, confident.

"Thanks, Scriver," Holt replied in a flat tone. "Those were really just some ideas for Killory, that's all, you know."

"Bosh. Rubbish. I do know. You wrote the speech." He leaned forward in his usual confidential manner, his voice smooth as piano keys. "You wrote it. It was your speech; and you did one hell of a good job."

Holt saw that there was no escape from Scriver, although he sat at his typewriter, obviously impatient to proceed, his thin fingers resting on the keys.

"We needed it, Holt," the intruder continued. "We needed it badly after that Boston fiasco. Why, everybody and his brother was ready to throw in the towel and write off Frank entirely after that collapse up there."

"I don't think Boston was—" Holt started to speak, but Scriver interrupted him with a wave of his pink, well-manicured hand.

"Now, now," he purred. "Usher brought you in just in time, my boy—just in the nick of time. Remember, I told you that when you and I first met."

Holt had no recollection of this, for it had not happened, but Scriver grew even more confidential. Suddenly looking both distressed and exasperated he clapped both his hands on the table and dealt Holt a private surprise.

With all of the skill of a Rome gossip, Scriver waited a moment for his statement to make the proper impression; he had held it back, waiting to drop it well.

"I know what our crowd is paying you," he said in his whisper, "and, frankly, I don't think it's enough. No, I don't think it's enough."

Surprise and embarrassment broke across Holt's face and as he started to say, "Why, sure it is—" Scriver broke in protestingly, firmly, quickly: "No, no, Ed. You leave this to me," he said. "Just leave it to me."

"But, Scriver, there's no reason why I—"

"Quiet, Ed; just keep up the good work. The very good work. We've all got a lot riding on you, boy. You're the most important thing around here, along with Frank himself, so far as I'm concerned. Just keep it up—" and before Holt could do more than realize that Archibald Scriver was no longer there, Scriver had gone, the door closing softly behind the retreating back of his sober dark suit and the homburg hat on his head.

"I'm afraid Holt is a little dissatisfied," he told Frank at lunch.

"He's what?"

"A little dissatisfied. After all, we're working the hell out of him. I saw him this morning and something he said to me made me feel that his nose was a little out of joint."

"What did he say? I thought he was doing fine."

"Well, it wasn't exactly what he said. And he is doing fine. It's just that I think he feels he ought to get more money. He's riding himself hard. Moreover, I think we have to have a happy ship around here."

"Why, of course. Naturally. I'll be damned if I didn't think we had just the situation with Holt that he wanted. I wonder why he hasn't spoken to me?"

"Oh, come on, Frank, you know better than that. Do you suppose he would ever complain to you? You're a big man, Frank, and while I wouldn't say these people are scared of you, because they're certainly not and have no reason to be—"

"Scared of me! Why, what the hell, nobody has ever been scared of me in my life, or had any cause to be. For heaven's sake! Scared of me—"

"Of course not. That's what I just said. But you have to realize that they would tell me things, naturally, that they wouldn't tell you. And, anyway, I think Holt is dissatisfied and just because he doesn't squeak to you it doesn't mean he shouldn't get some grease."

"I haven't the faintest idea what we're paying Ed. Isn't he still on Usher's payroll, too?"

"I suppose he is. But we ought to make him happy."

"Why, of course. Work out something better with him, Arch. Naturally. You do it. And thanks for the tip-off, Arch. Tell Sam to change the pay check."

"This is just among us girls, Frank, you know," Scriver said with emphasis.

"Oh, sure," Frank answered. "I realize Holt must be pretty touchy on the point."

"He is. Very dissatisfied, really, but remember he didn't say anything about it."

Archibald A. Scriver had opened another door. He had extracted an alliance with Holt, or at least a promissory note on the man's feeling—somehow— of indebtedness to him. No student of the lives of sycophants can fail to recognize here the sly and ruthless maneuverings of a cunning man.

Meanwhile, young Watson was engulfed in the Killory Clubs, driven hard by the developments, conflicts, crossed authorities and general exuberance. The kits that were made up to supply the clubs with needed paraphernalia—blown-up pictures of Frank, banners, buttons, envelope stuffers, automobile stickers and what not—had to be ordered. Meecham & Meecham, one of Madison Avenue's most aggressive advertising agencies, volunteered for this and did the purchasing. Then the clubs paid the Meecham firm at cost in a mutual labor of love.

Ben Watson's problem, however, was what the clubs could do to keep themselves busy. Activity was the only cement that could hold members together. They solicited the local newspaper editors for co-operation in reporting

heir doings, and generally got it. They recruited other members, and with
mazing success. They brought in what speakers they could. Ben was recruiting
dditional speakers to sustain what interest he could. Putnam turned to the
ports world, Scriver turned to the theatrical world, Usher turned to the busi-
ess world for these.

Notices of Frank's air talks were carefully forwarded to every listed club
y Meecham & Meecham, urging that these nights be promoted as local "get-
ogether-for-Killory nights." On each occasion, volunteers made the most of this
noment in more than three thousand cities and towns. Still, about thirty days
fter each new club was founded, there was what came to be known in Ben's
ffice as "The Lull." This was Ben's nightmare: The Lull.

"I think we ought to quit signing up any more clubs for about three
veeks," Ben announced, red-eyed from weariness, hair disheveled, and thor-
ughly groggy. Frank and Gibbons had dropped by to see him at the end of a
lay and came in unexpectedly.

"You look absolutely pooped, Ben," Frank said, voicing the honest sym-
athy he felt at seeing this quiet man who had come down from Ithaca to help;
eserved, self-effacing, sitting there with two cups of coffee on his cluttered
lesk, one of which he had forgotten to drink before it got cold.

"Mr. Killory," Ben said, awkwardly, "there just aren't enough things we
an give all these members to do steadily over the stretch of time. We're kept
usy around here, and so is Mr. Morton in Chicago, explaining to them why we
ave nothing more to explain to them. They're explaining to us why they have
othing more to explain, too."

"You think we started too soon?" Frank asked, genuinely concerned.

"Well, maybe. But could we turn a thing like this on like a faucet? We
tarted on the up-grade after the Chicago speech. We had to start then. Mr.
Morton's twenty-eight-city nucleus comprised about the only organization open
o us. We owed all those people something. Moreover, we had to build on that.
Ve had to use it to expand. We couldn't let the Morton momentum die. No, I
lon't think we started too soon."

"You mean I made the Chicago speech too soon," Frank chuckled, smiling
quietly at the forthright, able young professor.

"Maybe," Ben grinned, "but, anyway, we need more Killory for President
Clubs just now about as much as we need a hole in the head—unless we can
ind more to do for those we already have. But if we sort of put off soliciting
any more until about the middle of June we should hit the Kansas City conven-
·n on July fifteenth with these and new ones at their peak. Mr. Morton in
Chicago, Jennings in San Francisco, Bliss in Texas, and the other sections will
ust have to keep the present clubs drifting along, I guess, until we get to the
home stretch."

"How long do you call the 'home stretch,' Ben?" Gibbons asked.

"Well, we're figuring on a final three-weeks push. We're calling that Kick-
off Day. K.O. Day. It's June twenty-first." He pointed to the wall. There was a
great red circle on the calendar.

Frank looked around the shabby room, bulging with shipping containers and littered with all the gadgets and gear that emotionalism could contrive in Frank's behalf.

He looked out the window through the deepening twilight to where the lights were springing up against the encroaching night. Broadway, a few blocks across midtown New York, was already ablaze.

He knew that Ben, doing so much, wished to do more; splendidly unselfish, dedicated to a crusade. This young supporter touched his heart. A wave of protective tenderness, almost paternal, swept over him. The key factor in any man's character is the way—Ben's way—that he responds to the demands of loyalty. Sitting in this torn-up room was a wellspring of hope and faith. Frank stood up. "Ben," he asked, a trifle unsteadily, "do you think we're going to come into that convention with a bang?"

A deeper color came into Ben's cheeks. As though stung by a wasp, he sat up in his chair. His eyes caught Frank's fixed unremittingly upon him, and he said readily, "Mr. Killory, I think we're going to come into that convention with the biggest bang in the whole history of the United States."

Against all this background, Scriver had come up with an idea for the convention—which he kept to himself.

In the twisted, tortured, boiling political world that makes up a national convention, tickets for the big Kansas City gathering were severely rationed by the party's Convention Committee, as usual. Scriver's idea involved printing identical tickets in a great secret bundle. Killory gallery rooters would be told to come to the auditorium early. Scriver visualized a picked crew to pass out these unauthorized tickets to known Killory fans: anyone wearing the big Killory campaign button. The gallery would be swamped with Killory rooters, every seat full, every throat yelling for Killory, and every delegate listening even before the proceedings started. And the call "We want Killory" would never stop.

The yells would be honest yells by those who wanted Frank, although they would be disproportionate. Completely disproportionate. The roar of this privately contrived thunderbolt would hover over the whole proceedings. The effect on the nine hundred delegates, assembled under the signs of their states, sitting in row after row of yellow, folding chairs, would be powerful. Could they ignore the call of "the people"?

But this packing of the galleries with demonstrators there on forged tickets, who would shut out Means' and Willis' supporters and distort the voice of "the people" was very touchy business, as Scriver well knew. It remained his own secret, only to be sprung—and sprung by him—at the opening doors of the convention itself. A New Jersey printer would deliver the tickets to Scriver's house. There they would rest under lock and key.

But where was the base, the delegate base—the state around which other states could be made to rally—without which there was nothing?

"We're still out there talking with the public," Frank had said to Sally, "but there's no progress with the politicians." True. And there was no more time to lose.

The turn came, and from a completely unexpected quarter.

The string that drew this event to Frank stretched back to Braidwood and
a forgotten man.

The time was back in the weeks of Frank's arbitration of the dreadful
Herrin strike and the horrible fratricide that followed. This had been a long
time ago, of course, and as far away in terms of intervening events as though it
had been in another century. The forgotten man was Glenn H. Patterson,
former Governor of Illinois, whose telegram of congratulations had been waiting for Frank in Braidwood when he returned from Herrin.

Glenn Patterson telephoned to say that he was in New York. Frank
brought him to Glen Cove to spend the night. A hurry-up call sent out from
am to Walter Karnes and Ben had brought them there too, for dinner.

Karnes said this was, or could be, the first break that held out real promise
or at least some direct action in the problem of the State of Illinois.

Former Governor Patterson had finished his term in office in Springfield
shortly after the Herrin affair and, although he lived in Danville, on the eastern
border of the state, Frank had known him in Will and Grundy County affairs.
Patterson, of course, had never lost interest or contact in state politics from
Cook County southward, never been known to miss an important party meeting in the state, and would be a leading figure in the Illinois delegation at the
national convention.

They were not close friends, of course, and neither Frank nor Janet had
thought of Glenn for years—"How long has it been, honey?"—and now he just
dropped out of the blue.

Janet took Glenn's arm and led him into the living room. He had gone
right out of her head, leaving no memory behind, and then suddenly he came
back to her when she saw him again.

She saw a man of middle height who might have been in his late fifties. He
had thinning hair, soft and neat, a long nose, and dark but cheerful eyes. He
was thin, but he had a belly. Somehow he gave her a feeling of assurance that
ere was someone they could rely on.

"My goodness, it all seems so long ago," Janet gasped, a little panicky as
Glenn told them many things they knew but much they did not; apparently still
another family, the third since they had left Braidwood, had bought their
house; Dr. Gunther's son, who had taken over his father's practice when he
retired, was fitting in nicely although, of course, no one would ever be like his
father around that town; Jim and Olive McCarthy's boy was at the Rolla
school of Mines and their daughter at the state university.

"That's where I met Frank, you know," Janet told him, smiling, and then
she spoke of Mr. Mayo.

"I will always miss Mr. Mayo, always," Frank said. Mr. Mayo was dead.
His adopted son had turned out well, very well, at the bank and in the Big
Four Coal Company.

The neighborhood had not been kind to Aunt Margaret's house, which was
a boarding house now, badly run down. "I don't think I could stand to see the
Ridge Street place full of strangers," Frank growled. "There's some kind of
desecration in a house full of strangers who know nothing, and care less, about

what's gone before. I wouldn't go back into Aunt Margaret's house for a million
dollars. Or our house either." This was home country they were talking about.

Janet sighed and Glenn went on. Frank's office in the Forrest building was
a contractor's office now; an extension to enlarge Masonic Hall next door had
closed up the parking place between them.

Lawyer Jack Collins represented the United Mine Workers of America
but he also remained a builder of castles in Spain. He still had great projects
and no money.

"Frank lost a case to Jack Collins once," Janet laughed, "just after we've
been married."

"I simply do not believe it," Glenn smiled.

The Harpers had made what was really a fortune by branching out beyond their United Motors dealership into real estate—a fine development
called Braidwood Hills, although there were no hills. Their career had been
rainbow, really, ever since the crisis of the United Motors suit. Frank knew this
for the Harpers wrote him occasionally and, in fact, sought his advice in this
expansion.

"Oh, Frank, how old we grow," Janet remarked. Her sigh was like a short
sad poem.

The Braidwood saga went on until dinner was announced, an excellent
dinner, and afterwards Janet and the girls left the dining room while the four
men sat at the table.

Patterson came quickly to the point as the cigars were passed and it was
immediately evident that he had much on his mind that he wanted to say and
also much to ask about. "Gentlemen," he began, "I've long since given up any
belief in premonitions. I've had thousands of them. But I do think Frank
Killory is a much stronger contender in the convention than most people realize, just as Walter does." He paused, pushing some crumbs into a small design
with his forefinger and musing as he spoke. "But for the life of me I don't see
how you can get your convention problem off the ground without Illinois."

"We don't either," Karnes replied, with simple directness. "Can you help
us?"

"Well, I don't know. I want to, Walter, and whatever happens I would like
to have you know that." It was an appeal for understanding from an old
political associate and friend. Then Patterson looked at Frank. "And for you to
know it, too, Frank," he added.

"Glenn, anything you can do would help a lot," Frank answered, "and just
knowing you want to help means a great deal to me."

"I ought to be able to do something in the grass roots through the state
around Danville, Springfield, Peoria, Rockford, Moline; nearly any place outside Chicago and Cook County. I'm to be the delegate from the Danville area
and there'll be delegates from all those sections, of course, and I'm glad to
know Mr. Watson here is in charge of the Killory Clubs."

Then Patterson made his first offer. Turning to Ben he said: "Mr. Watson

1 back you up in developing these independent groups any place you want
e to in Illinois."

Ben's elation was obvious. "Why, that's wonderful," he beamed, "and the
ily place, so far, where we'll have sponsorship from a member of the regular
irty organization. That's our worst weakness all over. We may never over-
ime it but we're trying and Illinois—with your help—would be a pattern
e're praying for. It's a problem, a rough problem, Mr. Patterson."

Walter nodded, but Frank was waiting to hear more.

Glenn spoke in a low voice and smoked one cigarette after another as he
ent on. "However," he said, "I can go only so far in nailing down delegates, or
ven in drumming up their interest."

The same old subject going round and round, Frank felt, just round and
ound. "But a lot of those delegates have been in politics with you a long time,
lenn," he volunteered, rather restlessly.

"Oh, yes. And it's easy for them to tell me Frank Killory will be their
econd choice. They'd do that, some of them, and be honest and straightfor-
ard about it. But no individual delegate who does this helps you at all, right
ow, as Walter would most certainly agree." Another nod from Karnes.

"So, let's come down to cases. What delegation leader will speak out and
ommit his delegation? Who will stand up for Frank Killory as first choice,
nd his down-to-the-last-ditch choice, and buck the sentiment for both Means
nd Willis when everybody is sure one of them will win and be the nominee?"

Frank cut him short. "Who do you think the Illinois delegation will go
or?" he asked with a slight harshness that nevertheless caught Glenn's ear.

"Why, it's too early to say, of course," he answered. "My guess, however,
ould be Senator Means. Certainly Means is the top man in the delegates'
reference in Illinois. At the moment it's like watching a dog fight under a
lanket. You know something is going on, but you don't know just what. But
ur delegates like Means and his people a good deal better than the Cali-
ornians. That's the best answer I can give you, Frank. But it's too early. And
me can't fix it for you, Frank.

"The leader of our delegation is Governor Byrnes. As Walter well knows,
yrnes will really have the say. Byrnes is the best political leader our state has
ad in a coon's age, and the most respected. Our delegates are certainly not
oing to defy Mike Byrnes. On the contrary, they'll follow his lead and stay
vith his decision a hundred percent. Moreover, they know that a split-up
elegation has no political force anyway. When Mike decides, Illinois will be
olid.

"But he has to make up his mind first about who he thinks the nominee
hould be, which is the better man for the country, whether Means or Willis
as the better chance of beating the opposition in November, if nominated,
nd how the party within our state is going to emerge in all this. Then it's
one. The delegates will follow him because they believe in him."

"Do you think Byrnes has made up his mind, Means or Willis?" Frank
sked.

The room was so quiet that the men heard a dripping in the kitchen :
Patterson paused. "I know damn well he hasn't," he replied, his arms ou
stretched in front of him across the table, "or else there would be no dam
sense in my being here."

Frank wanted to know if he had talked with Byrnes.

"Yes. He doesn't dislike you, Frank," Glenn replied, bluntly. "You're sti
an Illinois boy, he agrees, and a very good one."

"How far would he come my way?"

Glenn fingered the handkerchief in his pocket, rubbed his glasses slowl
with it, and took a long time to answer.

"Governor Byrnes has no earthly reason to buck two powerful Unite
States Senators, one of whom may very damn well be President of the Unite
States, ignore their long services to his party and to the nation, cross up th
regular party organization. He has no reason to instigate a battle for a complet
stranger to him and to politics; a stranger, moreover, who has only an outsid
chance, at best, for the nomination and who has no record whatever as a vote
getter—never having run for public office in his entire life.

"But you ask me how far Mike would come if he came your way. I ca
answer that. He would come all the way—all the way—if he came at all. That'
Mike."

The room was warm and stuffy. Frank threw open a window and leane
out for a breath of fresh night air. "If Mike would do this," Karnes stated, "an
give us the base we need in the form of the Illinois delegation and fight fo
Frank in advance, I think Frank can be nominated."

"By God, so do I," said Patterson. "I never thought I'd live to see a wild
outside chance like this really happen in politics. But, yes, gentlemen, if Byrne
would do this you're really in the fight, not just making noises like the rest o
the hopefuls do every four years who have no more chance to win the nomina
tion than a snowball in hell."

Ben came up with the obvious question. "But for all the good reasons yo
just mentioned, Mr. Patterson, Governor Byrnes hasn't any reason to do it
Have you any idea what could bring him to us?"

"I have," Glenn replied as Walter showed his surprise, "and that's what
want to talk with you about. Mike has a mind—and a very good mind—of hi
own. Sometimes he makes up his mind, as Governor, to do something he think
should be done, come hell or high water, and devil take the consequences so fa
as its effect on him is concerned.

"Walter can tell you he has almost cut his own political throat severa
times by going all out on something he thought should be done when the whol
party thought he was as wrong as a summer oyster."

"We sure have," Walter agreed as Glenn continued, looking at the ceiling
"In this respect Mike is a maverick. And the key to Mike is loyalty. If he
believes in a man, he'll listen. And if that man has a cause or a person that he'
urging on Mike, Mike can be converted. Once converted, he can talk the ear
off a cornfield. With his mind made up, there's no stopping Mike Byrnes."

Glenn leaned across the table and took a drink of water as they all
atched him intently. "But the trouble is, it would be impossible for me to
nvert Mike Byrnes in this. Walter couldn't be expected to, either. He just
kes us, that's all."

Frank sat motionless, pressing his hands across his eyes. Patterson took a
iece of sugar, dipped it into his coffee cup, and sucked it. He looked at the
aree men, his lips puckered and his thoughts clearly revolving in his mind.

"But now I've got to ask you a question," he said, "about the only living
ul I think could convert Michael Byrnes and bring him your way. And, my
riends, the man who could do that is the man to thank for any future that
nere is in this whole Killory affair." He turned slowly in his chair and looked
irectly at Frank as his words sunk in.

Frank jerked forward. "My God, Glenn, who is it?" he asked in undis-
uised excitement. He was holding himself in with difficulty.

Patterson shifted his weight. "Well, it's very good news. The world turns
ound in a funny, coincidental way." He smiled and then rapped out a name.
Philip Winston Allen," he said.

A look of absolute incredulity spread across Frank's face. Karnes stared at
atterson, as amazed as if he had vanished from the chair. Frank bent forward,
ompletely puzzled.

"What on earth," Frank said at last, "has Philip Allen got to do with all
ais, Glenn, and with Governor Mike Byrnes of Illinois?"

"I'll tell you exactly what he's got to do with it. I know he's your partner,
'rank, of course, although I never met him. But this much I do know. It just so
appens that going back through the years and to this day Mr. Mike Byrnes
elieves with all his heart and soul that the greatest man alive on the face of
he earth is a man named Philip Winston Allen. Maybe it's been years since
1ike has seen him, I don't know. Maybe you think I'm overstating this, but I'm
ot. I may not know much but I know Mike." Patterson turned squarely to
'rank. "If your partner believes in you and will ask Mike to help put you over
ecause you're the right man for the job and he wants you to win, Mike Byrnes
vill go along with Philip Winston Allen, of that you can be as sure as of the sun
1 the sky. Frank, will he do it?"

The bluntness of the question took Frank aback. He had not had a real,
olid talk with Allen since he had returned from his holiday in the south of
'rance after the coal case. In fact, although Frank had not taken a leave of
bsence from the firm there was something of a tacit understanding that the
iew course of action which was sweeping Frank along was paramount, or at
east until it developed further.

Without any formal discussion about this deviation, Allen had seemed to
ccept it as a matter of course, and no issue had arisen about where he stood in
espect to all this. As for his attitude toward Frank's being the man who should
>e nominated, Frank was startled to discover that this had not entered his mind
ne way or the other. This is what shook him in the blunt question.

It now crossed his mind that he had not the faintest idea whether the old

patriarch had long associations with Senator Means or Senator Willis, or even
knew them. Allen had been in Antibes when Frank made the turn into politics
This die had been cast without any consultation whatever with him, his knowl
edge or his consent. These were hardly needed, Frank thought now, but in an
case, somehow they had been neglected. The event transpired with Allen a
unadvised as the man in the moon. And now the man he had ignored, for tha
is what it amounted to, was to be asked, as the first sign of attention, a vital
indispensable, favor. It was not the least irony in Frank's history clogged with
ironies.

Suppose Allen has reacted badly to my political plunge and all this and
merely been politely quiet, Frank thought. Or perhaps Allen feels that politic
is, after all, a "special business" and that either of the two distinguished and
able Senators, equipped for it, should have the reward and the responsibility of
the nomination. Or maybe Allen would like to see me nominated, but feels tha
he should not or could not actively intervene against Means and Willis in a
political affair. And, surprise of surprises, what is Allen's relationship with
Byrnes? Will Allen do it?

It was as if, all of a sudden, in a dark but familiar room which one
believed was empty a hand had suddenly reached out and placed itself on one's
shoulder. It was a friendly hand, surely, but it was an arresting hand as well. A
consent was needed. How constantly we take things for granted. This one all
was essential, apparently indispensable, and even that wasn't the whole story
No man's claim on another man can be asserted without its being impaired
Allen would have to offer this support to Frank and assume the responsibility
of persuading Byrnes very willingly, indeed, or there would be no remedy a
all.

"Will he do it?" Frank repeated. "Glenn," he said quietly, his face still full
of the surprise that had flashed these dismaying thoughts through his mind
"Glenn, I just don't know."

"What!" Patterson bellowed, sitting bolt upright in his chair. "Why, Frank
Philip Winston Allen is your partner. He's your friend. That's the whole point
Allen is proud of you, proud of you, respects you, I'm sure of that; good Lord
have you had some trouble with the old man?"

"Oh, heavens, no. I suppose he will do it. Why, yes, I should think he
would. But I can't say he will, Glenn. I haven't talked with him about any of al
this, as a matter of fact. I can't sit here and tell you or Walter or anybody tha
Mr. Allen will do something when I haven't any line on it at all."

Patterson was not prepared for this. "You better damn well find out," he
said. "You better damn well find out."

"I'll see him in the morning," Frank answered, with a finality which
seemed to close the subject.

When Frank finally came to bed and was ready to turn out the light Jane
was sleeping. As he leaned over to kiss her gently without waking her, she
stirred. "Oh, goodnight, darling," she said, when he kissed her on the cheek. He
put his arms around her, her head on his chest, and hugged her to him like a
little girl.

# 14

.s SOON AS Philip Allen came in the next morning Hazel told him that Frank
vas waiting to see him.

"Come in, Frank, come in," he called through the open door, indicating
vith a glance the chair at his desk. He was searching for something in a
rawer. "I'll be with you in a minute," he said, rummaging deep in this cavern
f picturesque timbers.

The stir of his rummaging mingled with the tick of the tall Versailles
lock. Frank was seized by a feeling of helplessness, or perhaps a loneliness, as
.e reflected on how inscrutable the turns of life can be. One sits here and won-
lers about it; that he should be brought back to the need of this man so de-
ached from the new world he was living in and whose life was on a completely
lifferent course; brought back to the need of his benign influence, wise, pater-
.al, as if Frank were tied by a silver cord.

Maybe nothing much can be known about ourselves. Just the illusion we
.ave. Maybe a man's illusions about his own talent may only make him ridicu-
ous to a wise man who knows him well. Frank was struck, suddenly, by a wave
.f self-condemnation and contrition. How quick he had been to turn his back
.n this mentor and find interests separate from the magnificent man who was
nterested in him.

He must somehow make reparation. Yes, after all, his actions had been "off
vith the old shoe, on with the new." No denying that. Why hadn't he realized
his as he leapt along? There was something just not right about it. An apology
vas required. A kind of exhilaration surged in him. He decided that he was
eally there for a reparation. Afterwards, he would bare the other matter: his
light. Then he would ask the great favor.

He saw with considerable surprise that Allen's hair was solid white, whiter
han he would have thought, although it could not have changed at all in these
.ast months, except that he had not gazed at him for a long time, and that this
.ade him look like a somewhat ancient version of the Philip Winston Allen he
.new.

Then Allen lifted his massive head, closed the drawer with a bang,
.rought his great frame up out of the chair and motioned Frank to the library
end of the room.

"Well, Frank," he said, "how are you?"

"I owe you an apology, sir," Frank began.

"What! For heaven's sake, Frank, what for?"

"Well, I suppose I felt I should be paddling my own canoe. But I've never

covered this political tangent of mine with you, or even discussed it. I'm sorr
Mr. Allen. I talked it over at the start with Bill Shaw, of course, and a litt.
with Alfred Caxton, from the firm's standpoint, but I haven't—"

"Nonsense, Frank. Nonsense. They speak for the firm, as you know. I wa
in Antibes, you remember. I was way over there in France before you eve
returned from Washington after the coal case. If any man in this town (
anywhere has been busier than you since I came back from Antibes I'd like t
know who." But, thought Frank, that had been a long time ago, or so it seeme
now. Allen put his hand on Frank's shoulder. "Forget it, my boy," he smilec
"You know we don't stand on ceremony around here."

Allen did not even seem to ponder the matter of Frank's neglect. At lea
this much of the growing anxiety that had so disturbed Frank last night ap
peared to have no place in Allen's thoughts. Perhaps it was something lik
those terrors which descend when you are in the woods and night falls and th
trees close in, and then you walk a little further and find that you are on th
edge of a clearing and that this is the way home after all. For before Fran
could make any further explanation or act of contrition, Allen asked him,
deep seriousness in his voice, gently, "Frank, how are you coming along?"

Frank paused. His answer came slowly. How was he to begin? A summar
of where his political effort stood was not easy, with Allen lacking its back
ground of events, ideas and personalities. The fact that he could feel thi
lostness here in this office made him wonder what had happened to his life.

"I think I'm doing all right," Frank said, simply, "but it's very complicatec
the picture as a whole." Allen nodded. "I think one side of it, the side of publi
interest, is in pretty good shape. I have Usher and Marshall Putnam to than
mostly for that, with their publications."

"I saw the spread in Usher's magazine, of course," Allen interrupted. "Tha
fellow Usher certainly stepped in with both feet. I've met him, and I like him
Putnam, too. Excuse me, Frank, I interrupted you."

"This is the side that's coming all right, I think."

"You're getting a good response from the country, then?"

"In many sections, yes, but in others it's not so strong. This is hard t
measure. The advertising agency people are starting several kinds of privat
polls on it; but you can read even the earliest findings a dozen ways fron
Sunday. What we're trying to do is spray the interest and enthusiasm outwar
and upward from multiple centers in the Killory-for-President Clubs. A fin
young professor from Cornell volunteered to organize and push this in th
grass roots. This has given me a wonderful fellow who's busier than a bird do
with those clubs—very effective."

Philip had moved to the sunlit windows and then back to his desk. Fran
seemed restless in the chair opposite him. His eyes shifted from the ceiling t
the walls and then back to Allen, as if to say: What is he going to do about me?

"Adding up all the activity, what is your progress?"

"I suppose it's too early to tell," Frank answered.

"Yes, I suppose it is."

"But you see, sir, the activity has us sort of going around in a circle."

"Eh?"

"It's the other side of the problem that stumps us; the side requiring itical acceptance of me by the party to the degree that I'll have at least one id group of delegates, one major state delegation, fighting for me on the nvention floor. This political base is, I'm sorry to say, just nonexistent." Frank v his big question looming ahead. "Mr. Allen," he said quietly, "we're sort of dead center."

Allen pulled out a cigar, bit off the end and dropped the plug in an ash ιy. He blew out a great cloud of smoke, waving it away with his giant arms, d leaned forward, close to the younger man. "Maybe you can spell that out a tle more," he said.

"It's the problem, sir. We haven't a base. No anchor in a delegation leader fight for me and back me with his state prior to the convention and on the nvention floor. Mr. Allen, all this activity is heading toward a fizzle for that ιson. In fact, on the basis of our present situation we don't even see how we'll included in the delegates' balloting."

"Well, you answered the question all right. Who in your group knows ɔst about this sort of thing?"

"Walter Karnes. A veteran. A very fine man. Moreover, he's on the party's tional Committee."

Allen nodded. "What does this Mr. Karnes say?"

"He says everything hinges on our having such a state to support me now, d from here out, and on the floor, and stick with me come hell or high ιter."

"I see."

"It's something like 'for want of a nail—'" Frank added. "But it's a very g nail." He must ask the possibility of Allen's intervention now and ask the vor. He looked tired. An involuntary sigh escaped him as he said: "Mr. Allen, 'alter Karnes finds that at least a dozen states will enter the convention tensibly backing their governors or somebody as favorite sons. This of course merely form without substance. A very different matter. Many state delega- ɔn leaders will use that method as an excuse to avoid commitments to Senator ɛans or Senator Willis until the balloting shows which contender will prob- ɔly win. This revealed, their delegation can then back the winner."

"I can see how a certain type of political leader might well do that," Allen ɾeed, "if the contest between Means and Willis is close. Is it?"

"Yes, it is."

"I wouldn't call their method a very inspiring spectacle, but I can under- ιnd it. This is the over-all situation you face, eh?"

"But, in addition," Frank continued, "nearly all the other states are already ɔmmitted to Means or Willis. And, besides, there is only one state I can ɾoperly have as my base." He rushed at the word: "Illinois. Mr. Allen, either I ιve the support of the State of Illinois or I might as well pick up my marbles ɔw and quit. As a matter of fact, what with the expenses and all, if I'm

without the support of the State of Illinois there's really not much point
going on. That's how it is, Mr. Allen."

"Well, Frank," Philip answered, "wouldn't it be very embarrassing for yc
to pull out now? A lot of people are rooting for you—really rooting; tho:
Killory Clubs and all, and many others who believe in you. Surely they wou!
feel you let them down if you quit. They could make the fight with you and t
losers with you. That's one thing. But they wouldn't like to quit with you."

"Of course not, sir, but they're whistling in the dark without knowing th
are whistling in the dark. But I know it and I'd be knowingly letting the
spend their hopes, time and money on really what is only whoopla after all."

Philip looked at him carefully, thoughtfully. He stroked his chin and fe
silent. "I'm afraid that very little peace of mind accompanies politics at tl
level you're striving for," he said, "and that it forecasts much inner torment in
good man. There would be compensations in winning, surely. I wouldn't expe
anybody who has gone as far as you have in all this to believe the compens:
tions may not be satisfying. But, in your case, do you think you had bett(
think it out again?"

Frank started to answer, but Allen held up his hand and went on, smilin;
He did not want the thought that came to him to sound harsh, and certainl
did not intend it to be. "You know, Frank," he said, "there's a verse in tl
Koran, spoken to unbelievers who are about to die. It says: 'Now taste tl
torment of fire you called a lie.'"

There was a strong streak of chivalry in Allen's nature and, sensing tl
younger man's uneasiness, he leaned forward with a movement of affectio
Then he asked the question that seemed to be troubling him, putting it for
flat yes or no. "Frank," he said, "do you want to go on?"

"Yes, I do, Mr. Allen," Frank answered quietly. "I want to go on and
have come here to ask you to help me." Silence. "I'll go on anyway, because
lot of other people, as you say, are in this with me. There's nothing else to d
I'm sure, but go through the motions the level best I can. There is no i
between for me that I can see. But if you can help me I'll have a fightin
chance, a real fighting chance. In that case, there would be good reasons for tl
people interested in seeing me get the nomination to keep on trying to win."

"How can I help you, Frank? How?"

"Mr. Allen, do you know Mike Byrnes?"

"Yes, I know Mike."

"Do you know him very well, sir?" Frank began to walk up and dow
groping for the right words to ask for Allen's decision.

"Yes, I know Mike very well," Allen replied.

"He's the key to the whole thing, sir," Frank said, rushing into a rounde
description of how Patterson's visit to Glen Cove and the previous night
discussion had led to Governor Byrnes and led to Allen himself as the only ma
who might persuade Byrnes.

If Philip was taken aback he gave no sign of it.

"You know, your friend Mr. Patterson can be overstating this a lot, so f;

s I'm concerned," he answered slowly, "and politics, Frank, as you have said,
s a 'special business.' "

"It's absolutely all we have to go on, sir, this hope," Frank replied. He did
not intend this to sound like "any old port in a storm" and Allen did not take it
that way. "Anything that comes out of this will be riding on—and due to—any
help you can give us."

Important moments often come quietly and important decisions are frequently heard with a minimum of excitement or drama; and this is the way
Frank heard the decision now.

Philip walked over and opened the door. "Hazel," he said, "get me Mike
Byrnes on the telephone at the Governor's office in Springfield, Illinois."

Frank stood up in a surge of emotion that almost brought tears to his
eyes. In fact, he turned his back on the giant figure walking toward the desk
and stared out the window, but the sight was dim, for his eyes were misty; the
involuntary tear which is the unfeigned tribute of a grateful heart.

The buzzer rang and Philip Allen spoke quietly into the phone.

"Hello, Mike. How's Kitty?"

The answers were coming from Springfield in long and short pauses at
his end of the line.

"Mike, I want you to do something for me."

"It's this, Mike. And it may be very hard for you. Very hard, I'm afraid."

. . .

"I have a friend and partner, Mike, that I brought out of Braidwood and
out here in New York. It's Frank Killory, as of course you know. Now, Mike, I
think Frank has made a very serious mistake. He went ahead in politics without
realizing that this must directly involve the State of Illinois if it is to mean
anything, and by failing to talk with you first."

. . .

"No, I'm sure he didn't realize it would come to a question of Illinois. But
he's an Illinois boy, after all, even though he didn't take the look before he took
the leap. But I most want to get that part of all this on the record with you,
Mike, because certainly you're entitled to a clean breast of things so far as I
know them."

. . .

"But, dear Mike, here is the important thing. Killory is a good man. He's
honest, he's intelligent. I can't tell you I think he would make a better President
of the United States than either Means or Willis, if it gets that far. I don't
know. But on this I'm sure you'll agree as I am that I'm sitting in this chair:
Killory should have this chance to be judged by that convention. They can take
him. They can leave him. That's up to the delegates and to the party, and no
holds barred. But I gather that in spite of the public commotion for him, and
certainly much of this is genuine, he's up a dead-end street.

"By God, Mike, Killory deserves a count and he ought to get that chance.
I'm told, and I believe, that you're the only man in America who can give it to

him." Allen was singing now from his heart. He held the phone closely. Frank moved to the edge of the chair, nervous but expectant, as Allen continued.

"I want you to give Killory that chance, Mike. Give it to him for the good of—of—well, Mike, just for the good, that's all. For the good of everything because, by God, it's wrong and stupid to have politics sewed up on a shut-out basis. If our country gets that impression, and it already has that impression, Mike, that's a bad thing. And if it works against Killory it will hurt in Kansas City, hurt in the election, and hurt in a lot of hearts. They tell me you can save that happening, my boy, with your great State of Illinois. I know you can. Do it, Mike. Do it, my boy."

. . .

"What?"

. . .

"Maybe. I would say so. I'm told a former governor of your state named Patterson brought Killory this analysis as his only solution and that it would require your support of him now, your fighting for him in the period before the convention and sticking with him at least through the first ballots."

. . .

"Yes, they say it means no commitments to either Means or Willis before you go all the way with Killory."

. . .

"Partly, but who knows? Killory is a man I feel certain of. He has convictions, Mike—convictions."

. . .

"Yes, he admits he has no more base than a rabbit, nothing to rally his supporters around or any bloc of delegates to gather more states' delegates in advance of the opening bell in Kansas City."

. . .

"I imagine so, but, of course, I really don't know. But I do know this: I believe in Frank Killory."

. . .

"This Illinois boy has to get fast recognition from you, Mike. And, if you can swing it, the backing of your delegation. And right now. Declare for him now, Mike. Make him your state's favorite son. You and your Illinois people are open to do as you please at a suitable time after the first ballots. I can see this would mean burning your bridges with both Means and Willis. But burned bridges never worried you, my boy, and I know, by God, they never will."

. . .

"Mike. Mike."

. . .

"Well, I'll be damned!"

. . .

"Oh, my boy, my boy. You're a chip off the old block. I tell you, Mike John would be proud of you. Just plain proud. I am, yes, I am. Tell Kitty I love her. And take awful good care of yourself and both of you. Goodbye, Mike. Killory won't let you down. I promise you Killory won't let you down. He deserves this, Mike! Goodbye, and get that message to Kitty that I love her. Goodbye, Mike, write me soon, you two!"

He hung up the telephone. But his face was clouded. He looked across the room at Frank standing by the window. "Frank," he said, in a solemn voice, the great crags and wrinkles in his face a study in seriousness, "Mike is going to declare his support of you. He will stand with you and he will stick with you. He's going to declare for you at six o'clock tonight, Springfield time." Allen hesitated a moment. Then he stood up slowly and walked toward the younger man, and said, "Don't let Mike down, Frank. No matter what happens, don't let him down." There was an iron look in the old man's eye as he reached out and put his big hand on Frank's shoulder.

For forty-two years in the little town of Moline, Illinois, Mike's father, John Byrnes, had worked his way up in the Rock Island Tractor Company. He started as a furnace boy in the plant's foundry when it was the Rock Island Buggy Works. In the first eleven years he never missed a single day at work. Then, after a brief layoff of three days, he was back again. He had never been to school, had taught himself to read and write, and, although there was not much to marry on, he had married at twenty-two. His wife, Kitty, had worked in the paint shop.

The fumes brought her an illness that necessitated some months of medical care, and this disaster fell heavily on the two. It threw them badly in debt to the doctor and to neighborhood stores and it was nearly three years after Kitty recovered, pale as eyelids, and returned to work to earn her share before they could pay the bills and be even.

Fallen helpless? Both enrolled in the opening class of the Randolph Night and Mail School when it started in St. Louis. John and Kitty studied together in the evenings: arithmetic, writing, geography, some history, some literature, but mostly in the general range of books on the school's directed list. After seven years of mail courses both won their diploma, their names entwined together on it. This hung in the hall of their small, two-room dwelling near the Chicago, Burlington & Quincy locomotive roundhouse.

That diploma looked down on poverty, unrelieved. Hardships, but hardships together.

John advanced in the foundry's section gang to foreman. In industry, the foreman is the first line of management. This is the first break-away from the ranks of the hourly worker onto the lowest rung of management. A factory is essentially a tool box. How each tool is used, when it is to be used, and how it can be used better, is the responsibility of the foreman. A good or bad foreman can make or break any section in a plant, and John began to make his good record there.

As the years went by he became mechanical superintendent of the engine

section when the buggy works started to make tractors and changed its name
its business and its future. Kitty was able to quit work when Mike was born
their only child. She never had to return to the plant. John grew with the
business and as it prospered, the small family prospered.

The Rock Island firm, now a leader in its new farm implement field, was a
family company. The three brothers of Moline's Warren family had founded it
in 1865. All had died long ago. The daughter of the youngest brother, Myrtle
Warren, age seventy, was now the only owner; an odd little spinster with
puckered lips, soluble eyes, nose-glasses which added to the pinch of her face
and an enormous air of solvency about her. (For reasons never clearly known
she had moved to New Haven years earlier and lived there.)

John had been in charge of the company several years and lifted it to
prominence in the industry before Miss Warren accorded him the honor of the
presidency. It was at this period that Philip Allen conceived his idea of an
amalgamation of midwestern farm equipment firms. This brought him to John
and Kitty.

He knew John's record thoroughly, and when he met those two staunch
souls his affection for them was all but instantaneous, as it was for their only
son, little Mike. His heart leapt up whenever he was with these two and their
little boy. It was his interest in, and respect for, John and Kitty that actually
fired his interest in the merger; they were the center of his wishes for this. To
them, in turn, it was music in the night; a dream that can be heard. But the war
intervened. The tractor plant was converted to making tanks for the army
based on a caterpillar design. Allen's project had to be suspended. "Never
mind, John," he said, "we'll go ahead with it some day."

Promptly after the war Allen resumed the plan; Rock Island Tractor Company had grown, and John had grown with it. The firm was to be the bell
wether of the amalgamation, with John president of the combined companies.

Then the blow fell. Miss Warren decided that, come what may, a lawyer
in New Haven for whom she had an attachment was to be president of the
merged companies. "Otherwise," she insisted, "there will be no merger." John
Byrnes was frozen out.

The unexpected development took an additionally ugly turn. This lad
and Lockhart, the lawyer, confronted Allen with the claim that John Byrne
had falsified entries in the company's books and had, in fact, been guilty of
embezzlement.

They gave this as their reason for John's dismissal in favor of Lockhart
whom Miss Warren—as she put it—"could trust." They purred that no claim
would be pressed, however, and all would be forgotten if the merger proceeded as she wished, with John out and Lockhart the president.

The Legion of Honor in his lapel, Philip Allen had returned from the
Peace Conference. A mountain of work as well as honors awaited him in New
York and Washington. The merger was only one matter. But he was thunder-
struck when the Warren lady and her young lawyer walked into his office to

tate their suspicions of John and their intentions, all of which they had previ-
usly aired to a hundred ears in Moline.

John. Kitty. As Allen spoke their names to himself he could hear the sound
1at hearts make when they break in two. He left for Moline the next day. John
nd Kitty met him at the station. On the steps of the Pullman, even before his
eet touched the platform and with these two there below him, he blurted out
1e only thing he wanted to know. "John," he said, "did you do it?"

Kitty was standing beside John, her head high, her eyes up, her shoulders
quare. "No, Mr. Allen," he answered, "I didn't do it."

The question had to pass between them. It had to be answered, and it
ras. John and Kitty were both in his immense arms, held close in his hug like
wo children while the tears ran down Kitty's face and all Allen could say was,
There, there, Kitty. Don't you worry. Don't you worry for one minute." But
he held onto him as strongly as to life itself and the train had pulled out before
1ey left the platform.

"They've gone a long way in this blackmail, John," Philip said later, "and
1ey're going to sue you to keep up their bluff."

"I know, Mr. Allen. It must be that lawyer, Lockhart. I never thought Miss
Varren would do a thing like this."

"Well, she is going to do it. And that lawyer himself is as dangerous as a
amel's kiss. Moline is a small community. This town means a lot to you and
Litty and you both mean a lot to this town. It's the dirtiest trick I ever heard of
1 my life!"

Philip Winston Allen called off the merger, pending the outcome of the
uit. He turned his back on New York and Washington. He went to Moline and
efended John Byrnes himself.

John was acquitted. And that hot, dry, windy summer morning when John
ralked back into the implement company office, Kitty on his arm, John re-
lected president of the company that had been his life, Philip Winston Allen
ad vindicated the Byrnes name forevermore.

The merger went forward with John at the top of the amalgamated com-
•anies, in which capacity he served with distinction until the day he died. Kitty
till survived him and the years which had passed over her head had left only
heir springtimes behind. Their son was always at her side and as time went on
\.e furthered his father's good name well: now he was Michael W. Byrnes,
:overnor of the State of Illinois.

# 15

By APRIL, Edward Holt and Walter Karnes were Frank's chief advisers and confidants. This brought Holt up, hard, against Karnes and all others.

There was a curiously underdeveloped strain in Holt's mind and character. Essentially hard and arrogant, he knew much about many things; but where feelings were required, he knew nothing.

Given to long insistences about subjects in the speeches, he brought a brilliant brain to the task. But he was impatient, imperious, and had an annoying conversational habit of driving every nail to the board.

He was quick with a quip. There was often a barb on it and no one could be sure whether he meant it or not. "A smiler with a knife," Karnes called him.

Moreover, Holt so tightened the access to Killory that little could reach Frank from outside the circle—and not even from within it—that did not clear through him. In order to "keep Killory posted" he insisted that he himself be fully posted. What began as a move for efficiency degenerated into a personal clamp on Frank.

"It's simple as ABC and obvious as the Empire State Building," Karnes had told a complaining Putnam and Watson. Even Jake Morton telephoned from Chicago to protest that he could not break through Holt to Frank. "And never if it's bad news," Morton said furiously.

"Ed is just in the ancient process of trying to take over somebody," Karnes replied. "I've never known it not to be tried in politics. There's generally one who gets a long way at it and perhaps a basketful who always try. Holt is just the one who's gone a long way, that's all."

"Well, why in hell can't Frank see this?" Morton bellowed. "Frank is no child!"

"Now, Jake," Walter answered. "In a thing that's ballooned as big as this you can't entirely escape a lot of rancor and pettiness, and you know it. This Holt thing is coming to a boil down here, too. We're no happier than you are. Still, don't be too hard on Ed. This is the first time in his life he has been out of an ivory tower, busy with his Big Think. If we can't handle this, we must be children ourselves."

"I say it's up to Frank to settle it, and put that arrogant fellow in his place."

"Well, Frank likes Ed. He puts a lot of store in Ed's loyalty, you know."

"Oh, for heaven's sake. Who isn't loyal? Just tell me that. Who isn't loyal—and going right down the line being loyal? My God!"

"But it's up to us to get along. Ed has his work to do, too, you know. And guess everybody is under something of a strain, anyway."

Jake remained adamant; he saw the Holt development as a major loss for the campaign.

"Frank refuses to wake up," he told Karnes. "I've made the issue for the last time."

"No, Jake, I can't take Frank's attitude in this that seriously," Karnes answered in simple honesty.

"Well, I can," said Jake, "and I think it all to the insufferable bad. Just tell Holt I think he's too big for his britches, that's all, Walter—and tell him I have things to tend to with Frank that must not be blocked. I'll decide what Frank should know out here and on the West Coast, not Holt. I say to hell with him, Walter. And I'm just about ready to say to hell with Frank Killory too, at this moment. Goodbye, Walter. Hello to everybody." Nothing was going to appease Morton.

Scriver stayed out of this fracas entirely. Caress the favorites, avoid the unfortunates, and trust nobody. If Holt had an ally it was Scriver; fully sensible to all that was going on, reluctant to risk Holt's disfavor and yet determined not to be caught in the middle.

Karnes told Killory of Morton's call.

"It sounds as if Jake blew his top like a prima donna," Frank said, nettled and annoyed, "and I don't see much point in pampering prima donnas."

"Easy, Frank. Take it easy. Jake is no prima donna, and you know it. I'm no prima donna, either. I can tell you this. I think Jake is right. Ed has developed a genius for putting his worst foot forward. He's giving everybody a rough time. He obviously takes some pride in paying no attention to what anybody says except you."

Frank laughed. "Well, he doesn't pay too much attention to what I say, Walter. That's why I like him. I need yes-men around here about as much as I need a hole in the head." He chuckled again. "You'll certainly admit Ed is no yes-man."

"We're not talking about yes-men. Sure, Ed is no yes-man. Neither are Watson, Patterson, Morton, or any of the rest. Why the mystery? Holt simply isn't a team player, that's all. He's a solo flyer; which may be all right. But he's lying obstacles in the way of the team players. That's wrong."

"Cool off, Walter. We need Ed. I'm depending on you. I'm depending on him. See if you can't work it out between you." Frank paused, giving Karnes a friendly glance, as if this had been chatter and it was dull. "Moreover," he said, to Karnes' amazement, "I think you should be chairman of the party's National Committee."

"I should be what?" replied the bewildered man.

"Chairman. That would certainly put the power behind us that we need."

"Why, Frank, that's an astounding thing for you to think. The chairman, as you know, is elected by the Committee as a whole. There won't be a new chairman until the Committee meets at the convention. The day after the nomination a new chairman, if there's to be a new chairman, will be elected on the recommendation of the party's nominee, which is proper. The nominee and chairman must work closely together. How on earth can the party have a new chairman meanwhile? Bill Perkins, as national chairman, has exercised his duties exactly as they should be exercised—neutrally. Everybody knows that and approves of it. Perkins has shown no preference for any candidate for the nomination, and will play no favorites before the party chooses its nominee."

"Maybe Perkins could move over into chairman of an executive committee, or something."

"Perkins will not and should not move and nobody is going to permit him to move."

"Well, I don't think Perkins is for me."

"Oh, I don't think so, either. But officially he's been absolutely on the square. I think Perkins is for Means. He ought to be. Means has supported him a dozen times to Means' own disadvantage. In any case, Means would certainly not expect Perkins to be his man now. Neither would Willis. Until this very moment, I would have assumed this would also be your thinking."

Frank did not disguise his annoyance. "Maybe Perkins might figure that by his negative attitude he's standing in the way of what the American people want," he said. "The party has no future by doing that, you know."

"Frank, that question covers a lot of territory—most of it still unexplored. Most of it is like the South Pole; uncharted territory. Both Means and Willis think the American people want them. Also, somehow there must be a firm line drawn between what is usual and what is understandable in a matter like this; what is 'official,' in a sense, and what is personal, with no attempt to bridge the gap. What you're talking about is neither usual nor understandable. It's so purely personal. In addition, it would be dangerous even to have your idea get around and be known. This talk must remain only between you and me."

Frank seemed taken aback. "I just thought it would be good for the cause, Walter, that's all. Naturally, I thought you'd go along with it or I wouldn't have raised the point. I'm sorry I spoke of it. I didn't think you'd take it this way. But I just can't help telling you I'm a little disappointed."

The telephone rang. "Governor Byrnes," Mary-Louise told him. Frank answered, "Yes—Hello Mike," and was nodding into space as Walter left. He clamped his palm over the receiver and called after him. "Walter. Mike Byrnes out in Springfield says we're doing fine." He was waving goodbye to Karnes with the other hand.

Both subjects in the incident disturbed Karnes greatly. He never spoke of the chairmanship proposal. But he did say at lunch, "Frank is wrong to brush off Jake Morton like that." Unfortunately he said it in Scriver's hearing. By mid-afternoon Scriver sat in Frank's office.

He came with his usual pseudo-anxiety, a puzzled look on his face; urbane but solemn, solicitous but firm. He waited until Frank had signed some letters and then pulled a chair close to Killory, asking in a low tone: "What's the trouble between you and Jake? I think I can straighten it out."

"Trouble? I'm in no trouble with Jake."

"Yes, Frank, you are. You just don't know it. You know, in an operation like this, as in the White House, the man at the top often is the last to get the facts, if they're unpleasant. I've heard you say that yourself. Of course, it's true. How right you are."

Arch traced a little design with his finger on the desk, the Father Confessor ready and waiting. Frank had gone back to the letters for a moment. Then he looked over the rim of one and answered.

"Arch, I'm in no trouble with Jake," he said slowly, "you know better than that. I'm depending on Jake, not only in the Midwest with the clubs but even out on the Pacific Coast through Jennings, and in a score of other places, of course. Jake's taking the load off here, he feels. Jake wants recognition, you know. There's a little vanity in him I suppose. Now, Jake somehow had a beef about Ed Holt shutting him off from me. Ed always speaks his mind. That suits me; but others sometimes don't understand it. Jake is just feeling a little neglected. I wish the prima donnas would get out of my hair."

Sympathy flooded Scriver's face as he cleaned his glasses with a handkerchief. "I don't blame you. But you're above such foolishness. You're a big man, Frank, a big man. You expect such things. I was saying to Ed only this morning, 'I don't see why everybody keeps horning in on Killory.' "

Frank was indulgent. "Nothing bothers me," he said, "except to see this nomination campaign through. We can take care of that kind of stupidity later. What have you lined up in Delaware?"

"Some think Delaware is too close to the Pennsylvania line and Senator Means' territory for you to invade with a major speech. They claim the Wilmington party organization is solidly for Means—a hundred percent—and might resent your coming in, and that it would backfire."

"Who did you get that from?" Frank was all attention now.

"Principally Walter. I don't agree with him," Arch said, as he rose to leave, "but, after all, he's a leader in the party's regular organization and ought to know."

Frank looked at the ceiling, a stony glint in his eye.

There was petulance in his voice when he broke the silence and answered Scriver. Arch was surprised—genuinely surprised—to see him suddenly break a pencil in his fingers. Frank's words came with the same snap, and hard. "I'm mighty damn glad I'm not having as much trouble with the American people as I am with the regular organization," he said. "I think the regular organization is disloyal to me."

Many were to hear this many times.

In politics rumor spreads at the speed of sound. In most political campaigns the real ruler is King Rumor, and it was in this one as well. The rumor somehow spread that Killory had cooled on Karnes. It could not help Walter's authority.

Thus Scriver had a problem. How close could he now afford to stay to Karnes? How quickly could he tie exclusively to Holt, and should he do so? "Something's up between Frank and Karnes," he told Grace. His wife gave him the uncertain smile of an airline hostess when you ask why one of the engines has stopped. "I hope we're not involved in this," she babbled.

He pumped Holt. "Oh, I think Frank has full confidence in Walter, I guess," said he coldly, dismissing both Scriver and the subject. He pumped Usher and Putnam. The result was meaningless. Glenn Patterson waved him aside. But from that time forward Archibald Scriver was never known to set foot in Karnes' office. Yes, caress the favorites, avoid the unfortunates and trust nobody.

How could it be, and so very soon—and was it true—that the heady air had made Frank somewhat giddy? Was it the suddenness of the climb? Had this always been latent? Surely Janet (although not her father), old man Mayo, and all of Braidwood would have vigorously denied that. Was Aunt Margaret looking down on him now, puzzled, her eyes moist, her fine hand offering him her heart? In one direction or another, behind the scenes, Frank was beginning to create intensely unhappy feelings. Magnanimity? It was disappearing. Moreover, he seemed less and less interested or successful in healing the breaches.

Janet was disturbed when Frank pointedly criticized Karnes shortly thereafter. Physically removed in Glen Cove, and heavily occupied with Jan and Margaret, she was completely detached from the inside workings of the campaign. She did not have the faintest idea about the background of Frank's displeasure. But the attack was both sudden and ungenerous and entirely unlike him.

"But he really started you in all this, dear," Janet suggested, "right from the very beginning. Wasn't it Mr. Karnes, dear, really?"

"I know."

"You've often said you couldn't do without him," Janet persisted, "in all these months."

"Nevertheless, I just somehow don't feel sure about Walter."

Suspicion. Suspicion. How can it set in about nothing, about nearly everybody, nearly everything? How?

"Well, what did he do specifically?" croaked Jan. "He must have done something, Dad."

"I guess he forgot he's supposed to be working in the campaign instead of running it. Anyway, let's not talk about it." Frank was looking up at the ceiling. "He made me damn mad," he said, "I can tell you that."

Jan was her irrepressible self. "You sound like Mr. Kill Joy in the funnies, these days, Dad," she injected. "There's something wrong with everybody and everything."

"Janet!" her mother scolded. "That was utterly uncalled for and utterly unfair. Let me remind you that your father is pressed on all sides and under great strain. Frank, it was certainly not very nice of Janet to say that." But Jan, having made her inopportune remark had, as usual, left the room.

Janet went to the bookcase and was fingering through a book from the shelf. Frank was running a pencil along a margin of an interview he had given the newspaper. "I don't think they got that right at all," he mumbled. "They really botched it."

Janet laid down the book. Her face looked tired and her eyes seemed anxious. "Please put away that paper," she said.

"What is it, honey?" he answered, dropping it to the floor.

"That was a terrible thing for Jan to say—"

"It's a little late for us to be surprised by a crack from Jan, isn't it?"

"Can you imagine how strange it makes me feel to realize I am sitting here right under this roof with the man who may be the next President of the United States? The man sitting right in that chair?"

"We're still a long way from there," he smiled.

"But, Frank, if you don't get this nomination all the work, all the people's efforts—and their fights among themselves, too, as I assume happen—will be for nothing, absolutely nothing. Friendships and loyalties cannot be broken on the way to that. If so, what do you or anybody have left over? You'd really be much better off if you hadn't started in the first place."

"What are you leading up to, honey?"

"On the other hand, if you win the election you're going to have to live with a great many people. You'll have to trust the people who helped you, which is only the start. Then you'll have to begin trusting actually hundreds and hundreds more as President."

"Of course, I know that."

"Well, I think you're losing your willingness to trust people, at least in the way you've always done before. You say you don't know this, you don't know that, about how much they are for you. This isn't like you, dear. Not at all. How many times have I heard Mr. Mayo say to you, 'If you don't trust people, people won't trust you'?"

"Janet, you can't trust everybody."

"You know perfectly well that's not what I mean."

"I think you're just forgetting this is all a different business. You haven't a very close look at it, you know."

"That's true. But I have had a very close look at you, and for a good many years, and I love you, and I don't want anything to make you think you're learning about people and life for the first time now. What you've known about people and life—and about yourself, too—for a long, long time will stand by you like a solid rock."

Janet said no more. A shadow of melancholy, however, hovered over her heart. And if Frank seemed to be listening to a recitation, it was an honest lesson, honestly taught.

"I know, honey," he answered gently. "Just you go to bed. And please don't worry. You know me pretty well. I've got my feet on the ground."

In any event, there was little tranquillity, as might be expected, and less every day as the Killory name went higher and higher on the lips and in the hopes of the public.

Karnes backed Watson to the hilt in disputes with the regular party organization on one hand, and met internal criticisms of the clubs' disorganization with: "Let them go ahead. We don't care how assorted the people are who work for Killory, or how much they work, just so they keep pushing. There isn't time to be efficient. We're cheer leaders. Cheer leaders may not get much smooth music out of the cheering section. But good ones get a hell of a lot of noise." Watson grinned, and they both helped mightily to soften local frictions. Millions became emotionally involed. It turned them from spectators into participants.

Money was coming in to Scriver in large amounts separate from the ordinary fund-raising efforts now under way. "Nothing too much extra," he told holt, "but we've always had what we needed when we needed it, haven't we?"

Scriver's reports to Frank were even less detailed. "I've got a book of the best givers," he mentioned one day, "the real people we should remember come November; the real people we should take care of." Frank had frowned.

"Arch," he said, "I just never realized all this was going to require so much money." But that was the end of the subject. Frank broke off in palpable eagerness to turn the conversation.

Sam Welsh was astounded by the deposits he made. His knowledge of what was really happening remained largely an unworked mine. In fact, he had all but lost touch with Frank and was quietly upset when—twice—Frank was talking with Holt and others in the elevator and did not even see him, although no hint of his New York isolation reached Janet in Glen Cove.

"How's Sam?" she had asked one evening.

"Oh, I guess Sam's fine. Very busy," Frank answered across a newspaper.

"You know, I think it's a shame that Sam and Min live way over in Atlantic Highlands, New Jersey. We really ought to have them out for dinner sometime, and have a nice evening with them. They must think we've forgotten them entirely."

"Well, honey, Sam works late, like I do. Then they'd have to go way back to Atlantic Highlands."

"Of course not, they could spend the night here. But I know. Anyway, dear, it was just an idea. He must be terribly excited."

"Sam's a little over his head; not able to help too much."

Janet looked up rather sharply, but Frank was still deep in the newspaper. "Over his head?" she replied. "Well, if it wasn't for Sam doing everything before we got here, would this house be over our heads?"

Frank laid down the paper. "Honey, Sam would like to be useful, and I suppose he thinks he's helping in all this. But you know Sam as well as I do. He's in the big league now and he's just not up to it."

"Well, I understand that, naturally. But that's no reason why you shouldn't respect him, Frank. Certainly you can respect him for whatever he can do, after all these years."

"I respect him," Frank mumbled. "What ever gave you that idea?"

In truth, Sam entered Scriver's office every morning for his orders; delivered in Scriver's patronizing way. His true association with Frank was merely his own persistent recollection. On one occasion, however, he was shaken when

Arch handed him ten thousand dollars and told him to put this in the safe deposit box downstairs. "And do it now," he added.

Surprise is easy to see on a good, open face like Sam's. "That's an awful lot of cash out of nowhere, Mr. Scriver," he volunteered in a dismayed voice, speaking mostly to himself.

Scriver turned toward him slowly. First he patted the erect man's skinny back. The air was all spice and the heavy scent of greenery. The touch was of a sanctimonious friend. Then he looked at Sam with the cool, fixed and colorless eye of a shark.

"Sam," he stated, "let me tell you something. You have one task around here, and only one. And that is to keep your damn mouth shut."

Arch was amazed to see him toss the money back on the desk. Sam's months of hat-doffings and genuflections to Archibald A. Scriver were over. Sam brushed past Mary-Louise and went in to see Frank.

"Frank," he announced to the startled Killory, "I want to talk to you."

Interrupted as he was, Frank hardly noted the first flush of anger he had ever seen on the faithful Sam's face in all the years since the first years in Braidwood. Waving his hand to the chair he said, "What's up, Sam? By the way, have you got the travel schedules made up yet for Kansas City?"

Sam ignored the question. "Mr. Scriver has given me ten thousand dollars in big bills to put in the safe deposit box," he exclaimed, "and I don't like it."

If Frank was stunned he certainly did not show it, although it was obvious that the news did surprise him.

"Well, he's probably been saving it up from a lot of smaller contributors," he answered. "What worries you, Sam?"

"This isn't 'saved up.' They're all big bills; one solid bundle of big bills, Frank. I think you should make it your business to know where that kind of money comes from!"

Frank's quiet reply was an echo of nearly his exact words to Scriver himself. "I never realized this was going to take so much money," he said, "and, Sam, I'm just staying absolutely out of the money side. You know that wouldn't have any influence on me afterwards."

"Yes, Frank, I do, but—"

"Oh, Sam, a great deal of all this is new even to me, and surely to you. Arch Scriver is an old hand. It'll be all right, and, for heaven's sake, I wouldn't have it involve the later pay-off to a living soul—not a nickel of it, all of it."

Sam knew this was true and he nodded, but before he could speak Frank went on. "On the other hand, just as a tip for your own good. Don't push into things—things of any kind—that are really not your business. Remember, this is a big operation now, and you're a little over your head in it. Just work along and be happy, Sam." Frank smiled, but it was a patronizing smile and, good as Frank's intent was, his words stabbed straight to the bottom of Sam's heart.

"Oh, Frank," he said, "Frank, Frank, what's happened to you? Don't you remember how we could always talk about anything and, anyway, just be together on it—all the cases, and everything, and the way you felt one day and another, and everything? Maybe it's New York—although I don't think so. Remember how we worked on *De Laudibus Legum Angliae* right here in New York, too?"

"You were a big help, Sam."

"Help? Frank, I'm your friend!"

"What exactly did Scriver say that got you so excited?"

Sam blushed. "He said 'Sam you've got just one job around here; and that's to keep your damn mouth shut!'"

"You want me to be honest with you about this, don't you?"

"Why, certainly."

"Well, I think Arch gave you some very good advice."

Frank had seldom seen tears come to a man's eyes before, just the sudden wetness from a deep blow.

"Oh, Sam—Sam," he said. "You know—" but Sam had lost his oldest friend. Sam walked out.

In the worthwhile mortal there is a throne room. Its door opens silently, magically, whenever one dares to be creatively useful; to benefit large numbers by breaking new trails, building new structures, awakening new deeds and restoring valuable ideals. Frank's purpose remained, without deterioration. But the good man with that purpose had not. Motive? None. Reasons? Historic. Results? Well, matters were now developing very fast.

The move into Kansas City was important. Moreover, Karnes had timed it well. The convention—mid-July—would be held there soon, of course. Officially, the city's slogan is "The Heart of America." Everyone in the Killory group realized it was the hub of important grass-roots sentiment, diversified in its interests and activities and also a wide-area captial of its own, being extraordinarily separate from its sister city in Missouri, St. Louis.

Behind the banner of the *Kansas City Star,* civic outrage and new pressures for better government boiled there. Although the burden of boss Tom Pendergast's machined had not become too burdensome and embarrassing until late in Pendergast's life, it had reached this stage now.

For years on end, Pendergast had been merely a true-green Tammany-type kind of fat cartoon politician with a whiskey voice. His control followed the semi-benevolent pattern of "Hinky Dink" and "Bathhouse John" in the early river wards of Chicago.

But somehow, in the twilight of Pendergast's life, a demon struck him like a bad attack of the seven-year itch. He sprouted, quite suddenly, an actual mania—nothing less—for betting on the horses. Refusing to recognize that a horse is an animal that can take a thousand people for a ride at the same time, as often described, Pendergast moved his gibbous frame out of the rocker landmark on his lawn in the Mission Hills district and into the Twelfth Street betting parlors.

In this belated metamorphosis he then proceeded to lose such large sums aboard the telegraph wires to the tracks of the nation that the pressure for more and more money opened the door for an intensification of Kansas City's corruption and its blood-sister, vice, on a scale that brought national notice.

The vigorous, articulate, sweep-clean determination of local grass-roots groups fighting Pendergast was an ideal setting for Killory.

Glenn Patterson had close ties there. Kansas City would be his show, as Boston had been Scriver's. He had arranged a citizens' reception for Frank in the William Rockhill Nelson Gallery of Art, a gift to the community by the late founder of the great *Kansas City Star*. Then Frank would speak that night at the Auditorium downtown.

Jake Morton and his key men came from Chicago. Lester Bingham traveled over from St. Louis. Sam Welsh went out from New York two days earlier, alone. Karnes, Holt, Watson, Putnam, Usher and Gibbons went out with Frank. This was also the first trip on which he took Sally.

But she saw the Kansas City trip as a problem. She really did not want to go. She was not intimidated by the social rules, but she did not intend to be tripped by them either.

"First," she told Frank, "it's certainly not intelligent for me to travel out with you and Usher and Putnam. They buy my articles from Bixley. At their high level the newspaper world is a small world full of personal, private chit-chat and chirrupings, and you and I as human beings are none of their business. Next, there's Holt, Gibbons, Mr. Karnes, and young Watson, to say nothing of your good Sam Welsh from Braidwood. And Glenn Patterson besides. Frank, we'd just be asking for trouble. You'll defend my honor, I suppose, and ruin my reputation in the process."

Frank nodded, but the "birdwatcher" expression was there and she knew he was not concentrating on what she said.

"But I'll miss you, darling," he interrupted. "I don't know why, but it seem a long way out there. Funny, with all the traveling around I've done, too. But somehow it seems a long way."

"Next," Sally continued, "it would be hard on me to be there differently than you and I are here. Where are the group's headquarters?"

"The Muehlebach Hotel."

"Well, I certainly cannot stay in the same hotel, I wouldn't think. Braid-wood, stop and think a minute. It would feel strange and hard to get out there and be shunted off, buried someplace else, away from you."

"Why can't you stay at the Muehlebach? There'll be lots of newspaper people in the Muehlebach, anyway. Actually, it's the only hotel in Kansas City where anybody would stay. You're writing about this campaign in a very big way. Couldn't be more natural, Sal; not possibly."

Moreover, he argued, what she called a "gathering of the clan" was, in fact, a consequental gathering of the clan. At this assembly of the group many campaign questions would be settled, future plans and strategy arranged, personalities sought out for co-operation, objectives established on a state by state basis. This decided it for Sally. She flew west and checked in at the Muehlebach.

The group's large suite was a series of paneled sitting rooms and bedrooms far from Sally's on the top floor. Sam Welsh promptly reserved the same accommodations as Frank's headquarters during the July convention.

Below the window, Twelfth Street's blazing lights lit an up-down path like a roller coaster along the avenue's long, undulating hills. A red neon sign blinked from the Hotel Baltimore across the way and you could even see, in far-off Union Station Plaza, the tall memorial beacon to the fallen of our wars.

Not for Fame or Reward
Not for Place or Rank
Not lured by Ambition
Or goaded by necessity
But in simple
obedience to Duty
As they understood it
These men suffered all
sacrificed all
Dared all—and died

Sally had seen this inscription on the beautiful beacon that morning. She had quoted its words as the lead in her day's article to Bixley, the article now fanning across the country with her Kansas City dateline.

Her supporting words began:

By many lands, across many a sea, their brothers stood near the sad dust of these men, so far from home. They represent the load of grief that rolls down the years across the shoulders of the living. Their dust is not under their names. But it can be called sacred, deep among the never-to-be-forgotten.

War is a stairway of agonies which they climbed on bruised and aching knees. Each name is a man who died. One man. He is lost, to everyone who loved him and to the world. He, one man, who might have changed the world had he lived.

Men in their prime, dying one by one. One man in a struggle complex beyond all measure.

None of our political leaders has ever heard his name. Yet it is he, not they, who does the fighting and the dying.

In our accelerated age another storm cloud is mounting and darkening, its crimson rim reaching out to suck down the sun. We are charged with the knowledge that a new world war may be creeping upon us across the gullies of history—doubling our claims upon each other and upon life.

The convention of one of our two great parties will be held here in Kansas City soon. Will these good responsible men and women who are delegates and the aspirants who are candidates turn their eyes, their minds, and their hearts toward the dutiful implications in this beautiful inscription to our fallen dead? Or will they turn toward politics as usual, represented by the neon cheapness of nearby Twelfth Street?

Candidate Frank Killory is speaking here tonight. He has a great oppor-

ity—and responsibility—to be worthy of respect and thanks for doing his
t selflessly for our nation.

She concluded this with particulars bearing on the events.

In *The Kansas City Star* office, Editor Sherman Humphrey handed the
ets to Managing Editor Jerry Simms. "Some time since I've seen copy like
t," he said. Simms nodded. And might have added, "Thank God."

But when Sally had filed this article and gone to the cool oasis of the
ıehlebach's downstairs grill to lunch with a *Star* editor, trouble struck.

She encountered Edward Holt. This was her first encounter with Holt and
· disliked him on sight. When he walked by the table he stopped to speak to
· editor, telling him the time mimeographed copies of Killory's speech would
ready for newspaper release.

"Your publicity people, Sam Welsh and a few others have already told
," the editor replied, a little sourly.

Hold brushed this aside and turned to Sally, an awkward note in his voice.

"You're Sally Bryce," he said, looking over the top of his glasses.

"Yes, I am, Mr. Holt."

"Arch Scriver tells me he knew you in Rome years ago."

"I knew Mr. and Mrs. Scriver there. He was representing some American
vie interests. As I remember, the Mussolini government was delaying a lot
I making it somewhat hard for him."

"Not too hard, apparently," he said, squinting down at her and then taking
his glasses as if he preferred a better stare. The gold bridge had left a mark
his nose and his eyes seemed to float, naked, in their large sockets.

"Well, I don't know," said Sally. "I've lunched with Mrs. Scriver several
ıes since I've been back in this country. She's a very attractive woman, don't
ı think?"

"I really couldn't say," Holt replied, somewhat unnecessarily, "but I under-
nd Arch was a good friend of your husband."

"Oh, yes, they saw a lot of each other in Italy."

"They're still friends, I'm sure."

"Why, certainly, although I don't suppose they've seen each other for
ırs," she answered.

"Where is your husband now, Miss Bryce?" There was a deliberate bite in
· voice, loaded with insinuation. "Now, really, Miss Bryce, where do you
e?"

"London. We live in London."

"Your husband is still in the Foreign Office?" He gave a meaningful laugh.

"Still in the Foreign Office, poor dear. But away from London is the only
ıce to be in the Foreign Office. However, Charles was due for rotation
me."

"Do you think he will be coming over here?" Holt leaned closer with a
art little spy-about-town look, tapping his cigarette ashes onto the edge of a
ıte.

Sally looked squarely at this thin, angular man with the chill blue ey〈
Does this aggressive man have a purpose, Sally thought, or is it just his ma〉
ner? He's such a bloody snob. What's he driving at? Her annoyance cloud〈
her face, her smile dimmed, and she was having enough of enough. She felt〈
swift impulse to push over the table, seize a bottle and hit him full in the fac〉
Her teeth glittered as she touched them with her pointed tongue. Something〈
what he said and in the sound of his voice was insulting, full of implications〈
all the things she had ever done and of all the things which she knew some sa〉
of her. And sometimes in her hearing, too. She was able to speak French a〉
Italian perfectly, and Spanish admirably, and she knew enough German〈
understand and carry on a conversation. People were forever talking ind〈
creetly within the range of Sally's hearing in the mistaken belief that she d〉
not understand them.

Holt had spoken as if she were a trollop. The contempt was there, hidd〈
away beneath icy inspection. She knew what it was with searing clarity.〈
meant arrogance, intolerance, hypocrisy, repugnance toward all life outsi〈
Holt's own little circle.

Sally thought: I must count ten before I speak. It's always my tongue th〉
gets me into trouble, and I don't want any trouble here in Kansas City.

"Mr. Holt," she said evenly, her wide-set eyes staring straight at him, "〉
husband has never been in America and does not plan to come."

There, she thought, that should end this impertinent nonsense. But it d〉
not. Holt, impervious to the handsome woman's tightened manner, althou〉
easily noticed, moved into an area of remarks that ignited the explosion. H〈
glanced at the *Star* editor sitting beside her, only to make it worse.

"Arch says some London newspaper people had a nickname for yo〉
pieces from time to time." He paused, smiled, and lit a cigarette. " 'Sall〉
Fables,' they said."

Sally scanned him in calm, cold fury. There must be some kind of masoc〈
istic thing in this, she thought. She moved her gloves to one side on the tab〉
and toyed with her water glass for a moment, her stare never leaving his fac〉
She spoke slowly, deliberately, and for the equal benefit of the baffled editor.

"The man who said that was a rival editor of the great Vincent Emery, 〉
Holt. I worked for Mr. Emery. He arranged for me to work on the newspape〈
here. I have always appreciated Emery's testimonial that achieved that result.

"The last time I heard 'Sally's Fables' was in a London saloon. My stat〈
ment then about the rival editor was, 'This Hercules with the brain of Einste〉
—which might well apply to you, Mr. Holt—I'll take him apart, finger 〉
finger, right off his funny fat hand, and tooth by tooth.' You see, Mr. Holt, t〉
son of a bitch said what I wrote was not true." She rose to leave, adding: "An〉
Mr. Holt, if that's what you also think about one single word, well, you're a s〈
of a bitch, too."

"He had it coming to him," said the editor as they walked up the sta〉
from the grill, her sharp heels ringing like little hooves on the marble. "What 〈

rth does Killory see in that man?" her escort asked. "What is such a man ing behind the steering wheel?"

"I haven't the faintest idea," Sally answered, still boiling with fury. "Holt s, in point of fact, a brain of Einstein, you know. But I think he's a bastard, well."

Frank tried to mollify her. In his mind he damned Holt as a fool for allenging her, but this complaint passed away as he spoke. "Sally," he said, "I ow Holt. He didn't mean anything; just making conversation. Why, he's said ain and again your pieces are head and shoulders better than anything else it's going out. You know that."

"I'm not talking about my pieces."

"He was just reaching for conversation, nothing else. It's just an unfor-nate manner."

"I think he's a bastard, in spades," she answered, as she kicked her shoes o a corner and loosened her hair.

He felt her harsh, rebellious, distant. He forced her face toward him. arling, shush. For heaven's sake," he said in a warning voice. "Ed was talking out Arch and Grace Scriver, too, to make conversation; mutual friends, itual friends between you, what could be more natural? Am I so opinion-ed?" he asked. "Do I force my opinions on you?"

"No," she said, "but you always have one. And you can have Arch Scriver, ,. I think he's a lecherous old man. I don't mind a man making a pitch, but I te to be helplessly mauled." She pushed her lips forward in a grotesque itation of passion. "He had his hand on my knee under the table at every iner party in Rome, wiggled around to press my breasts whenever he could t his fat paw or chest near me, and stuck himself at me on the dance floor e a God-damn stallion. You can have Archibald Scriver, all of him, his cute le plots and all. His own special brand of smooth dishonesty is in his blood. hy, I wouldn't trust that man if I were you as far as I could throw the iehlebach Hotel. And, by God, I don't see how you can mix with him, either. t I don't see you resenting his obvious fawning and stuff, any more—if you er did. I think the man is laughing at you—I know he is!"

"Arch has worked hard. He's helped raise a lot of money, too, you know. ; been very expensive, Sal. Arch has come through." He sighed wearily.

"Bunk. There'll be a pay-off. With you, as in Rome, he could no more do nething without thinking of the pay-off than a bank robber, even less. Scri-r hasn't a drop of courage, a drop of loyalty, a drop of anything except ney and one scheme after another to grab coattails—"

"Stop, Sal," Frank interrupted, flushed. "Stop. It doesn't do you credit to n down two people like that, working as hard as they are; sweeping state-nts, one hundred percent condemnation. All black, all white. That's not isonable. Be fair, Sal. It takes all kinds of people to make the world. Both Ed d Arch could be your friends."

"They could like hell. I choose my friends. I may slip up occasionally. No abt about that. But I choose them for a reason, or a lot of reasons, and I ran

out of reasons the first moment I ever laid eyes on Scriver and Holt; Scrivyears ago, Holt today downstairs. I smelt them both. I felt them both. An
damn it, you should too." Her voice was suddenly tired.

"Let's not talk any more about it," Frank said. He smiled wanly an
reached for Sally's hand in a conciliatory gesture, but she had turned away
get a cigarette and look out the window in the grayish-black of the ear.
evening twilight. A fog was settling down comfortably outside.

"That's the best idea you've had," she answered.

"All right."

"Now go upstairs and join the clan, Frank," she said, taking off her su
coat and pulling her blouse up from the tight skirt, the other hand working th
zipper down in a fast, strong, petulant stroke. "I'm going to bed."

Frank had hardly returned to the headquarters suite before it was time
go to the Auditorium and to hold his rendezvous there with what turned out
be a great, resounding success.

After the Kansas City results there could be no stopping the bandwago:
Ray Jefferson, who would lead Missouri's delegation, had traveled over fro:
St. Louis to tap and explore sentiments. He came to the Muehlebach heac
quarters from the Auditorium, along with Karnes.

Jefferson was a jovial extrovert with thinning hair, a moon face, and th
small feet of a dancer, so often found on fat men. His giant stomach an
enormous black mustache made him look like a corpulent Sultan, and h
booming laugh was legend in the Missouri political world. But he had a toug
streak in him when he was opposed; not stubborn, only rigid; so very rigid.

Frank greeted this welcome stranger in a maze of smoke, ash trays, ic
buckets and milling people. Like Italians and Greeks, politicians are seldo:
happy except in each other's company, and Glenn Patterson was beaming whe
he told Killory that Jefferson was there.

It was Glenn's turnout for Kansas City, and Scriver paid no attention, bu
only sat drinking and staring at the crowd which kept pushing and bumpir
into his chair.

The place was so crowded, so public and so noisy that Karnes led Fran
and Jefferson to his own small bedroom at the end of the inside hall. Pattersc
signaled that he would stay behind.

Walter and Killory squatted on the bed. Jefferson took the chair, flickir
sparks and ashes as he made himself comfortable, a hair-embedded weddir
ring on his hand.

"Mr. Killory," he said in a voice surprisingly high for a man of his size, "I'
glad to meet you."

"I appreciate that, Mr. Jefferson. We all do. I've been looking forward
meeting you for a long time." Frank wanted this to be an easy-going convers
tion. He had thought it would be a reconnaissance.

"I'm very close to Mike Byrnes," Jefferson announced, "and I think th
world of Mike." Frank nodded; Mike was moving in all directions for hir
Jefferson went on: "He was in St. Louis shortly ago, talking about you. Mil

ʒed me to come over here. I should tell you, Mr. Killory, I came on account
Mike. Did Mike tell you I was coming?"

"No, he didn't. Maybe he wasn't sure."

Jefferson gave Frank an odd glance. "I told him I'd come," he said, some-
ιat flatly. Picking up a drink that Walter offered, Jefferson continued. "Then I
ınt to the proceedings with Walter. Between Mike and Walter I've been
aring a good deal about Frank Killory."

He laughed. Frank shifted on the edge of the bed. Is this cat and mouse?
hat is the mission hidden back of those eyes? he wondered. When will this
litician come to the point?

"Well, I'm in the hands of my friends, you know," Frank said, smiling,
ıd Mike has been breaking his neck for me." Then he launched into a set
ιce against the Washington administration, running up and down its sins.

"There are a few questions I'd like to ask, if you don't mind," the Mis-
ırian stated, trying to fit his bulk more comfortably on the small chair.

"Shoot, Mr. Jefferson. I may not know the answers, but I'll try."

The visitor asked his views on a dozen issues. He was specific: domestic
licy, item by item, foreign policy, item by item. Frank's answers were to the
int. He was on his feet now, walking up and down in the small room. "One
ıng I'm not going to do to be elected President," he said, "is try to out-
ɔmise the present administration. I don't believe in that. A friend of mine
ce expressed it better than I can, Mr. Jefferson." He put his arm on Karnes'
ɔulder. "'False promises, unobtainable promises, broken promises: these
ree things are the curse of men and nations.' I agree, Mr. Jefferson. And
ease remember this; I don't propose to be all things to all men. I don't have to
· President of the United States, you know. I have to live with myself. No, I'm
ιt going to try to be all things to all men—"

"—and you are going to be President, Killory," the fat man answered,
aming. "Karnes was right about you. Walter is right. And the people want
u." Jefferson rose, and it was a brisk rising for such a weight; thrown off
ɪlance for a moment by the nearness of the bed.

"Would you declare for me?" Frank asked, rather tentatively. Walter was
raid he was pushing Jefferson, but Frank was ready for a frontal attack
ainst the sacrosanct.

"I'm meeting Sherm Humphrey of the *Kansas City Star* shortly. I'll declare
r you, Mr. Killory; they'll be good votes for you, along with Mike's, in the
issouri delegation. Maybe not solid on the first ballot, of course, but the
ajority. Mr. Killory, the White House needs a big man, the country needs a
g man. And you're a big man, Killory. Count me in." His heavy face was
ıshed with pride.

This was the second important break Frank had had at the delegate level
the campaign.

The *Star* put Jefferson's statement on the front page, of course, and the
ɪre service carried it throughout the country.

"I want to follow in the footsteps of Michael Byrnes," Jefferson's statement

began, "and see that our great country turns to Frank Killory of Illinois." It w
a blow deep into delegate territory regarded as solid for Senator Arthur Mea
except for four delegates known to favor Willis. The deflection would affe
Means most. Jefferson's hold on the Missouri delegation was real.

Means was flabbergasted. He telephoned Jefferson as soon as he cou
reach him. "Artie, the people want him," the Missourian answered, "that's a
The people want him—more than anyone. It's as simple as that. You shou
have seen the way things exploded at the Auditorium here. He's got somethir
I don't know exactly what, but he's got it. He's rolling. And he's plenty, plen
confident. Absolutely sure that he is in.

"The interval before the convention meets is a fine piece of time, in t
way the Killory crowd have this thing paced. Their timing is good. My de
gates are not going to stand against the groundswell, Artie. I figure I might
well be out in front. There's no use my coming in on the caboose. It's my l
I'm making tonight, that's all. And you know I haven't a grudge in the wor
against either you or Grant Willis, bless you both."

Means was too old a hand in politics to be mad. Following Mike Byrn
commitment in such a pivotal state, some other delegations were certain
follow his lead and declare for Illinois' favorite son. Byrnes would see to th
His influence among many delegation chiefs was decisive. But Means kne
Jefferson well. He respected the Missouri leader as a canny judge of pub
sentiment. This is what made the news so shattering.

Sally did not hear Frank's speech. She did not write her article. The S
editors thought this strange. So did John Bixley when it failed to arrive over t
wire in New York.

No one could know better than Sally that she was a difficult woman. S
realized that she had been difficult all her life, and it remained too much f
her to fathom the change in her feelings that was deeper than those merely
off by such an incident as that with Holt; changes from satisfaction to protes
tion or resentment that could alternate rapidly. Where does this back-and-for
nature come from? she would ask herself.

In responding to these changes Sally took orders out of nowhere. But s
was fully aware of an approaching change toward her resentful mood when
came; feeling herself engulfed by it in a way that carried all the mystery a
menace of a fog rolling toward you across the sea. She would ask herself: W
do I feel so intensely about things? Few things mattered much to Sally, b
those that did, mattered a great deal.

How long she had slept she did not know, and when she was awakened l
Frank's voice she was chilled and stiff. It was late, surely after three in t
morning, but the moment she saw Frank she sat bolt upright in bed.

Sally blew the hair out of her eyes and whirled prone on the bed, ha
turned on her hip, her long fingers seizing his arm and shaking him.

"And I'll tell you more about this son of a bitch Holt, and Scriver, to
she shouted. Brooding, frustrated, furious, restless and turning in the p
hours since Frank left, this awakening in the sudden light of the room caus

reak of near-frenzy in her. Something had seized all her latent emotions,
e kind of crystallization, some summary, entirely vivid, of what was hap-
ing to Frank; where he was with himself and others, although the attrib-
n of all this merely to Holt and Scriver was not clear, quite even in her
burst.

"They're everywhere, these kinds of pushers," she said in her fury, "and
met more than my share. Maybe I deserved to. I don't know. But I've
wn them so many times in so many places that by now, damn it, I ought to
w who the Holts and Scrivers are and the only sort of people who are ripe
them."

"I think I understand."

"As long as there is any 'thinking' about it, you don't!"

She clasped her hands over her ears as he tried to mollify her, refusing his
ening words, her head shaking from side to side. His calmness further
riated her. "Be quiet about that man, damn it, that's all," she shouted,
ing at him quite wildly. My superstructure is just going to explode one day,
thought, honest to God it is. Then she tore back into the subject. Her voice
pitifully hoarse and unsteady. Her naked breasts glistened.

"All snakes are deaf and look sideways. So does that man Holt." Her hands
e trembling and it all seemed to come out of an intense contraction in the
of her stomach. Frank got up and started to leave the room. Then he turned
k. "Just shut up, Sal," he said, furiously.

Sally's brows rose in a satiric arch. Her mouth parted in a slow way that
wed all her teeth. She was shaking.

"Oh, yes?" she answered in her rage. She kicked back the covers violently
pulled her knees high up under her chin.

Whereupon she called Holt's room on the telephone. Nothing Frank could
or do could stop her.

When his weary voice came on the line it was obvious he had been waked
by the ringing. "Mr. Holt," she began, frigid, precise, direct as a hammer, "I
't like people who talk behind other's backs. I won't talk behind yours. I
k you are a wrong man, Mr. Holt. A wrong—made-wrong man. You're
sfied that you know everything. Frank's getting like that, too. You have the
wers—fast. It must be done your way, played your way, or else. Most of the
e you're wrong, as in the trouble I understand you've been giving Jacob
ton and Karnes.

"You're hurting the Killory campaign, and hurting his chances of being
sident of the United States. But, chiefly, you're hurting Frank. Or you're
ing him hurt himself, it doesn't matter which. He's mixed up with a wrong
n, among others, in you. Frank is right here and he didn't want me to call
, but I want him to hear this." Her voice sounded totally unreal. "I'm
aking on the personal side about you now. In my book, Holt, you're a
tard. Now, you conceited little son of a bitch, go back to sleep." Then she
ged down the phone.

"That telephone call was a terrible thing to do," Frank said, livid.

"Stop it, Frank, just don't tell me what to do. I told you I have gypsy e
I told you I can see things and not to cross me. Those bastards that mean
much to you now, cross me. They don't look like the Devil, Frank. They do
impersonate the Devil. Oh, no, damn it, they *are* the Devil." Frank was
palled to see her shake her fist in the air, trembling with rage. "What do
expect? Scorching red skin, a hound-like face; all nose, eyes shifty as a cal
date for Sing Sing, a big leer, a large drawn-back mouth"—Sally had screv
her face up in leering pantomime and was acting it all out in comtemptu
gestures—"a spiked tail and the God-damn flowing cape that could not poss
contain anything but disaster? And the God-damn horns which, by themsel
would be enough to warn anybody—even the dumbest man on earth?"

He was watching her carefully. She popped up on the bed, her I
crossed under her, leaning forward on her hands, chin up, eyes blazing,
loose hair covering her face. As Frank—alarmed—tried to put his arm arou
her to quiet her she shouldered him away.

"The Devil isn't like that," Sally rushed on. "Oh, no. Otherwise so m
people wouldn't fail to recognize him; for he does exist, the actual De
Frank, without question!

"I've met him—many times and in many forms—like that faker who,
forty years, took the credit away from the village doctor for climbing M
Blanc, the son of a bitch that the French guide told us about at Chamo
Start in this world as I did, move in it as I have, and you meet the Devi
many times you can feel him as easy as a slimy spider crawling up your
You don't have to see him. You can feel the eager little bastard. And, tak
from me, at some time most people do meet him—the real Devil—in his p
form; otherwise there is no possible explanation for the likes of Archibald
Scriver and Edward Whosis Holt!"

In the expression in her eyes were insinuations, bitter and searing, b
out of their intimacy. "And that's where you come in, Frank Killory!"
pointed at him. "You! You! You! If you think so much of a man like that, .
cannot see what he's doing, or helping to do, to you, your brain, your cl
acter, your very nature, why damn it to hell, Frank, you've gone down hil
a hack.

"Holt didn't put something in you,"she gasped, "he brought somet
out that was already there. Your character! Where has it gone? Where is
Just tell me that. Plain, stinking self-interest—that's Holt. That's the guts of h
and it's getting to be the guts of you, too; you two together. The thing that u
to be you is gone. Frank, it's gone. God damn!"

Frank was appalled. He turned to her; her hands were gripping the si
of her head as if she were holding it on. He seized her arms. Then he let go.
must have been hurting her. She registered a most fleeting, searching lool
alarm, then let herself fall back on the pillow and half closed her eyes.

Thoughts rushed through her—what does anything matter, any time,
place?—and who gives a damn?—and why should I?—the sun will rise the
day no matter what, the birds eat the insects, the cats chase the birds and

wheels of the world will roll on no matter what, with scarcely a wobble in
sas City, New York, London, Rome or any place on earth to bear witness to
words, the books, the problems or the events anywhere. In fact, if all
kind were to give a single horrid shout and expire in a mass, the face of the
et would be marvelously little changed.

When she regained her composure, waves of faintness swept over her. Her
d ached horribly and she could feel the race of her heartbeat, odd and
ping.

"I'm sorry, Frank," she said, seizing him to her, "maybe I've run off the
s. That's unimportant. But you have, too. And that is important."

# 16

DVERTENTLY, it was babbling, rather witless Grace Scriver, always the echo
Arch, but at the moment more absorbed by an alligator pear—"Fresh from
ifornia by air. Aren't they wonderful! We never could get these in Europe,
ld you?"—who resurrected a name Frank had scarcely mentioned to Sally
l gave her news of a mentor about whom she knew practically nothing.

She was astounded by the facts in Grace's chirrupings about how "this
tner of his, Philip Winston Allen," had picked Frank out of nowhere,
ated his metropolitan life and his national prominence that elevated him to
political try, and how Allen had saved Frank's political life, as well, by
nging to him the indispensable Michael W. Byrnes.

The implications lost on Grace were not lost on Sally, and these meshed in
mind like the key to a puzzle.

In this dawning she perceived the broad consequence of Allen in Frank's
. She discerned in Allen the ichor of the wisdom Frank personified in the
l case. She saw Allen as a man of such loyalty himself that he could estab-
in his own life a loyalty deliverable—and indispensable—to Frank.

I can see all this from Allen only as a sign of admiration for Frank, she
ught, as Grace rambled on.

The picture of an umbilical cord began to form in her mind. Frank had
n lifted by a silver cord. In the process he had cut the cord. Much had
eded with the cutting. Much had vanished entirely. And in the fanning

breeze of popularity and the great lure ahead, he emerged as hardly more t
a talented man of ends and means; means and ends.

But in cutting the silver cord had Frank also cut Philip Winston All
friendship for him? Sally hoped, nearly prayed, that Frank had not.

"Did they have a falling out?" she asked, suppressing her anxiety.

"Oh, heavens no; I don't think so," Grace answered, nodding and wav
to an acquaintance who went by, lost in the lunar heights of public sweetn
good-fellowship and charm.

Could this mentor reach Frank through his self-respect, which in one fo
or another, she felt to be the toughest strain in his character?

Nothing in Sally's life had ever dulled her instinct for action. And she
responding to this, again, with approximately the speed of light. Within m
utes, babbling Grace found Sally saying a rather hurried farewell after a qu
glance at her watch; mumbling something about being late and what a sha
and bore it was in New York to always have to hurry, hurry, hurry.

Allen's Hazel made the appointment and Allen had no clue when he s
Sally's name on his pad: Mrs. Charles N. Benson—London—4:30.

She was waiting for him when he came in. The room itself, and wha
seemed to reveal about the man she was soon to see, gave her courage:
books piled high on the tables near the window that looked across the har
into the haze of the Jersey shore. The river. A gray, neuralgic day. But
beyond the reaches of the harbor the open sea sparkled like lightning.
crossed her mind that ports have a pulse beat inland cities never know. Alle
wide desk with the comfortable leather chairs beside it. Was it, could it
made of ship timbers? Very handsome, but very odd. Surely it must have
story. The soft, deep crimson carpet and the over-all quiet in this room. T
tick of the Versailles clock. Tick, tock . . . tick, tock. The sober elegance of
paneled walls and the lovely carved mantel that she saw had been shaped
beautiful proportions by an artist's eye. The bright force of the Gauguin a
the Piccaso that flanked the mantel on each side. Oh, no, there are no encircl
myrmidons here, she thought.

But she was not prepared for the sight, the sudden impact on her, of
massive, heavy-shouldered man who came in: the fine head bristling with wh
hair, the brow a broad, almost vertical, escarpment; the formidable jowl;
quiet blue eyes, so comprehending, and his obvious simplicity as he mov
toward her. She could feel the ambience of this man on her instantly, its a
spreading out to grasp at her mind as surely as if it were grasping at her slee
You cannot say to a stranger, and perhaps not even to a friend, "My God, w
a patriarch you really are, every inch of you." Yet this is what Sally almost d
quite involuntarily.

"Mrs. Benson?" he said. "I am very glad to see you."

She took a deep breath and swallowed a dry lump in her throat; and s
took his hand, her hand working in its imperceptible way that brought th
both to chairs. Within a moment, in his presence, she felt completely co
posed.

"Mr. Allen, I should introduce myself," she said.

"Oh, I'm very glad to see you. Thank you for coming in." He nodded asantly. "Hazel told me you said it was urgent. I'm always more than de- ited to see anyone from Britain."

"I'm an American, sir. I live in London, but I write for the newspapers as ly Bryce, and I have been writing over here about the Killory campaign."

"Oh! That's very interesting."

"I know Frank very well," she said, but in a way totally devoid of a veiled aning. "I am sure you have been following his campaign very closely."

"Miss Bryce," Philip answered, "I haven't. No, I haven't. I only returned ) days ago." A smile filled the crags in his battered face. "I have simply been ring the time of my life."

Sally's impression was already formed; no one could spend even these ments with this man she had come to see without reaching the conclusion t here was a forthright and valuable man, with something of the inside uty that long life of fine usefulness puts into a fine face. She could see that ; salty patrician would be as obstinately resistant to capricious minds as a idred square miles of stone.

"Why, Mr. Allen, that's wonderful."

"Yes. I'll tell you exactly what I did. Miss Bryce, you should have been h us. I'm sorry, you missed something, really. My partner, Alfred Caxton, a son, Al. Well, Al and his sweet wife have two boys, Billy and Jack—both ght as a dollar and, I can promise you, more fun than a barrel of monkeys."

Sally was glowing. So this is Philip Winston Allen. This is whose life is in ; consequential room.

"Well," he continued, rubbing his hands in glee, "I said 'Al, you may recall t your father is my partner. I don't know what he does with his time, nor ve I ever known for more than thirty years, but whatever he does with it he :s not do any work. He is always away some place, sunning himself, pamper- himself, reading detective stories for years on end, playing pool, I suppose. ally don't know what Alfred Caxton does. I am a patient man. But enough enough.' Then I unleashed my thunderbolt. I said—and the whole family s quaking—'Al, unless you completely surrender Billy and Jack to me, no ngs attached, and let me take them on a Mediterranean cruise, I will fire ir father! Out he goes from the firm, right on his head. Vamoose! Alfred xton, in the gutter, destitute, unemployed, a disgrace to God, to country— l to Yale.'"

"Why, Mr. Allen—"

"Billy and Jack and I went first to the Madeira Islands and then every- ere in the Mediterranean, and to Egypt. I even rode a sightseers' camel with m there. In fact, the lazy camel at the pyramids was so used to ordinary rists' weights that when I got on him he wouldn't get up. He just stayed wn, bleating like an ugly goat. The two boys were rolling in the sand with ghter." And, laughing himself, he added, "No, I'm sorry, Miss Bryce. I've en far out of touch. Shortly before I sailed Frank came to talk to me about a

problem he had. And I know that it was settled. I've just been wishing h
well, since then. Won't you please tell me all about it."

Sally felt a lump in her throat. This man was still Frank's friend—his ve
very important friend. How could she tell him what she thought? How cou
she ask him to help?

"Mr. Allen," she said quietly, "Frank is in trouble."

"Frank is in politics, Miss Bryce. When a man goes into politics he ma
himself vulnerable all round."

"No. Frank is in trouble inside himself."

"What do you mean?" He leaned forward with a look of concern.

"You are responsible for a great deal of Frank's thinking and charact
and a great deal of his success."

"Miss Bryce, Frank came here a self-made man."

"Sir, I am no talebearer. And, believe me, Mr. Allen, I have no axe
grind. No, I haven't. But I also am not guessing. Frank needs help, and not
kind you gave him with Mike Byrnes."

Philip's eyebrows went up. So she knew about that?

Sally leaned closer to the desk. She wondered if her voice was steady
must speak as clearly as I can, she thought, for he must believe me and he m
not misconstrue a word I say.

"Mr. Allen," she said, "I think you get a great deal more pleasure
understanding people than in condemning them. I am asking you to und
stand Frank now, not to condemn him. I just hope you will take what I
going to say in that spirit. Did you ever hear of a 'Morning Glory'? Not
flower."

Philip answered slowly. "No, I don't think so."

"Well, in England a 'Morning Glory' is a race horse that looks very go
and runs very fast in the early morning trials. But in the actual race he chang
turns out to be just another horse. There, where it really counts, he fades."

"I see."

"Frank, right now, is turning out to be a 'Morning Glory.' "

There was concentration in Allen's fine face now and he started to spe
But he stopped short and did not interrupt her.

"However, sir, it is far worse than that. What's happening inside him is
taking him out of the race. Far from it. He's gaining all the time. But he's ri
on the edge of becoming a phony, Mr. Allen. And, again, I'm not guessi
Somewhere along the line in this political thing Frank lost his bearings witl
himself. He's feeling, thinking, saying and doing things that I'm absolutely s
are no more the Frank Killory who had and deserved the confidence of a m
like you than just any other eloquent spellbinder off the street." Sally's dism
and sense of urgency were obvious. Her face was pinched and there were vio
shadows under her wide-set eyes. She looked strangely fragile and unprotect
as she appraised her hopes for this giant's intervention.

"But, Miss Bryce," he protested, "that is a very shocking charge to ma
You know, I'm sure, that Frank should be here to defend himself. It's ve

difficult for me to listen like this. I wish Frank were present. I wish he were with us, Miss Bryce." Allen was not angry, but he had turned very stern.

"I understand. And, as a matter of fact, Mr. Allen, I am coming to that. But may I be specific?"

Philip nodded, reaching for a cigar in the humidor. "You will excuse me?"

"In Frank's anxiety for this great nomination, and what he foresees through it, that he will be the President of the United States, which I believe is what would happen, Frank himself has gotten consumed by it. He started out selflessly. I am convinced of that. You know, I believed in Frank Killory, too, Mr. Allen. Then the challenge became greater and greater as he saw the prospect becoming more and more real—success a probability, not just somebody's dream. First a handful, then hundreds, then thousands and now millions of people moved in to push Frank up, up, up. As the cheers became louder and louder, the fan mail piled higher and higher, the publicity greater and greater and the manipulators moved in closer to his ears—and Frank went off the rails. The difficulty is there are two Franks: the Frank who was and the Frank who is."

Sally's spirits were rising. She knew she was going to be heard out. "If Frank Killory had walked straight from the coal-mines case in the Supreme Court to the White House, you'd have had one man. Today, we've got a different man.

"This new Frank is busy burning his own house down within himself, and his promises and his good sense and his mind's honesty along with it. He started out believing that 'false promises, unattainable promises, broken promises are the curse of men and nations'—to use Frank's own words."

"He's right."

"But now what does he believe? I don't know. Do you know, Mr. Allen?"

Philip looked down at the carpet on the floor, shifting his weight from one leg to the other. Suddenly he raised his eyes and said abruptly. "Well, I assume he believes what he says. What has he been saying?"

"So far it's more the trend in what he has been saying. But before long I think Frank Killory will be promising the American people anything and everything that comes into his head if he thinks it will help him win."

Allen scowled and relit his cigar, drew on it, and put it down to let it burn out. "Oh, Miss Bryce," he mumbled protestingly.

"Sir, he'd make even more promises, I think, if he weren't so busy breaking promises he's already made. Frank Killory's real worth is in a downhill slide. And much of the push is coming from people who care ten times as much about what they can get out of it if Frank is President than they care about Frank. Moreover," Sally continued, evenly now and in a precise way, "what looks on the surface so spontaneous is not quite that, of course. All this stirring of the so-called grass roots has another side to it. The stirring is being done by carefully planned operations and is organized."

"But it is in the grass roots, you agree?"

"Yes."

"Well, Miss Bryce, 'all this stirring,' as you call it, seems to me to be all to the good. What's more important than to get average folks thinking about their government and participating? Arranging politics through rigged ward club-houses and stacked primaries that mean a candidate must be endorsed by special groups before he can even become a candidate—and be beholden to them—before he can hope to get any place in the primaries; arranging primary voting days at seasons when no one is election-minded so that only organized forces participate; shut-out conventions that nominate hand-picked fellows—these are all really terrible things if we want any kind of good government. Ordinary folks get completely side-tracked.

"Yet they're the most powerful group in America and they could knock this whole setup into nothingness if they ever took the bit in their teeth."

The craggy face was relaxed now and Allen smiled, as if seeing the vision. "I say 'hurrah' for everything the Killory campaign has been doing to break up this contrived piracy and collapse it with a good, swift kick in the pants. That's one reason—so long as you mention it—that I did have a little talk with Mike Byrnes in Springfield when Frank brought his problem to me. And while I have been completely out of touch, as I said, I do know that when I sailed there did seem to be an awful lot—a wonderful, amazing large number—of decent and worried citizens in the grass roots working mighty hard for Frank's campaign for no selfish reason on earth. Surely, Miss Bryce, you don't think that's a contrived too?"

"No, I don't, sir."

"It's a little like when Lindbergh landed, years ago. My God, I'll never forget it. This was a great human moment. The nearly incredible response was the clear, clear voice of our great country's inner self; always just waiting to be given half a chance to show that the nation's true spirit is still there. The wish that never leaves our people is that good things can be done and that courage, decency and all the quiet dreams of self-reliance and hope be allowed to light the way. That yearning within the core of our country is always ready and waiting. That's what I see in 'all this stirring,' Miss Bryce."

Sally looked crushed. I am failing, she felt, I am failing. He just does not understand me. But then Allen placed his heavy arms forward on the desk and studied her quietly for a moment. She sat back with one hand over her eye and he could see the pulses in her neck throbbing.

"Now for the problem, Miss Bryce, as you see it," he said, "and I agree that it can be a problem. Does the man—Frank—deserve and justify the confidence of all these millions; the confidence of the American people? It's quite true, more is the pity—politics does have a Janus-head quality that often makes it difficult to separate the reformer from the political campaigner. In short, Frank on the level? You're asking me who is being caught—fish or fisherman."

"Mr. Allen, he has lost what he had. That is what I am saying. Surely you regarded Frank as a promising man. I am saying that Frank is a promising man who, inside himself, is breaking the promises. And with all this he's become utterly suspicious. He's putting his confidence where anybody should be able

it doesn't belong. He's withdrawn it from the best brains around him. As for
rest, Frank now seems to think his world of friends is full of strangers who
just waiting for a chance to become his enemies. Yet, Mr. Allen, where is
man who has been helped by so many people as Frank Killory?"

Philip walked to the windows. He spoke patiently, compassionately, over
shoulder; but he was clearly concerned. "I am in no position to agree with
, or to dispute you. This can happen, of course. Big, high goals can store up
nge things in eager people, not only in politics, but in business, in partner-
s, professions, the arts, the military or heaven knows what. These windows
k out on offices full of the problem, with all its sadness. That I know.

"A firm will say, 'My, my, aren't we lucky. When old Mr. Bilkins retires we
e fine Mr. Billups right there to take over.' Billups has been working intelli-
tly, co-operatively, selflessly, for years. He has everything. That's why the
le Board of Directors is so happy. But when the Billups I'm talking about
ally lands in the top authority all those years can sometimes seem to melt
rancid butter in the sun. Those who knew him best then don't know him at
The work of others that satisfies him for decades seems unsatisfactory to
. He questions everybody's judgment but his own. He begins to frighten a
of people about their own future. He has no reason to envy anybody
thing. No reason to be suspicious. Who knows why? I don't, although I do
w—and very well indeed—the tragedy and dangers that come from it; not
e to the man, of course, but to so many, many others affected by him
ugh all this, like innocent bystanders who get hit by the rock. So useless,
, such a waste!"

Allen spoke with feeling, and he continued. "But Frank Killory is no ordi-
y man," he said, flatly, "Frank is a good man, Miss Bryce, and while my
le point in agreeing with you that this can happen to good men—you'd
ect it of the smart operators and so forth—Frank is a whole lot better than
. His mace has been a long time at the forge. He has had a good self-made
He has intelligence, but Frank also has character. Moreover, he has always
character. You cannot unlive a life that produces a man like Frank."

"He is unliving it, Mr. Allen."

"The Chinese say such men blow hot and cold with the same breath—"

Sally pricked up her ears. "I'll remember that," she interrupted.

"But my information is absolutely nonexistent. I remember telling Frank
e that old Bernie Baruch said, 'Every man has a right to his own opinion,
no man has a right to be wrong in his facts.' I simply have no facts, Miss
ce."

The look of sharp pain, of near despair, gave a haunted expression to her
, and Allen felt his whole body stiffen. He turned and walked toward her.
sensed a change in his face. Anxiety had taken the place of sternness. Had
man really been as certain of Frank as he had said, or had it been more his
ing of affection and the momentum of his hopes?

"What can I do to help him, Miss Bryce?" Philip asked.

"I want you to talk to Frank and see if you can't open his eyes. If he won't

listen to you it's hopeless. Who else? Who else? The selfish men he's listening
now are worse than no help—they're hurting and are a part of the very dam
to himself that I'm talking about. Yes, you need the facts, sir. I understand t
But I am equally sure you will want to make up your own mind about them.

"You have been away. Will you from this moment forward—beginn
now—make it your deep, affectionate business to follow and weigh everyth
Frank says in the papers, on the air, anywhere, not against the background
the Frank that you have known? If you will put it within the framework
what I have tried so poorly to say, I can only hope you will get the project
that's absolutely necessary now. Nothing can come of this visit with you—
Frank or anybody—unless you forget the Frank who was."

Did Philip hear an echo of the toast to the Young Man Who Was? "Le
fill a cup and drink with love . . . to his dreams, for they were rainbow-color
to his appetites, for they were strong; to his blunders, for they were huge; to
pains, for they were sharp; to his time, for it was brief . . ." Perhaps, perh
But he only said, "And then, Miss Bryce?"

"Then I can only hope you will make up your mind to stand this g
man from Braidwood, Illinois, straight up on this carpet and bring him bac
his senses."

In the downtown financial district and at the Battery, it was late in
day, the twilight hour, and most offices were closed; the harbor lights v
coming on, the first few lights in the houses on the flat Jersey shore twin
through the haze of the lingering sunset; the beacon at the Narrows of
harbor was turning in its great arc and the winds from the ocean bent thro
the buildings and shook the windows mildly at this tip of Manhattan.

Philip had moved to the windows, deep in thought. The docks were
and the vessels with their cranes and harnesses were quiet for the night.
criss-cross streets below, shortly ago so busy, were silent as a stone desert.
voices and noises had been brushed away and Allen could see only the
vacant pavements for blocks on end. Slowly and painfully he made his cho

As Sally gathered her gloves and bag and arose to leave, Allen turned
came toward her and put out his hand, this towering man, speaking with
deliberation.

"You assume the responsibility for these charges, Miss Bryce," he
quietly, "for that's what they really amount to. And in your doing so I ac
your good faith, and I accept your good will, too, toward Frank and tov
me.

"The charges strike very heavily on a hope I've had, and still have,
Frank. The responsibility remains yours for this doubt of him and your in
ences to me. I will make the promise you ask, Miss Bryce," he stated, aft
pause. "I have great confidence in Frank Killory."

"Thank you, Mr. Allen, thank you," Sally answered. Her voice was a
plication and her face was turned away.

The breakthrough of the delegate barrier widened steadily after Jefferson
lowed in Byrnes' lead. Byrnes was pushing in every direction behind the
nes and calling on the loyalties and political acumen of his party colleagues
one state after the other. Delegation chiefs or highly influential figures were
rking openly for Frank in the delegations for Maine, Rhode Island, Ohio,
rth and South Dakota, West Virginia, Florida, Georgia, New Mexico, Iowa,
egon and the State of Washington. The last six states, in that order, had
ually declared for him.

Pivoting on Byrnes' Illinois support, Killory would go into the Kansas
ty convention with at least one hundred and twenty votes. This was practi-
lly the ideal base for the beginning of the first ballot. Not too many; that
ght include weak votes which would be lost to him on the second ballot. Not
few; so that he was simply another of the many contenders represented by
ttered votes that would surely go to the leaders after the voting counts
gan to jell.

"We'll hold back about twenty votes on the first ballot," Karnes decided,
taining agreement from Patterson, Byrnes and Jefferson. "This means we will
me out of the first ballot showing about a hundred delegates for Killory. And
th these twenty—or more—in reserve, we can be absolutely sure we will not
le downward on the second ballot. But if the large number of Means and
illis votes that appear in the first ballot contain weak votes, as I am certain
y do, one or the other of them—or both—will be fading in the second ballot.
th have been worried about a deadlock. Both have been playing for numbers
avoid this. Both have been trying to come into Kansas City as the leader in
at now turns out to be a stalmate between them. I say they are vulnerable—
nerable as hell—to fading downward from their first ballot strength. The one
ng we must be sure of is that *we* don't fade."

Byrnes gave this task to Ray Jefferson. Many of his Missouri delegates—
largest majority—would like to vote for Means or Willis first. Then on the
ond ballot they would switch to Killory. The fading effect on the two sena-
s could be critical. The gaining effect for Frank could be decisive; provided
s second-ballot advance occurred in enough delegations.

Jefferson undertook to duplicate the hold-back arrangement among the
legation leaders that he knew best. "If we hold back twenty or so votes on
first ballot," he said, "we should be able to get through the first roll-call
th at least a hundred votes; a very, very respectable start. Then on the
ond ballot we should pass that number halfway through the alphabet."

Patterson asked, "Ray, do you think we can come through the second
llot with a hundred and fifty?"

Jefferson hunched over his wide stomach. He squirmed a little in his chair
side Karnes' desk. "Does anybody know where Einstein is right now?" he
ked, laughing—but figuring steadily with his stubby pencil. In a few mo-
ents he looked up at Karnes and Patterson.

"Of the total 905 votes, about 75 will be scattered every which way. So,
out 830 is the real figure we're working on. Frank surely has 120 of these.

Means and Willis are even, with approximately 360 each. Each one has mo
than three times as many as Frank"—he looked up from his figures, smiling
"but we can come out on the second ballot with not less than 160 votes,"
stated flatly.

"And I think it can be as many as 180. Means and Willis would each dr
to about 320. That's the decisive thing. Frank on the way up, and strong
after the first ballot, the two far-ahead leaders on the way down. One ma
going toward the majority figure required to win. The two leaders going aw
from it. If we can do this on the second ballot, Frank can be nominated on t
fourth ballot.

"When Frank goes to 180, neither Means nor Willis can stand melting li
that. If most of the second ballot defection comes from Willis and drops hi
under 300 votes, and Means' strength stands firm, as I think it will, or ev
increases a little, say ten or twelve votes, Willis will be out of the running
the end of the second ballot. If the main defections come from Means, which
do not expect, and Willis stays steady in the second ballot, Means will be ot
No matter how it looks in the newspapers now, the nomination is not going
Willis.

"It's not to be Means or Willis against Frank. That's the first fact. It w
surely be Willis who fades on the second ballot. Accordingly, it will be eith
Arthur Means or Frank Killory who wins this nomination for the next Preside
of the United States. With the trend clear to the scattered voters and othe
Frank would equal or pass Means in the third ballot. The answer is: Frank w
be nominated on the fourth ballot. My good friends, with our hold-back on t
first ballot and the pick-up to a hundred and eighty or more on the secon
Frank is in, sure as God made little apples."

They telephoned Mike Byrnes in Springfield and paced him through th
calculations; delegation by delegation, the first ballot hold-back, the seco
ballot's big gain; Means' position and Willis' position then and thereafter. Wh
did Mike think?

"I think you're right. Absolutely right. I agree with Ray's figures, give
take a few here or there. But taking them as they are, I agree. It's going to I
either Means or Willis against Frank, after the second ballot. And it will I
Means, not Willis. Means against Frank. But please give Frank this message f
me."

He was talking to Karnes, with Patterson and Jefferson on extensions. "T
Frank to keep cool, now. Nothing fancy. He's much further ahead than eith
Means or Willis thinks. He's further ahead than he himself thinks. The impo
derables are working for Frank. Repeat that to him surely, Walter: the impo
derables are working in his favor. He can win this nomination. I believe that
things stand now he can win it on the fourth ballot.

"Moreover, if an outsider can generate this much enthusiasm and pun
against the administration, Frank must be reflecting even more national dissa
isfaction with the administration than is generally realized. Therefore, if he ca
get the nomination, he can beat the administration and win the election. T

ınk if he keeps his head he can be the next President of the United States."

Karnes told him. He found Frank as unsurprised as if he had said merely ood morning." "Why, of course, Mike's right. I think Ray's figures are even a le on the conservative side." Walter had seldom seen his friend so composed. ınk stuck Jefferson's penciled calculations in his pocket and hauled Karnes to lunch.

After they ordered—Frank very rarely had lunch with one person alone se days—he turned to Karnes with a certain abruptness.

"I wanted to bring you over here, in any case," he said, "and get something ng that has been on my mind some time. It's getting late for it, Walter, and his can be set up we'd better—you'd better—move fast."

Karnes was all attention. Then, impervious to Karnes' explanation made a nth ago, almost as if he had never heard it, Killory again launched into his ossible proposal that Perkins move out as national chairman and Walter e his place. This was an ominous encore.

"Frank," Karnes replied, completely bewildered, "it's silly to thrash that ıe wheat over again. I was surprised when you had the idea in the first ce. I certainly thought we settled that. I've said nothing to anyone about it :e then. I only hope you haven't, either."

Agitation sounded in Karnes' voice and he spoke very deliberately. "I have way to make any such idea possible. No one else has, either. It's a situation, chairmanship procedure. It's firmly fixed, for many, many years. It's right way it is. Other people are involved who are not only not your supporters who would be outraged if they knew you wanted to ease out a neutral irman and substitute your own man instead. You're on the make for the nination, my friend, and you'll look like you are trying to pack the National nmittee. The resentment would boomerang like a ton of bricks."

"Well, I'm more sure than ever that Perkins wouldn't support me."

"What you want to do shouldn't be done, can't be done and won't be done. ılly, Frank, you have to come down out of the clouds about that thing."

Karnes had discovered that Frank had two distinct methods of communi- ion; talking to a person and talking to himself. At the moment he could not ide which was happening.

"The organization is opposing me," Frank murmured, returning to the ıiliar theme.

"Why, you've had more and better organization support than any new- ner has a right to ask. First, Mike Byrnes: indispensable. Nobody could have ıgined he would take such a leap in ordinary politics, no, sir, not for a ıute. But he took it. Glenn Patterson is a party man. So is Raymond Jeffer- ı. And other delegation leaders are coming, too. Success breeds success in s business. Mike gave our game its ball park to play in.

"Well, if the rest had as much sense as they're supposed to have they'd see light."

"And dump Means and Willis, merely in the face of our blitz? Burn their 'dges and commit themselves to a man most of them do not know, have no years of loyalty to, and who is largely an uncertain political entity to the Why, Frank, what do you expect!"

"They might give some thought to what's good for the country."

"A great many people do not think either Means or Willis is bad for country, Frank."

"Well."

"They've been in government a long time. You don't get where they are the Senate, especially Means, who never dodged an issue, without hav something the country can use."

Round and round and round; but Walter could not seem to satisfy Kill that he must not try to press himself into the chairmanship.

"Sometimes Walter hasn't as much force as I'd like," Frank told Sally t night. "Oh, I know he's for me, but—"

"My God, if Karnes isn't, who is?"

"He's for me all right. But I think he could be a little more aggressive."

"Braidwood, every man has to do his own work in his own way; ev woman, too, for that matter. Now just please don't get too, too dissatisfied w Walter Karnes. Even I have some knowledge of how both parties and natio committees are set up identically alike. Even I can see Walter's point, if can't."

Frank smiled; he was patronizing her. He took the attractive woman in arms. "Sally," he whispered into her ear, "I don't know what I'd do with you."

"Well," she answered quietly, "you seem able to do without quite a people. I don't know." Oh, Mr. Allen, Philip Winston Allen, dear Mr. Allen, thought, are you keeping your promise?

Details were being set for a long trek to the Pacific Coast. Karnes, Pat son and Watson had chosen Portland for the Killory invasion. Los Angeles San Francisco were out: too bold a move into Willis' home state. Frank dissatisfied by the decision and Scriver had even said, "Frank, you should h the Hollywood Bowl." But Killory concurred in the Oregon decision Morton arranged a big outdoor rally in Portland.

Jake went out in advance and took charge. Jennings came up from Francisco. Patterson was the advance man from New York, taking yo Watson and Sam Welsh with him. Repetition had brought so much pract that it was incomparably easier to see that all the pieces fell into place. St ings of even a few months earlier seemed a nightmare of errors now. "I d know how this crowd of enthusiasts ever got anything done," said Putnam, " they did. Do you remember Chicago! It seems a mighty long time ago."

Both Putnam and Usher were feeding whole writing teams in from th papers to help Frank's speeches. The volume was satisfactory. The consiste with his earlier pronouncements was not. Frank's and Holt's rewrites made result hardly recognizable within the framework of much that he had p claimed in his initial appeals to the public. Then Frank would take off finally come out with something more, alone.

As if a ratio existed, the harder he pressed now the more he promised. irnes often did not see the speech before it was delivered; although Frank's w willingness to propose easy solutions to national problems and to expand ᵣ promises was mild at first.

The Portland address, however, caused alarm. Again, neither Morton nor tterson, who were out there with him, had seen what Frank intended to say. irriedly finished in his hotel room by Killory himself, and him alone, it had t even been mimeographed before; sticking the sheets in his pocket, he went once to the auditorium to deliver it. And, within moments, across the nation, e whole slippery tract of manuscript paper suddenly rose up and screeched at lly.

It was the product of a quick wit that now usurped the name of convic- ᵢns. It was certain that Frank could not fulfill these new promises, because ey were impossible.

Then Frank rubber-stamped the labor legislation of the administration, hich he had always opposed as jerry-built, inequitable and unenforceable.

Within three paragraphs he was endorsing the expansion of social security exactly the ways he had long condemned. With this he threw in a lot of fiscal racadabra.

In conclusion, he went all out for federal aid to education of a type that he d stated time and again would be ruinous to the independence and flowering the nation's universities.

He ended: "The road is still steep and rocky, but the outlines of the goal gin to rise above the horizon. Help us! Help me!" On the surface it was all lendidly encouraging. Actually, it was deeply misleading and the whole thing nt Frank rummaging in the debris of his earlier statements and expressed nvictions.

The first blast came from Sally. She and Frank had had nearly a solid eek together in New York before he left for Portland, and these had been aenadic nights. But Sally did not make the trip, and her piece criticising his irtland push was an all-out crusher.

It began: "A demonstration needs substance as well as show." It ended ith a statement and a question, hard and to the point: "Chinese say such men ow hot and cold with the same breath. Killory's convictions seem like a lost ip gone in the secret of the tempests. Is this a man of promise who is now ˙eaking the promise?"

Her switch surprised Bixley and he telephoned Sally before releasing her ece to her subscribers.

"This is no switch by me, John," she stated, calmly, as if expecting his call. ʰe question is, has Frank Killory switched? It was a very contradictory ᵢeech, from any viewpoint, it seems to me. Either Frank doesn't believe what ᵣ's been saying about numerous things, repeating them all over the United ̣ates and arranging chances to do so, or he doesn't believe what he said last ˙ght in Portland."

"I agree, Sally. But anybody is entitled to pitch one or two balls out of the

ball park. Killory's average in all this has been high. I think you hit too har
about this one."

"I hope I hit hard enough to help stop him from doing this again," sk
replied, as resolutely as a West Point drill sergeant.

Bixley laughed. "Have you heard from Killory?" he asked.

"No, I haven't. But you haven't released the piece yet, you know. I will
later today."

This was only the start of the commotion. Karnes, Patterson, Jefferson ar
Byrnes announced flatly to Frank that it was impossible for him to backtrac
like this.

"Backtrack?" he all but roared over the long distance telephone to Karne
"This is not backtracking! I'm looking ahead. If you ask me, Walter, I think i
probably the best speech I've made in the entire campaign."

"It hurt you, Frank."

"With the professionals, you mean."

"With anybody that wants to, needs to, and must respect you. You hav
convictions. You can't switch around like that, as a man of convictions. I dor
think what you said last night represents your convictions. And if you think th
is good politics, I don't think that either." Killory had never heard his frier
sound so angry. There was a pause. Then Walter concluded: "Never mind. O
swallow doesn't make the spring. Suppose we just try to treat Portland as
fluke. I think we can smother it some by hurrying your next big meeting. Th
would give you an early chance to make a talk that will take the bad taste o
of last night." They decided on this strategy.

Sally wrote that speech. It was for Baltimore, and the date was advance
one week. She began it on a low key, with a solemn expression of sympathy f
anyone holding the office of the American Presidency. Faced with the decisio
a President must make—the really vital decisions on which even the peace
the world might depend—could there be any citizen who did not say in su
hallowed moments: "I am glad I am not President of the United States"?

The text traced events, developments, the larger problems, and applied
these a symposium of solutions that Frank had previously proposed. Sal
ticked these off, one through ten; the speech would register as "Killory's T
Point Speech." Then Frank all but refused to deliver it.

"Darling, it's you," he said, reading her sheets over the room-service tra
"but it's not me."

"I don't care particularly if you're complaining—"

"I'm not complaining—"

"Complaining about the words. Go over this draft and put it in your ov
words, naturally. I've no pride of authorship, you know. It's your own gift f
oratory that started you on your speed run. But if you're complaining about th
substance in what I've written, and these ten proposals, don't complain to m
These are not mine; they're yours. I just expressed in different language wh
you've said again and again, as you well know."

"Yes, but I don't think reviewing these pushes us much ahead, maybe."

"Not as much ahead as Portland?"

"No, not as much as Portland. The professionals didn't like what I said in rtland. The American people did. In my view the professionals are a liability, l, as I've told you over and over again. If they were so smart no outsider like yself, a non-professional, could make these inroads. I think I understand at st what the public is looking for fully as well as they do."

"Frank," she answered, making no attempt to soften her exasperation, fter Portland you asked me to write this draft. It's the only time you have ked me to do so. If you think I'm trying to sell you the idea of using it, you ve another guess coming."

"Don't be angry, Sal."

"I'm not angry, honestly I'm not. You can take it or leave it. I just wrote at I believe you think; because you said you think these thoughts. And, cidentally, I think them myself."

She had moved to the bedroom windows, pulled back the draperies, and s looking up the avenue toward Central Park. There was the city's late night sh, lights only in the streets and the park, for the canyon's stores were dark.

"Before he released my piece about your Portland promises," she said over r shoulder, "John Bixley telephoned me and asked, 'Sally, why the switch?' I ld him my piece was no switch. You did the switch, Frank. And I thought rtland was God-awful."

Frank laughed. "Oh Sal," he said, "I've forgotten more about this sort of ing than you'll ever know."

Was it incapacity? One might as well say that a person succumbing to phus dies of incapacity.

There are many penalties to the quick mind. Vanity and pride can be two them. Yet Frank himself had said to Janet, in Braidwood, years ago: "Pride, re than anything else, I think, causes many of the troubles; corrosive pride."

"And greed?" Janet added.

"Well, greed mixes with pride, but pride and vanity—and I'm using them gether—last longer. And when pride starts its work it is impossible to meas-e what can be the effects."

They were sitting in the porch swing, looking up at the great purple bowl the sky. "My God," he said, "what a night. Look up there; outside ourselves."

The stars, appearing in a fragile, sparkling mass with the vast tapestry of e celestial needlepoint behind them, were radiant as a weave of silver from e horizon to another in the flat Illinois countryside.

The North Star flashed overhead, this gigantic atomic explosion, beckoning this little globe whirling along. The old benevolent constellations stared rough cold space at Frank and Janet's world.

The Milky Way, that Mississippi of the sky, rolled across thousands of llions of miles of space. "Yet," said Frank, "it's only a fraction of the universe yond."

They saw a meteor. "Oh, look, a falling star," Janet exclaimed.

"That's good luck," Frank answered. "Make a wish."

The comets went on their long errands, deep in the temple of the univers
The colored planets and moons, the dull masses, and the cold, dead worl
lying in the silent morgue of eternity told their unfathomable story to the
two.

Against all this the seven stars of the Big Dipper stood out so clearl
suspended, each alone and each alive, each in its place like a jewel in a velv
box, yet each traveling through the heavens with enormous gusto. There was
great glory in this sky.

Her cheek close to Frank's, sitting there with her thoughtful husban
Janet quoted Goethe. "Didn't he say, 'The highest to which man can attain
wonder'? Father often says that," she remembered.

Frank's eyes swept again and again across the magnificent night in t
slow back-and-forth pendulum motion of the swing.

"Honey," he said, "it all makes us seem so small. What a wonderful less
against vanity! Against pride! Anyway, we always overemphasize the things v
know and underemphasize what we don't know."

Yet now he could accidentally encounter Albert Winship, the Natior
Committeeman from California, Senator Willis' home state, in the St. Re∤
lobby and challenge this total stranger point-blank. He spoke to Winship
icy tones, cold as a glacier.

"I don't know whether you're going to support me or not," Frank volu
teered. There was not the slightest possibility of Winship's supporting Fra
against Willis. "Moreover, I don't give a damn. I think the professionals li
you are a liability!" It had broken up Winship's friendship with his fellc
Committeeman Walter Karnes. Senator Willis, in turn, was literally incred
lous. The Californian had telephoned him at once.

"What's the explanation? What's happening?" Willis asked.

"I don't know, Senator. I'm just telling you what Killory did. And I nev
saw the man before in my life."

Senator Means had the story from Willis later that day. He listened
Willis repeated it in the Senate corridor. When it was finshed they just look
at each other; old friends. Then the two men went their ways on the Sena
floor.

# 17

VALTER KARNES ran square into Sally at the St. Regis elevators. Prim and chic
n a smart gray suit, she stood preoccupied, looking up at the floor dial, idly
apping her room key on her shining purse and hardly noticing the shrill
vaspishness of an irritated, jostled elevator starter standing beside her.

Can we ever be as lonely as sometimes in a crowd?

Once when Frank had awakened and was sitting on the edge of the bed
vith his feet four-square on the floor, his back with its solidarity and strength
oused in her a sudden, compounded emotion. It occurred to Sally all at once
hat Frank was at the moment the person nearest to her in all the world.

Out of the countless people she knew, among all her friends—London,
'aris, Rome, and where not?—Frank and his solid, muscled back alone were
eal. All the rest, at this moment, were a phantasmagoria of ghosts and shadows
vhich could, if she permitted, immerse her in a dreadful feeling of loneliness.

That must never come, never, whatever else happened. Never that look,
mpty, envious, in so many women's eyes; grown hard like the agate marbles
he had played with as a little girl in Philadelphia. So many had it, all those
mart, chic women who passed in this elegant Manhattan lobby; who rushed
easelessly on their paths among the proper places in Europe with the clatter
•f silver spoons in their brains and mouths; through the corridors of the Ritz in
'aris, the Ritz in Madrid, into the ballrooms in her London, hurrying back and
orth across the Atlantic on giant, glittering liners.

Then Sally's moment of revelation and clairvoyance passed and she
hought: Loneliness is a frame of mind, plus idleness. Thank God, neither
.pplies to me; it never has and it never will. But she looked sharply, even now,
t the reflection of her own eyes in the mirror beside the elevator, searching,
»erhaps without knowing it, for any trace of the frustration which she would
tave been terrified to see. In truth, it was not there.

"I just got off the train from Baltimore," Walter said. "I need a drink.
Come on." His voice was flat and tired. Sally shrugged as he turned her around.
They walked through the crowded lobby. The crowd was waiting for Frank.
All her practiced senses became alert.

Snap-snap, tick-tack, all at once, a tiny excitement stirred and grew.
Karnes, recognized, was known to bear the personal carrying power of Frank
Killory's famous name. And on such occasions a New York crowd invades any
precinct by sheer weight of numbers, paying no more attention to the uptilted
»yebrows of reception desk attendants than to a robin in a tree.

Walter and Sally had to weave their way through the cottonwool of smiles

and handshakes of political pushers, implorers, well-wishers and fakes. Onl
the timbre and pitch of the voices conveyed any meaning. They were excited i
their different ways. And they were framed like a frail stockade by a circle
the urbane who belonged in this hotel's elegance: suave onlookers, extravagar
women and shameless young men and other surprised travelers whose gaz
seemed to suggest that urchins had taken over the candy store.

Urchins were included, in fact, and as usual; one confronted Walter an
Sally, baring his upper teeth and smiling like a puzzled chipmunk. A sallov
man, his face pale and his eyes full of the excitement, started to engage then
Sally threw Walter a quick, trusting, pleading glance and they hurried by.

A freeloader of unknown identity, a lizard-like stare in his liquid eyes-
their little pupils set in immense, bloodshot eyeballs—blocked their way. Mo
ing around him, Karnes merely forced a nod and gave him the unwillin
politicians' smile that tells you to come back another day.

A reporter fell into step; a threadbare boy from Brooklyn put slightly o
balance by a Harvard education. Karnes knew him, and his recognition wa
hostile and forbidding. Before the young man could speak Walter turned o
him with the hard word: "No." Sally saw the rebuffed one's temper explode lik
a celluloid collar, sulky and indignant, and full of groans and growls.

Walter did stop, however, as they passed the lobby newsstand. But Sally
piece for the day, which would cover the Baltimore splurge, was not in th
paper.

"I just couldn't write it," she said, tired and baffled, as she ordered he
drink. "I don't know whether it's because I'm so damn mad; or perhaps becaus
I pity him, Walter. Maybe you can tell me what the hell is going on. Nov
Baltimore!"

"Me? Me tell you?" he answered. "I wish to God I knew. Sally, what i
going on?" He broke the masklike rigidness of his feelings and thoughts b
jabbing his cigar hard in the ash tray. But there was more sadness than anger i
his look as he leaned across the table, a note of commiseration in his voice.

He was not a soft man, but he was not a hard man, either. He had seer
much happen for many, many years in both the back streets and the perfum
and glare of politics. The clamorous caterwaul of voices never confused hin
Moreover, he had that quality which Arabs describe as *baraka*: he had th
power to make life appear as better than before. This stood Karnes in goo
stead in his political calling. But as he sat there with Sally he was not
politician, he was a friend, which is a very different thing.

"I left before Frank finished the speech," he said, "and caught the firs
train back. I just couldn't face riding all the way here with him." Walter spok
in a tone of flat hopelessness that she had never heard him use.

"The applause nearly blew my radio off the table," Sally answered, with
dismissing gesture like the fluttering fan.

"I know."

"The response sounded terrific," she continued. "His voice. The slow, dee
tones. His basso profundo shook them to their heels. And those pauses; thos

long, long pauses. Then the stepped-up, straight punches. My God, how well he's kissed that 'unseen audience' jinx goodbye!"

"I know."

"Whammy, whammy, whammy. Absolutely terrific, Walter." But the handsome woman was holding herself stiff, like a watchdog at bay.

John Gibbons, Frank's rotund researcher, pouched and sallow, his night-gray eyes twinkling above their black sacs, and a new light mustache carrying little conviction of masculinity, waved from another table; spirits high, the epitome of confidence and good cheer.

Frank needed facts. Facts. But Karnes and young Watson had quarreled with Gibbons more and more, lately, about the debatable figures and comparisons he fed Frank. They challenged these bluntly after the Portland affair, only to be met by Gibbons' flashing eyes and a voice like ocean waves. He was practically drawing Frank's triumphal car; close in and chock full of get-up-and-go; and here in the bar his mood was one of jovial aggressiveness. "Hi, you two," he called, tilting a tall glass. "*Prosit.*" Walter looked like a locked house.

Sally spoke to Karnes again in pent-up words. "All that political whang-dang and witless logic Frank let go with! Full of eloquence and body English." She twisted in the chair. "Caught up in an avalanche, riding ahead with the whole push of the crowd!"

"Why, sure, Sal, the crowd was in Frank's bones, taking him right along and along and along. With the offers he was making, in another ten minutes he would have thrown in the family silver."

Sally replied with an inflection of tenderness. "But, Walter," she asked, "do you think he was in the crowd's bones?"

Walter's hand tightened around his drink. He drummed the table vigorously with his other fingers. "I know very damn well he wasn't in their bones," he said, looking at her squarely. "It was the show, Sal; just that, the show. Like Portland. Jovian fireworks. Just the show. Frank refuses to believe that. In it, he sees nothing but approval bursting out, noisy as five hundred Fourths of July.

"You heard what he told them, all over again, Portland redoubled in spades. You'd think he'd just forgotten something out in Oregon and wanted to be sure to put that in, too, the next time." Karnes crushed a new cigar hard in the tray and pulled a package of cigarettes from his pocket. "Most of those promises are utterly impossible, and Frank ought to know it, and the rest are questionable. All in all, it was as phony as a wax apple."

The distressed woman spoke as if to Frank himself, someplace removed. "You hardly know what to feel," she said, "except pity." She was speaking with sympathy and understanding for the man on his way back from Baltimore. She gave a deep sigh, took another sip from her glass and went on, tapping her rings against the rim. "Well," she said, "now who can do what?"

Walter smiled. "My dear father used to say," he recalled, "that if you tell a man something that is clear and you tell it to him five times and he still will not believe it, there is only one reason. He just doesn't want to believe it."

"No, Frank doesn't want to believe it."

"I know you tried to get to him after the Portland thing. My God, Sal," he grimaced, "that piece you wrote about it. I know he asked you to draft the Baltimore come-back. And I also know he didn't use your draft."

"Is it hopeless to bring him back in line now, Walter?" Sally asked, reaching across and putting her hand over his. "He's really quite a guy, really quite hell of a guy, and he's worked so damn hard." There was pleading in her eyes, nothing short of that, and they were moist. Walter had never found her gentle, pitying, compassionate. The simpleness of these feelings in her touched him; that's what he found so appealing now—her spontaneity. Ready-made regrets were absent, along with any petulance or anger. She was patiently picking up the stones with which Frank was shattering his own windowpanes.

Walter stared at her. Memories mixed with beauty. He saw passing before him those women of his springtimes who disappear among the flowers, the music and the lights of successive memories, like swans swimming toward radiant climes. They go to join many other charming memories while other waves of beauty, diamonds, flowers and feathers roll by at the sound of Rossini's music; but Sally fitted no memory he had.

The waiter came and Karnes motioned him off. He was sketching small circles slowly on the tablecloth with a pencil; stopping and reversing, starting again. The room was full of the buzz of people at the nearby tables and booths. Yet the helplessness at this table was being defeated even under the same roof.

These two did not know it, of course, but as Frank came in the lobby and stopped by the desk the message was there.

While the buzz in the King Cole room droned on, he was pushing south through the Fifth Avenue traffic, caught in the river of snorting automobiles, called to the very tip of Manhattan by a low, quiet voice that said: "Frank, dear boy, I wonder if you might drop down to see me?" Philip Winston Allen.

The lights were out in the firm's reception hall and only Allen's Hazel was on hand, gathering her things to leave, when Frank arrived.

He had not seen this room for months. Frank felt strange here after the rumpus-room atmosphere of so many political hallrooms and dens. Nor had he laid eyes on this massive, heavy-shouldered man who sat behind this desk since the first big break—the Illinois break—in the campaign.

Philip's glance was cast down now onto some papers and he had not yet seen Frank Killory standing at the door.

The life of every man is a diary in which he intends to write one story and writes another.

History is the story of innumerable biographies. It is also the story of the development of individuals; of lost illusions, the clash between the thrill of expectation and the arrival of the truth, and too often of useless sorrows strewn along the way.

When Alexander's homesick army refused to cross the Indus this was the end of Alexander the Great, and he died before he could return home, aged thirty-three. Napoleon, still only forty-six, was enchained on St. Helena longer than it had taken him to conquer all continental Europe; the victim of his own useless conquests.

Evil men are self-betrayed by immoderation more than anything. Bismarck was an evil influence in Europe, but he was a moderate, who knew where to stop. The others are out for the full, rich life and if their course leads downhill they are still determined to proceed at full speed. They are like the first adventurous boatman who rode the smooth river from Lake Erie to Lake Ontario. The river is broad and smooth and carries the boatman rapidly and easily. The speed of his progress and success of his whole enterprise is remarkable to behold. But the cataract of Niagara is near. The boatman may—or may not—finally see that the current is a current of destruction. In either case, it is too late. If he tries to retrace his way the current is too strong. Down he goes over the sharp rocks, and the waters with him.

But the waters, maddened into a frenzy by the swift descent down the Falls, only boil and thrash for a time and then flow on again as ever. However little such men may care for the idea, the march of mankind soon covers each of them with a shroud.

This inexorable expansion of the universal life which flows and swallows up all eras and which effaces man's existence, except in a few hearts and not always even in one, is the ephemeral drama of humanity as Philip Winston Allen understood it.

Others rise like a rocket, claim their headlines, and burst, leaving little if any trace behind them. What of the hopes so extravagant or simple, but so shot through with sad self-betrayal and debris. These men are singular and in many ways they are unique. What can you feel, except pity?

To their mind they themselves become the only worthy cause; the rest belongs to the moon. Their smile can acquire the spontaneity of a mechanical tiger, nodding and grimacing come what may. As soon as they can describe something they think they understand it. Their judgment can disappear as completely as if anesthetized. They grow never to realize victory or recognize defeat. Nevertheless, sometimes when they are found dead they are found kneeling across their bed in prayer.

The jugglers and dancing bears and herb salesmen who come to surround them take a heavy toll and somehow dull the excruciating conflict of conscience. Warnings have the look to them of something spurious. Early illusions and subsequent self-discovery leave them as disarmed and de-fused as Samson with his hair gone. And all they see remaining is the purposeless spite of men and women. Yet as a leader whom can they blame? To their virtues be kind, to their faults a little blind.

They are the victims of the unfathomable chasm of this world in which such men trample underfoot the positions they had created for themselves through their decency, dignity and good judgment, and seem to do so with a shameless ardor that suggests a thirst for construction but which the inner eye of many others sees as being self-destruction. They can become as confused as the gypsies that cry at weddings and dance at funerals.

What observers may view with sympathy and concern they view as victory. They can also grow to view other's sympathy and concern with suspicion. For personal charm, unfortunately, has no connection with a willingness to trust. Even the apparent simplicity of outlook in others becomes suspicious. And Frank had grown very suspicious. As Sally had said, he did, in fact, feel that his world of friends was now full of strangers who only awaited the opportunity to become his enemies.

This conclusion itself served as a premise now for this decent, generous man. And if you urged the reasons on him for his changed frame of mind, you were only met by polite incredulity. Yet old friends still retained for Frank a sort of Rousseauesque attraction, a nostalgia for simplicity, and the reassuring world he had known. This is mostly what touched him as he stood at Allen's door. But it was mixed with strong impatience.

Tick . . . tock. The early evening light flickered across Allen's shoulders. You could even hear the scratching of his pen. Whatever this is, I wish it could be another day, Frank thought to himself, for it had seriously interrupted his time to come here straightaway on his return from Baltimore. How many decisions were waiting for him at the St. Regis?

The big man looked up. "Come in, Frank, come in," he called, motioning him toward the library end of the room. He stood, came around the desk and shook Frank's hand as he walked him toward a chair. "Thank you for coming down here like this," he said, settling comfortably by the round, leather-topped table, "and directly from the train, too. I'm afraid I must have interfered with your schedule."

"Oh, not at all, Mr. Allen. Thank you. It seems very good to be here," Frank said, and looked it. Allen took a cigar from the humidor as Frank refused one and reached for his cigarettes.

"People used to call those things 'coffin nails' when I was a boy," Allen chuckled. "The first I ever smoked was named 'Cubeb'—supposed to be without tobacco. Awful, just awful." He screwed up his face as if it were only yesterday. "I guess that's what drove me to cigars."

All right, now, Mr. Allen, thought Frank, why am I here? What do you want? He wasn't uneasy but he was anxious to be under way.

The older man appeared in no hurry. He puffed little rings at the ceiling, thoughtfully. His deep wrinkles were relaxed, and his eyes seemed pensive. They heard the hum of a cleaning woman's vacuum in the far distance, down the long, deserted corridor behind them.

Mr. Allen, please, get on with why I'm here, Frank thought; this is only the beginning of the evening, the workday, for me. His mind was away on the problem of what time it would be before he would see Karnes, who apparently had missed the train in Baltimore. He could have used those hours to talk with Walter, but, damn it, Walter wasn't on the train.

Allen's voice sounded again. "Frank," he said, turning directly to him, "I have been more or less driven into something, really."

"What, sir?" He answered with a smile that was more dutiful than spontaneous.

"When you were last in this office I asked you how you were doing. I wanted you to come down here now, with the Kansas City Convention only a

ew days away, and tell me how you're doing now." He paused and leaned
orward. "Please do, Frank."

Oh, here to report the score and satisfy curiosity, Frank thought to himself;
vell, that's natural and understandable but certainly very inopportune. I wish
his could have been postponed until the pressure of these days eases, some-
ιow.

"Mr. Allen," he replied, "the clubs young Ben Watson organized are really
;oing at an amazing rate across the country." He would begin there. "Young
Vatson, none of us, including myself, could have expected anything like this."

Allen nodded. "Must be several million," he guessed.

"Yes. And, further, newspapers are reporting my speeches more and more
ompletely. Instead of just a capsule, radio stations nearly everywhere are
•roadcasting whole sections of them. We see this as not only helpful to the
:ause, but a significant sign of public interest and enthusiasm. Very important."

"I should think it is."

"It's apparent that the American people have really come along with us. I
;ather Senator Means and Senator Willis realize that, too," Frank smiled
luietly. "At least, that's what I understand."

Allen got up and sauntered to the windows, looking across the harbor as
'rank, warming to his report, spoke on. "This public enthusiasm is reflected by
he break-throughs and defections our way at the delegate level. You saw that
tay Jefferson, the Missouri leader, declared for me?"

"Yes, I did. And I saw nearly the same gains announced in six states." He
urned and looked at the younger man. "Florida, Georgia, New Mexico, Iowa,
)regon and the State of Washington," he said.

Frank was taken aback. Why, he can even tick them off, he noted, and
lead right he is! He's really been right in there watching, hasn't he. (Oh, yes,
·ally, he had.)

"Well, sir," he laughed, "I didn't know you'd been following things quite
hat carefully."

"I have."

"Of course my people have been counting delegate noses very carefully,
Λr. Allen. In this home-stretch stage they've arrived at the mathematics of my
ituation. Karnes and the others figure that I'll enter the balloting with not less
han a hundred votes. They're clear on that. However, we have a solid hundred
.nd twenty. We plan to hold back about twenty, including a lot in Jefferson's
Λissouri delegation. We want the count to be a hundred on the first ballot.

"On the second ballot the twenty held back, and more, who voted first for
Λeans or Willis, will switch to me. The fading away of their strength will be
erious for both senators, surely."

Allen was following closely, nodding assent. Frank was on his feet now,
valking back and forth, spelling out the situation with greater and greater
ntensity.

"We'll finish the second ballot with more than a hundred and sixty votes,"
ιe stated, speaking as much to himself as to Philip, "and probably as high as a

hundred and eighty. When we do that neither Means nor Willis can afford this show of strength and the effect of the defections. Not on this scale.

"If most defections are away from Willis, and Means holds roughly the same count he had on the first ballot, Willis will be out of the running in the third ballot." Frank's hand came down on the table, firm and flat, and there was a ringing note—even a challenging note—in his voice and manner as if the Klieg lights were already sputtering on the convention floor and he were reaping the rewards there now. "This is the way it shapes up," he went on. "Willis out. Out. Then it will be only between Means and me."

These revelations, sharp as bird tracks, were delivered with finality. "All the talk to the contrary by Willis and Means is largely ridiculous," Frank added.

He came up close, his eyes fixed on the big man. "Yes, Mr. Allen," he said slowly, "the nomination will not be between Means and Willis. It's between Means and me. And the imponderables are working in my favor against Means."

"Imponderables? What imponderables? What do you mean?"

"Yes, the usual imponderables," Frank said, rather patiently, "the unmeasurable things stirring in people's minds at the end of a campaign. Sir there's a great deal of certainty in all this now, in answer to your question."

"I see."

"Finishing the second ballot with a hundred and eighty votes or more, expect to be nominated on the fourth ballot. The fourth ballot, Mr. Allen."

The big man sat down in his chair. This was the attention Frank had seen on the deep-wrinkled face in the room spread with partners during Allen's outline to them of his marshalship in the coal-strike case. The same attention in this listening; a very concentrated mind.

The hum of the cleaning woman's vacuum had stopped. Only the tick-tock . . . tick-tock. And Frank himself was speaking more quietly, soberly and in measured words. "In addition," he continued, "I'm sure you'll agree that when an outsider can create this degree of response from the American people it shows that there is surely much more dissatisfaction with the Washington administration than is generally realized. My analyzers of what's happening concur. They say that with my nomination proving this dissatisfaction, I can beat the administration and win the November election."

Allen looked at the ceiling. The picture was clear. Frank would be in. The next President of the United States.

But Allen's thoughts were his own. How many years ago had it been, he asked himself? He usually dined with Woodrow Wilson upstairs in the White House. That night others were with them in the large room on the first floor.

As the President and guests arose and left the table to have their coffee elsewhere, Wilson had taken his friend by the arm. He led Allen to the dining room's broad fireplace, cheery and bright with high-burning logs. Wilson pointed above the tall mantel. Allen looked up at an inscription. The President read it aloud to him, his voice in soft tones. Philip's memory of this clung to him

ind like the gentle trace of perfume upon a sleeve. Did Allen see moistness in
e eyes of this dear, lonely friend?

> The Best of Blessings on
> THIS HOUSE
> and on all that shall hereafter
> Inhabit it. May none but Honest
> and Wise Men ever rule under This Roof.
>                               November 2, 1800—John Adams

"Ah, yes," Wilson said, as he drew Allen away. "Adams was not my favor-
₂ President, but I had great respect for him." Then he stopped at the thresh-
d of the broad doors. The three great, brilliant chandeliers of the main hall,
₋arkling their beautiful light off the white walls and stately cornices, lit the
sta ahead. The other guests were assembled there, waiting.

Wilson, bent now by so many cares, heartaches and misunderstandings
₁d the willful spites he had not expected, squared before the big man. His
₋ice was firm and strong and the affection in it was utterly unembarrassed.
₋nd I have great respect for you, dear Philip, as well," he said, "even though
is difficult for me to express myself as I would like to. Although you and I are
. opposite political camps, I am one of your many admirers. Bless you for
₋lping me."

And this was the evening, after the goodbyes had been said, that Allen
₋und, wrapped in simple paper, untied, no ribbon or mark, waiting with his
₋t and coat, the photograph that the President had inscribed: "A man to ride
₋e river with." It stood on his desk now, not ten feet away.

Allen leaned forward, his elbow on the table, with his massive head sup-
₋rted on his hand and those astonishingly alert eyes under their bushy brows
₋ed quietly, kindly on the younger man. His voice was tentative. "Frank," he
₋id, "I heard your Portland speech. Now I've heard your Baltimore speech."

"Yes."

"What was the response to these?"

"Well, sir, I'd say the response to Portland was even better than any in the
₋mpaign. There was a little rhubarb, a little kick-up about it among some of
₋y circle." He looked down, slightly, and rubbed his fingers along the edge of
₋e chair. "But every man has to do his own work in his own way."

He said this more with petulance than defiance, and Allen sensed that
₋rank was trying merely to be better understood. "I have to tend to my own
₋usiness. One thing is certain; the response to Portland from ordinary folks
₋ere and across our country was excellent, very fine. It's too early to tell much
bout Baltimore. I'd say, however, that the response will exceed even Port-
₋nd."

"How did you happen to make them, Frank?" It was a very searching
₋uestion, going to the root of Sally's contention.

"What do you mean, Mr. Allen?" he said, chilled, at a loss.

"Just how did you happen to make them, that's all?" When Frank hear Philip say this he did not know that Sally floated before the big man's eyes.

"The Kansas City convention is only a few days away," he answere guardedly. "I know we're doing all right. However, I simply did not feel w could take any chances on the outcome. I know I went a little far here an there in this windup; but I don't think anything is sure, after all, until the cour is in. I felt I had to rivet the nomination. I don't think I should take an chances."

What was Allen driving at? Frank wondered. He was on the edge c indignation. How can these men realize what it means to be directly involvec the weight of the guessing, the constant improvement in the odds, the numbe of times they're wrong and you're right?

Allen had tensed. He saw this as shilly-shally and shift. Killory, restles disturbed and frustrated, knew the older man was annoyed; it simply could no be helped. Frank glanced at the tall clock and eased himself in the chair as preparing to go. But Allen interrupted him. He felt a sudden twinge of exas peration, detained still longer.

"What are your relations with Senator Arthur Means?" Allen asked, t Frank's surprise.

Hoping to leave a discussion of that question, or any further questions, i the deep freeze, he merely answered: "Why, I haven't any. I'm just out to be: him, that's all." But Allen persisted.

"You say every man must do his own work in his own way," Allen musec "That's true." Then his words came very deliberately. "But isn't it also true tha how a man does his own work shows his way?"

"Certainly." He had hoped not to reveal the impatience that pricked hin his anxiety to leave for uptown and get reports from Karnes. But he could no just rise and escape. His eyes rested on his wrist watch, but Philip did not see to notice.

"All right, now," Philip said. "You explain that you 'must tend to your ow business.' What you say to the American people may be your own busines Frank. But I don't think it is entirely your own business. A large number c people were attracted to you by your thoughts and principles. You've mad these abundantly clear and convincing from the beginning—starting way bac with the coal case plea before the Supreme Court; starting right there. Th very beginning.

"You chose to support those principles in politics. And those who believe in them have chosen to support you. They even gave much money to advanc this; some of it selfish money, but most of it not. But, most of all, they delivere to you their convictions. You owe them something, Frank. In fact, you ow them everything."

Allen stood up, and walked back to the window. He broke the silence wit an explanation. "I asked you to come down here now," he said, "because I pai close attention to what you were saying after I returned from the Mediterra nean, and I became deeply worried. Then when you even built on your Port

nd promises at Baltimore I just had to know, first hand, what you're think-
g."

"Oh, sir," Frank answered, somewhat patiently, "politics just isn't that
mple."

"I know it isn't simple. But I did need to know whether you are more
terested in the politics of what you're saying about fundamentals than in
hat you believe. In short, what do you believe? A man may be better than his
eputation, but he is never better than his principles. If you cross up what you
ave claimed you stand for by scrapping it as politically inadequate, I just
on't see much point in people electing you. So far as I know, there wouldn't
e even a demand for you—and there certainly is—if people hadn't felt sure of
ou."

Nothing was going to stop Allen now. He idled with some books on the
ble. As Frank listened to the voice, anger took possession of him. He sat still,
ushed, the hard-set muscles showing along the line of his jaw. But he let the
lder man have his say. And he meant to compose himself fully now; slow or
st, but surely.

Allen continued: "You have stood your friends and neighbors on their ears.
ou tell me your Portland promises, and confirming them—and more—in Balti-
ore, pushed you ahead with the American people. I disagree. In the first
lace, a vast population's subsurface reaction, its inner thought, its inner eye, is
ery hard to judge. Certainly harder to estimate than a jury's. I'm sure you'll
gree, Frank, that judging a jury's inner thoughts is hard enough. Yet you're
cing those twelve people day after day, looking straight into their faces.
ou've announced to me a very difficult judgment about many millions."

Was it not enough, day after day, to gnash one's teeth with frustrations,
rank thought, feeling himself so inspected; and now these accusations. Was he
xpected to sit there high up in this New York building and shed gouts of
lood? Surely he had been modest in reporting the nation's demand for Frank
illory. Why, he might have insisted that it was too real for anyone to miss;
lain, loud and clear, and what was all this about the inner eye? Why read the
rystal ball when you can read the book? It's a pity Allen had not been in
ortland to see for himself how things went there, and in Baltimore, too.

Philip did not stop. His cigar had burned out, forgotten. "I don't think the
merican people thought better of you," he stated, "for the reasons you just
ave me. At least, I hope not." His broad hands were flat on the desk and his
oice was hardening. "Oh, no, Frank, what you say to the people is not entirely
our own business.

"The Presidency of the United States is the greatest office in the world; the
reatest compliment and the greatest responsibility that the world's greatest
eople can bestow. You appear to be very near indeed to having this bestowed
n you by our great people.

"You know as well as I do that we've had great Presidents, mediocre
residents, and a few—very, very few—bad ones. But in exchange for his

opportunity, each faces a moral problem—and so does every man who asks fo the opportunity."

Frank found it simply impossible to keep from looking at the clock a Allen went on, slowly, deliberately. And did Philip hear an echo of Sally in th room? "The democratic process serves us as voters well, but sometimes it doe awful things to the office-seekers. Power, even the yearning for power, ca become heady stuff, as everyone knows."

Yet Frank's look was symptomatic of a what-has-it-got-to-do-with-me be wilderment; this complaining, expostulatory monologue. And with Karnes an all those men waiting at the St. Regis! Their errands for him were surely mor important. He simply could not postpone his meeting with Karnes any longe He glanced at his hat and coat on the chair by the door. Could he grade he retreat gently?

"Yes, I know, sir," he said, in a voice that sounded chill and stiff. "But it a really looks a good deal different out on the firing line. Maybe you just don understand politics—not right out on the firing line, anyway." He started to ris and leave. "I'm dreadfully sorry, sir, but I really have to do this in my own way you know."

Allen stroked his chin as if reluctant to say more. But his hand motione Frank to sit down. There was authority in it. (No, Sally, the big man had no finished.)

Frank resumed his chair. He felt a slight warmth of self-consciousne creep up the back of his neck.

Allen spoke on. "Frank," he said, "I am sorry; very sorry, deeply, deepl sorry." And moving the desk telephone toward him he picked up the receive Within moments the big man was speaking to Springfield, Illinois. The silenc in the room was almost three-dimensional. Frank, puzzled, could even hear th voice at the other end of the line.

"Hello, Mike. How's Kitty?"

"Oh, Mr. Allen. Fine, fine; she's just wonderful. She'll be so happy to kno I've heard from you—"

"Tell Kitty I love her. And, Mike, forgive me."

"What?" Byrnes did not seem to understand him.

"I asked you to do something. I knew it would be very hard for you to de I'm afraid."

"Frank Killory?"

"Frank, yes."

"Well, sir," the voice came. "I heard you'd been away these months. Bu you haven't a thing in the world to worry about. Not a thing. You can imagin how it makes me feel—and Kitty feel—to be able to tell you that. Welcom home, Mr. Allen! Mr. Allen, Killory is in. Sir, we're in. I believe Willis i finished and out of it after the second ballot. It will be between Means an Killory. We're a little jittery after Frank's last couple of speeches; but th momentum is left. Are you there?"

"Yes I am, Mike."

"If nobody rocks the boat, we're in, sir."

Frank settled back, his tensions gone. He felt that Byrnes' confirmation of hat he had told the big man made everything so much less complicated and fficult. Mike had laid it right on the line—"We're in"—direct to the big man. ertainly this, beyond anything else, should enlarge Allen's hopes and diminish llen's apprehensions. The score in hand from a competent score-keeper. There as a long pause on the line.

"Are you there, sir?" Mike asked again.

"I want you to listen carefully," Allen replied, in hushed tones. "Very refully. I thought we should have the courage to try the untried. And may at be truly said of us, you and me. I asked you to depend on my man and my dgment. I told you I couldn't say that Frank Killory would make a better resident of the United States than either Means or Willis. I told you I brought m out of Braidwood and put him here in New York. I said he may have made mistake by going into politics. But what I presumed to suggest to you, Mike, as that I strongly felt that he should have the opportunity to be judged by the nvention. I said he deserved a count."

"Yes, Mr. Allen, I agreed."

"Agreed? Why, Mike, there would have been nothing in all the Killory tivity without you stepping in. He and his own people made that very clear, deed, to me. They told me only you could save him with your great State of linois—its Favorite Son. And you did it, Mike, my boy. And he'll be nomited, you say?"

"I have the count, Mr. Allen. I know nearly every delegate it includes, eyond my own delegation. We will come out of the second ballot with a indred and eighty votes, or more. Means cannot stand the additional defecons I've lined up, sir. By the third ballot others will be trying to smell out ho's to be winner, so as not to get left at the post. I don't believe the balloting ill even finish the fourth roll call, in fact. I can hold my votes in line. It's illory on the fourth ballot, Mr. Allen . . . "

But now Frank somehow felt a sense of alarm and of strange clouds oving and gathering on the horizon as he peered questioningly at the big an. The ether was beginning to wear off. He shifted uneasily as Allen interpted the speaker in Springfield and continued.

"Whoever has the ignorant man's ear has his mind, Mike. To sound right, ot to be right, becomes the *summum bonum*. And there's nothing easier for an nbitious orator to dull than the sharp edge of principle. Moreover, there is othing more ugly to see than an eloquent man not telling the truth.

"Mike, this is my fault. I told you I could feel certain of Frank Killory. You ccepted him on my say-so. Well, I must tell you that I do *not* feel certain of im. My hopes have come apart. I'm sorry. Forgive me, Mike. For any excuse r none, Frank is the man of Portland and Baltimore now, and several other nings. In any case, that is what happened. I don't know how. It's hard to xplain. It would take some time. But that's the fact; all else is explanation. I do not believe it is right for you to feel certain of him. I do not think the America people can feel certain of him."

Philip paused again. Slowly, without looking at Allen, Frank took out hi handkerchief and wiped his face.

"I hardly know Senator Arthur Means," he said, quietly, to Mike, "and don't agree with everything Means believes in, surely. But I know Mean believes in everything he says. He has conscience, brains and integrity. That's lot. And that's his record. It's a mighty good one for this country. The Behistu Rock on the road to Babylon carried an inscription: 'The Reign of the Lie.' I was inscribed by Darius the Great, asserting he had destroyed it. The problem is to keep destroying it, because it always comes back. Mike, answer me this do you feel that anyone—everybody and anybody—is justified in feeling cei tain of Means?"

"Well, Mr. Allen, of course. That's been Means' obstacle, being right ou in the open for the opposition brickbats. I've always respected Means, wheth I thought he could win the party's nomination or not. I've always tipped my ha to Arthur B. Means."

Had Frank been exploded by mines of his own making, had he dug an opened the tunnels and trenches that besieged his own citadel?

"Mike," Allen continued, in a tone that was clear and final. "You and I ha an understanding in this. Oh, Mike, you're a chip off the old block. John woul be proud of you. I'm proud of you. Mike, forgive me. I asked Frank to do onl one thing. I told him you believed in principles and not to let you down, n matter how much he wanted what you made it possible for him to get.

"There's no use reviewing this past mistake; what we must face is wher we are now; where we are with this prospect for the next President of th United States.

"Unwind it quietly, Mike. Unwind what you have done. Don't hurt any body's feelings if you can help it, son. Change your own mind, Mike, which yo are entitled to do, and which often comes of thinking. And above all give Fran no black mark with all whom you've involved in this. But in the days remainin before the convention, release your Illinois delegates from the commitment t Frank. Release the other delegates, too, and their leaders, and all who hav followed you, state by state. And then, Mike—then turn these good people t Senator Arthur B. Means."

"Oh, sir," came the low voice over the wire. "That's a relief . . ."

Allen had not only sawed off the limb. He had chopped down the whol tree. And this is how it came about that Frank Killory was defeated for th nomination.

Sally had forgotten about the Roman rain and how long it was able to last But there was the promise of spring. The almonds were out and the days wer longer, the mornings balmy. She told the maid to open all the windows.

The maid in her black uniform was on her knees before the wardrob trunk, her button-like eyes carefully scanning Sally's clothes, her big hand

acked with labor, her dull eyes twice too old for her face, a face tanned to the
lor of a dark leather; born in the south where the whole of you weeps from
e heat. The trunk stood open in the middle of the floor, and on the gilt chairs
the suite's sitting room lay undergarments, blouses, little bundles of hand-
rchiefs and scarfs, and—cut short for her to wear—a rose.

The boy from the hall porter's desk, gay as a candy cane, delivered the
ble, bobbing for his tip the way beach boys dive for lire. Sally signed the slip
a small scrawl and handed back his stubby pencil. There was ample light to
ad near the windows and she sat down there, listening to the rain, rain, rain
at came from the waters that separate this shore from Africa.

The cable form was spread in her hands. A magic word: Urgent. Now she
as not listening to the rain. She was listening to life; this fond, familiar tyrant
at rules so strangely in our debate with fate.

SALLY BRYCE—EXCELSIOROTEL—ROMA—OR FORWARD. AN OLD MAN WHO WAS
AN ADMIRING READER OF YOUR KILLORY CAMPAIGN COVERAGE SENDS WARMEST
CONGRATULATIONS TONIGHT'S ANNOUNCEMENT THAT YOU ARE CHOSEN FOR
THE PULITZER PRIZE.

PHILIP WINSTON ALLEN

# HOW TO WIN
# AN ELECTION

# HOW TO WIN
# AN ELECTION

## THE ART OF POLITICAL VICTORY

### by Stephen C. Shadegg

To my children—Cynthia, Eugenia, David and John—who in their years of childhood accepted without question or criticism my weeks and months away from home, the price they paid for my participation in managed elections.

# Contents

# 1 · *The People's Choice*

ᴇ ᴘᴇᴏᴘʟᴇ of the United States of America will determine the shape of tomor-
v's world. The sovereign voters of this Republic with their ballots control the
st powerful military weapons ever developed, dictate the expenditures of
re than a hundred billion dollars every year, decide the fate of nations and
people. The voters in America bear an awesome responsibility.

The man who is now President of the United States first won election to
· U.S. Senate by a margin of 87 votes. The echoes of that political contest are
l reverberating.

There is no prize for second place in a political contest. The margin of
tory is not important. Once in office the successful candidate may move a
le more boldly if he has enjoyed a tremendous plurality over his opponent.
t whether the margin was 50 or 50 thousand the victor enjoys the power and
rquisites.

Political campaigns which seem to absorb the attention and energy of the
tire nation are soon forgotten. The loser fades into obscurity; the winner
rms himself before the fire of public applause.

Nobody asks: how are elections won? because that stamp of approval
ich goes with the majority opinion in a democracy smothers the question.
hat difference does it make how he won? He won, didn't he?

In the aftermath of almost any hotly contested political decision we hear
· charge that votes were bought and sold. "Victory was the result of a
litical machine." A few examples can be produced to support these conten-
ns of vote buying, but the truth is that candidates and campaigns are organ-
d to spend money to influence the voter's ultimate decision. Every political
tory is the result of organization and planning and unified effort. The ob-
tive of all political parties is to provide a powerful organization which on
ction day can give the party's candidate enough support to insure victory.

No one knows precisely how much money is spent each year on political
ivity. The present system of reporting is grossly inadequate. It is probably
ie that a minimum of $500 million is spent every four years on behalf of
litical candidates. Some observers put the figure as high as $1 billion.

A candidate for the U.S. House of Representatives, running in a rural
trict, might conduct an effective campaign on less than $50 thousand. But in
· urban areas, and particularly in the big city districts, a race for Congress

can cost as much as $300 thousand. And 435 members of the House must r
for re-election every two years.

One-third of the U.S. Senate is elected every two years; senatorial conte
are state-wide. They can cost as much as $2 million in California or New Yo
The minimum required to stage an aggressive campaign in a small state wou
be around $200 thousand.

Every four years we have a presidential campaign and each party, throu
its National Committee, raises millions and spends millions.

The states must select fifty governors. In some states there is a gubern
torial race every two years, in others every four years. Add to these famil
political contests the races for attorney general and state legislatures, for va
ous administrative commissions, and it soon becomes obvious that the $5
million figure is probably conservative.

Hundreds of thousands of individual Americans engage in political act
ity. 68,836,000 voted in the presidential election of 1960. The qualification i
voting varies with the states. Out of an estimated adult population of 1
million people, 63.8% participated in the last national election.

After a national election, the commentators and the analysts engage in
great season of second-guessing. Many of their explanations are quite val
The point is they are all made after the fact.

In football and baseball the coaches start with the recruits. They teach t
fundamentals of the game until a shortstop, presented with a double pl
opportunity, moves almost entirely from reflex action. The quarterback with
option play knows precisely the choices open. The good quarterback makes t
right choice.

In the field of politics there is no such opportunity. Candidates come
varying sizes and shapes. Some are well qualified. Some have almost no qual
cations. Dunces and dullards have been elected to high public office. Sol
candidates move from victory to victory. Others are defeated their second ti
out.

The national political parties maintain offices in Washington, D.C. staff
with experts. The committees make studies and reports and offer what wou
be valuable assistance if the candidate knew how to apply the informati
supplied. Unfortunately, most of the candidates—particularly those withc
prior experience in the political field—don't have the slightest idea how
make use of the information supplied.

In the presidential years the national committee centers all of its attenti
on the party's presidential candidate. The man nominated by the party for t
presidency has the deciding voice in the selection of the national chairman.

Long ago the members of Congress recognized the national committees
one-track-mind affairs and organized their own groups within the Congress
assist incumbent members seeking re-election. The Democrats and the Repu
licans both have senatorial campaign committees and in the House there a
the congressional campaign committees.

These groups, organized to provide effective political assistance, are, so i candidates for the House and the Senate go, far more helpful. But frequently ere is a sad lack of co-ordination between the party's national committee, the rty's senatorial committee, and the congressional committee.

The aspiration of representative self-government is to provide the people th leaders in political office who possess an uncommon competence. The eory behind popular election puts great confidence in the ultimate judgment the electorate. There is an assumption that the majority opinion will elevate e nation's best to high office. Our political history seems to deny this as-mption.

Politicians are fond of viewing a current election contest as being of su-eme importance. In every election the future of life, liberty and property ngs in the balance. Political power in every public office has increased tre-ndously as we have delegated more and more authority to our elected icials. It is this very fact which makes each succeeding election increasingly portant. As our involvement with the rest of the world increases, the political cision becomes increasingly critical.

The dearest persuasions of the past 6,000 years are being threatened. Our ng-accepted Judeo-Christian concept of the nature of man has been effec-ely challenged by the doctrines of Marx and Engels. If democracy is to rvive, if we are to march forward together into a better tomorrow, then we ust soberly examine how political decisions are made, how elections are won.

What segment of the population makes the ultimate decision in any politi-l contest?

Is the personality of the candidate or the political philosophy of the can-date the deciding factor?

Does the average voter know why he voted for the candidate of his oice?

Can public opinion be manipulated or controlled to produce a desired sult in a political contest?

Does the average political candidate tell his constituents the truth?

What part do public opinion polls play in determining the outcome of ections?

In November, 1960, nine incumbent Republican U.S. Senators were re-ected. In Iowa, Jack Miller won a Senate seat on the Republican ticket; and Wyoming Keith Thomson, a Republican, was the victor. In a number of ese states the same voters who returned a Republican to the Senate chose hn F. Kennedy over Richard Nixon for the Presidency.

This apparent inconsistency went unnoticed entirely or received only pass-g mention, the majority of attention being focused on the change in the tional administration. Once the votes are counted very few people ever ask hy this candidate was successful or why that one lost. Obvious anomalies, ch as the election to the Senate of Leverett Saltonstall from Massachusetts—hile Kennedy was winning the state by a tremendous margin—are dismissed der the general heading of "that's politics, I guess."

No two election contests are ever identical. No two candidates possess th same assets or the same liabilities. When a Republican candidate can sweep t victory in a precinct or a district where the majority of registered voters ar Democrats, there is always a reason for the contradiction.

In our highly competitive world of commerce we have learned to view success objectively. We analyze the factors which mark the difference betwee success and failure. We have learned that an aggressive sales effort frequentl enables an inferior product to dominate the market. We know that the man agement of distribution and transportation will influence the acceptance of on product over another. We know that in some instances a company with lowe gross sales will make more net profit than the competitor who is outsellin them.

In business the objective of all this effort on the part of management is t make a profit. In all campaigns the objective is to influence the voters to make decision favorable to the candidate.

The introduction of a new commercial product is usually preceded by very careful market analysis. The merchandiser wants to aim at customers wh have a need or a use for the product, who are in an economic position t purchase the product. The approach is made through a proven medium capa ble of reaching the consumers who are potential purchasers of the particula product being offered.

In political campaigns such a practical approach is the exception, not th rule. Candidates and campaign managers—much like Mr. Leacock's famou horseman—ride off in six different directions all at once. Candidates wast hours of valuable time expressing their favorite views on subjects which hav little interest to the potential customer—the voter.

There is a market for ideas and concepts just as there is a market fo girdles and mink coats. The campaigner who fails to aim his remarks squarel at the major interest of his audience is engaging in non-productive exercise.

In politics the candidate is the product. He may be superior, average o inferior. Voters are emotional as well as rational creatures. They refuse t conform entirely to any set pattern or to respond invariably to any particula formula. But, with few exceptions, it can be said the body politic on an election day is more influenced by the campaign than by the candidate.

To the uninitiated it might seem impossible to separate the two. Th citizen whose interest in politics is casual and passing will declare that th candidate is the campaign, that what the candidate did and said is responsibl for the voter's decision.

But what did the candidate say? Where did he say it? How was it said fo him?

"I liked what the candidate said," says the voter.

Yes, of course you did. But why did he say it? When did he say it? Ho did it happen that you were listening?

"That fellow came to my town and I could tell he was interested in m problem," says the voter.

Yes, of course you could. But how did it happen that on that particular day
ıe candidate managed to address himself to your problem and to speak in a
nguage you could understand and accept?

"I didn't like what his opponent was saying about him, so I voted for the
ıy," says the voter.

Of course you didn't like what his opponent was saying about him. But
ho helped you to arrive at this understanding of the opposition tactics?

"I didn't like the folks who were supporting that other fella; I didn't think
ıything they wanted would be very good for me, so I voted for him."

Of course you didn't like the people who supported the opposition. But
ho helped you to understand who they were and the ways in which they were
ıpporting the opposition?

The candidate was the major instrument in presenting all these factors
hich created a favorable reaction. But it was the management of the cam-
aign and the timing of the campaign that caused the voter to see the candi-
ate in such a favorable light. More importantly, this favorable impression was
reated at about the time when the voter was required to take action, to
egister his opinion at the polls.

After thirty years in the arena of practical politics—as the manager in
ommand of campaigns, as a specialist advising campaign managers—I can
ocument the following conclusions:

Only a very few successful candidates have any real understanding of why
ıey were victorious.

The segment of the population which is least interested in politics actually
ecides the outcome of most elections.

The party organization can help a candidate tremendously, but it cannot
lect him.

Party labels are misleading and party registration is never the key to a
andidate's strength.

Millions of dollars are wasted in every political contest.

Elections are more often lost than won—by that I mean the errors or
ıistakes committed by the loser have a more profound effect upon the out-
ome than does the positive performance of the winner.

There is no surer way to lose an election than to think you have it in the
ag.

Virtue in politics is not its own reward. And while the big issues count,
ıore often than not the little things make the difference between defeat and
ictory.

The prevailing notion that a candidate, by his campaign, must persuade a
ew more than 50% of the voters to give him their ballots is a grossly misleading
ssumption.

Two men were contending for a seat in the U.S. Senate in a Southern state.
hey were both good campaigners. They belonged to the same party. One
andidate, when addressing his rural audience, would always slip in a state-
ıent something like this: "Now I don't believe in downgrading my opponent—

that ain't the way Americans settle things—but when a man is seeking to serv his home folks in the U.S. Senate, those folks are entitled to know all there is t know about him.

"Now, I'm gonna campaign in every county in this state, and I'm gonn talk on the issues, not on personalities. But I'd be shirkin' my duty if I didn tell you that my opponent once matriculated and that his wife does not den the fact that she was once a thespian."

There then followed the usual emotional campaign speech. When th votes were counted, the loser—with some bitterness—admitted he had lost th rural vote because the backwoods voters didn't know that matriculation : the act of entering college, that his wife was a "thespian" because she had ar peared in amateur theatricals.

In 1958, a Republican incumbent was running for re-election to the U.S Senate. He was defeated. It is reliably reported that the following campaig tactic contributed materially to that defeat.

The Senator, although no one knew it at the time, was suffering with brain tumor. Because of this illness, he was subject to dizzy spells. At times h had difficulty in remembering names and carrying a discussion to its logica conclusion.

This situation was seized upon by the opposition as an opportunity t employ the following device:

Six weeks before the general election an attractive man and woman woul present themselves at the home of a farmer. Their introduction was routine.

"We're representing the XYZ Opinion Research Poll and we've been ser to ask you some questions if you don't mind."

If the farmer's wife agreed to be interviewed, the callers would produce typical questionnaire form. They would inquire about the make of tractor use on the farm, the type of implements, the household appliances, etc.

At some point in the interview, when confidence had been established, on or the other of the team would casually remark: "Isn't it too bad about Sena tor————?"

If the housewife responded by saying: "What do you mean?", the follow ing explanation would be given:

"About his drinking."

If the housewife defended the Senator, the survey team would explain "We don't believe the story either, but we were over in another county las week. The Senator was making a political speech and one of the ladies w talked to told us the Senator was too drunk to sit on the platform, that h mumbled when he got up to speak."

The small communities of that state have a strongly religious characte: The effect of this tactic was devastating. It was successful because the Senator management was not prepared to detect and combat this type of assault.

All sorts of people get asked to manage political campaigns. There ar almost no professionals in the field. With the exception of the national con mittees of the parties, there is no full-time employment opportunity. But 43,00 people run for office every two years. Every wise candidate has a manager.

There is no school for candidates or for campaign managers. There are housands of excellent textbooks on political science, but there is very little written about campaign management.

It is my purpose with this book to offer to those seriously interested in olitical action an understanding of campaign management, campaign techiques and procedures.

My answers to some of the questions raised in this first chapter may be hallenged. But there is one promise I can make: the opinions and conclusions resented herein are not theory, they are not arrived at through abstract discusions. Every technique presented can be documented and supported by its use n actual political contests ranging from Massachusetts to Arizona.

I make no apology for my conservative political beliefs. Voters don't elect hilosophers to public office, they elect candidates. Approached in the right ashion at the right time, a voter can be persuaded to give his ballot to a andidate whose philosophy is opposed to the cherished notions of the voter.

# $2 \cdot$ *The Paradox of Elections*

EVERY CANDIDATE for elective office is consumed with a desire to win—to be irst over the finish line. At the outset of a campaign this desire is frequently oncealed by such statements as "I want to serve my country," or "Our viewoint needs to be represented," or "A great many people for whom I have the leepest respect have asked me to make this race." The candidate may be incere in his desire to represent a viewpoint or to contribute his special talents n the service of government. But he also wants to win.

Election contests are bitter affairs. The punishment inflicted upon a candilate can be more brutal, more lasting, more destroying than the punches xchanged by prize fighters in the ring. A candidate for minor office in a small onstituency will devote at least a month of full time effort to winning the job. Anyone who wants to be elected the governor of a state or to the Congress of he United States will have to spend a least a full year campaigning. Most uccessful efforts are launched ten to twenty months before the fateful day in November.

In his narrative poem describing a hillbilly fiddlers' contest in Georgia Stephen Vincent Benet says: "Them that got the mostest claps'd win the bestest prize." The claps for a politician are votes. The procedures for recording the decision are well established. But the serious business of selecting qualified men to serve as temporary rulers of the city, state or nation is frequently referred to as "the side show of politics."

This tremendous expenditure of effort and time and money would seem to require that the aspirant for public office achieve an understanding of how political decisions are reached and just who among his peers will make that final decision.

In every campaign a multiplicity of organizations is enlisted to "get out the vote." "This is the priceless privilege of our free society." "Failure to vote is a denial of responsibility." Service clubs organize campaigns and frequently give out little tags on election day which proclaim: "I voted . . . Have you?" Editorial writers pontificate on the subject. Now and then some revolutionary suggests that if people don't know why they are voting, it would be better for society if they stayed away from the polls.

Political decisions are made by the Indifferent—by that segment of the body politic which really couldn't care less. This is the enormous paradox of democracy—a paradox which has gone almost unnoticed in this nation which prides itself on self-government.

Most managers—indeed, most candidates—are accustomed to the traditional practice of cataloguing their constituents on a basis of economic level, residence, occupation and membership in minority groups. These divisions have some validity. A far more helpful approach and more productive from the standpoint of winning is to classify the voters according to their degree of interest in political matters.

Voting habits or probabilities often reflect the economic level or the affection or disaffection of a minority group. Some political observers believe the rural voter follows one pattern and the urban voter another. The apparent differences charged to these groups is actually a reflection of interest. In all of these accepted subdivisions we find the truly meaningful divisions between the Committed, the Undecided and the Indifferent.

The first classification is by far the most numerous. It embraces all of the voters who are firmly aligned with a particular political philosophy, as well as the more aware among us who view an election as something more than a contest between two attractive personalities. In this Committed group we must include those who are strongly prejudiced toward one party or the other—a condition described in colloquial terms as being a yellow-dog blank—interpreted to mean that a voter would give his ballot to a yellow dog if such were on his party's ticket, in preference to bolting the party.

The Undecideds are frequently those who are truly best informed. They recognize that often times only slight shades of gray separate two candidates. They understand the niceties of the situation. And because in their thinking so many complexities are involved, they frequently find it difficult to reach a decision.

The Indifferents are those who don't vote at all, or vote only in response to an emotional appeal, or as the result of some carefully planned campaign technique which makes it easy for them to reach a decision. The Indifferents decide elections.

During the Truman-Dewey presidential election contest, commencing in June and ending in November, 1948, a research group surveyed a selected sample of the voters in Elmira, New York. The results of this effort were published by the University of Chicago Press in 1954. The authors—Berelson, Lazarsfeld and McPhee—provide evidence to document the argument that it is the Indifferents who decide elections. The descriptive term they use is "the unstable voter."

In that contest 71 per cent of the voters remained constant in their affection for one or the other of the candidates. Thirteen per cent wavered between party and neutral. Sixteen per cent wavered between the parties which, in this instance, must be regarded as shifting back and forth from Dewey to Truman and vice versa.

The authors say: "The people who change most during a campaign are the people who change most between campaigns." At another point. . . . "The resultant fringe of instability surrounding the solid core of more stable American votes arises simply from not caring much one way or the other about the election."

If this construction is correct, we should not be dismayed that sometimes the democratic way of decision seems to elevate the least qualified men to public office. Rather we should be prayerfully thankful democracy works at all, that men of quality and ability are selected by an obviously imperfect system.

When candidate Jones secures the Republican nomination to the United States Senate, he can count on receiving the vote of all the Committeds who give their allegiance to the Republican Party and to the Republican philosophy.

When candidate Smith secures the nomination on the Democrat ticket, he can likewise put down in his column the number of committed registered Democrats in his state.

I do not mean to suggest that a candidate can measure the strength of his party registration and then determine the outcome of the election contest in advance. If this were true, we could do away with elections and declare the winner on the basis of party registration. But the committed vote *is* dependable, it can be determined in advance, and except in those states where there is an overwhelming imbalance between the parties, the committed voters do not have the power of ultimate decisions.

Any study of election day returns over a period of years will demonstrate that in both parties we can find and identify this hard core of immovable voters who cannot be persuaded by any blandishment to desert their party candidates.

It is the continuing ambition of party organizations constantly to enlarge their groups of committed voters. The real health in the democratic process can be found in the fact that neither party has ever been able to enlist and hold a majority of committed support for all of its candidates over any great length of time.

The area of all election contests is limited by a geographical boundary. The smallest unit is the precinct. A number of precincts joined together make up the city or the county or the state. Elections within the states are all determined by the popular vote. In presidential contests, under the present rules in most states,* a candidate who wins a majority of the popular vote within the state receives all of that state's electoral votes. Students of our election practices from other countries are frequently dismayed when they discover that although Franklin Roosevelt was elected President of the United States four times, the people did not vote directly for Roosevelt—giving their ballots instead to electors who were pledged to vote for Roosevelt.

The number of committed voters in any precinct or in all the precincts of a constituency can readily be determined. This process of identification is simple but only a few candidates and campaign managers recognize the value of making such a determination.

A review of voting history in the precinct will reveal that the poorest Republican candidate has historically received a certain number of votes or a certain percentage of the total votes cast. The term "poor" is used here not as a judgment on the candidate's qualifications but at an indication of his showing in the contest. The number of votes cast for the poorest Democrat candidate added to the number of votes given to the poorest Republican candidate will reveal the probable total of committed votes in that precinct.

This reconstruction of voting habits will be of no value in a one-party state where the outcome is determined in the primaries. But in a state which has selected its leaders from both parties in recent years, an analysis of prior election returns will prove to be of significant value.

If, from the standpoint of the votes received, the most unsuccessful Republican candidate has enjoyed thirty per cent of the total votes cast, and the most unsuccessful Democrat candidate has enjoyed forty per cent of the total votes cast, the astute campaign manager will recognize that since the committed voters amount to seventy per cent of the state's total, the remaining thirty per cent hold the power of decision.

In making such an analysis it is important to study at least the three most recent elections. Figures should not be compiled entirely on the outcome of the races for the top offices—that is, for governor and for the Congress.

That segment of the thirty per cent who are truly *undecided* will probably reach their own conclusions independently. It is their full understanding of the points at issue which contributes to their indecision. They are acutely aware of their responsibility and will probably not be greatly influenced by the campaign devices designed to reach the indifferent group. The undecided almost always vote, but the indifferent voter must be prodded into action or he very likely won't vote at all.

---

* A few states have freed their electoral college delegates from commitment to any Presidential candidate on the ballot.

The candidate whose party's nominees have historically enjoyed a smaller number of committed votes must make a greater effort to win. But, essentially, the task confronting both candidates and both managers is the same—to reach the thirty to thirty-five per cent of the voters, undecided and indifferent, who when their votes are added to the committed votes will give one candidate or the other a majority.

By this analysis the target area comes into sharp focus. The two candidates are not competing for the approval of all the voters or for the approval of 50.01 per cent of the committed voters. Their task is to reach enough of the undecided and uncommitted or indifferent voters to bring their total to 50.01 per cent. Thus, the Republican, who has at the start a committed vote amounting to thirty per cent of the historic total, must persuade a few more than twenty per cent of the remaining voters to place their stamp of approval upon his candidacy.

Most analysts agree that in the presidential contest of 1960, candidate Kennedy was tremendously benefited by the Catholic issue.

From a truly objective viewpoint, it makes little difference whether the man in the White House is a Protestant or a Roman Catholic. It is to be hoped that any aspirant for such high office will be guided by deep religious conviction. But the Kennedy campaign exploited the opportunity to emphasize the Catholic issue out of all true proportion.

During the campaign the candidate stressed his identification with the Roman Catholic Church. In his speeches and in the public statements of his supporters, there was the undisguised suggestion that to vote against Kennedy was an act of bigotry, the protest of a voter moving not from logic but from passion.

It is probable that a substantial number of the indifferent voters gave their ballots to Mr. Nixon because of prejudice. But the Kennedy campaign which faced the issue in the early days of that effort made it difficult, if not impossible, for the Nixon supporters to ask the Indifferents to vote against Kennedy *because* of his Roman Catholic religion.

Political campaigns generate and fatten on a certain type of hysteria. Campaign speeches frequently feature appeals based upon emotion rather than upon logic and reason. The voter is harassed by a host of candidates seeking his support. In contests where it is sometimes difficult to find a truly major difference between competing candidates, the voter is almost forced to rest his decision upon some relatively unimportant difference.

The experienced campaign manager will devise his strategy to sharpen the differences between his candidate and the opponent. These differences may have no real bearing upon the candidate's competence. But if they can be displayed in such a fashion as to be easily recognizable, the Indifferents will show their gratitude for this assistance by voting. And if the manager has been successful, if the differences reflect credit to his candidate and imply discredit to the opposition, the Indifferents will vote for his candidate.

The indifferent voter—the voter who is not solidly and completely committed philosophically or emotionally to one or the other of the two major parties—is representative of those who fail to vote.

We can boast that approximately sixty-three per cent of the qualified population participated in the 1960 presidential contest. But we must not lose sight of the fact that almost thirty-seven per cent of the free American citizenry regarded that election as so unimportant as not to demand their attendance at the polling places. These stay-at-homes frequently contribute vitally to the outcome of an election.

In 1936 Franklin D. Roosevelt received a total vote of 27,751,597.* His Republican opponent, Alfred Landon, earned 16,679,583 votes. In 1940 F.D.R., running for a third term, was given 27,243,466 votes. In the same year 22,304,755 citizens marked their ballots for the Republican, Wendell Willkie. The remarkable fact here is not that Willkie received more than 5,600,000 votes over Landon. The significant figure is that 5,117,041 more votes were cast. A portion of this increase can, of course, be attributed to new voters; but most of these ballots were cast by voters who had stayed away from the polls in 1936.

In the 1960 presidential contest we find some startling examples of what failure to vote can mean to the outcome of an election. Approximately 59,000 citizens in the State of Illinois marked their ballots for a congressional candidate but failed to indicate a preference for one or the other of the presidential candidates. Mr. Kennedy won Illinois by some 9,000 votes.

A majority of these 59,000 voters gave their support to a Republican candidate for the House or Senate. They simply refused to vote for Mr. Nixon or for Mr. Kennedy.

Students of the outcome in Illinois believe this failure to express a preference in the presidential contest must be attributed to the influence of those who were urging Republicans to disavow Mr. Nixon. This objection was based upon a belief that Mr. Nixon was not sufficiently conservative. It is quite fair to state that those who refused to vote for a presidential candidate in Illinois contributed materially to Mr. Kennedy's victory.

The indifferent voter can be reached and motivated by a variety of techniques. In 1952 Barry Goldwater, a Republican candidate for the United States Senate in Arizona, appeared certain to be defeated. Goldwater was challenging a two-term experienced Democrat politician, Ernest McFarland, who was then serving as Majority Leader in the United States Senate. From this position of incumbency and party leadership, McFarland appeared unbeatable.

The party registration in Arizona favored the Democrats by about five to one. It was obvious Goldwater could not win on the committed Republican strength. Many responsible leaders in the Democrat camp regarded Goldwater's challenge as an annoyance not to be taken seriously. In support of their position they relied on the fact that it would be necessary to persuade at least twenty-five per cent of the registered Democrats to cross the party line.

In planning this campaign we started with a detailed precinct analysis. This told us it was possible for Goldwater to win.

---

* *Voting statistics used in this paragraph are taken from the 1964 Edition of* The World Almanac.

Arizona had elected a Republican governor in 1950. In that campaign the Republican candidate was Howard Pyle—a radio broadcaster who had for years conducted a rather sentimental program reading poetry on behalf of a mortuary parlor. Pyle's voice and Pyle's name were known to almost every citizen in Arizona. But he had no political experience, no demonstrated competence in public administration.

The Democrat nominee was Mrs. Anna Frohmiller, an extremely capable individual. She had served 16 years as state auditor. During her administration she had established a magnificent reputation as an effective, efficient administrator. It can be argued that she would have made a better governor as a result of this vast experience.

Pyle, the Republican, was elected. The Democrats dismissed this upset as being based on masculine prejudice against having a woman as chief executive.

Women have been elected to the office of governor in other states. If Anna Frohmiller was competent to be elected and re-elected as state auditor—a responsible position—she was, on the basis of competence and qualification, eligible to serve as governor of Arizona.

There is no way of determining exactly why Pyle won. His victory demonstrated there were not enough committed Democrat voters in Arizona to determine the outcome of any election. Surely any citizen who would make his decision on the basis of the sex of the candidate has no strong commitment to party or philosophy. Such action is the result of prejudice rather than reason. And if these people had moved across the party line once, it was a fair assumption that they could be persuaded to do it twice.

Our study of that 1950 election convinced us that Goldwater could be elected to the United States Senate as a Republican, provided we could reach and persuade a sufficient number of the Indifferents. It is true these voters we needed were registered in the opposite party. But they had crossed the party line in 1950 for a relatively superficial reason. It was our job to persuade them to cross the party line in 1952.

We had reason to believe the overwhelming Democrat Party registration was not in any sense a reflection of solid commitment to that political faith. When Arizona became a state in 1912 the population had a distinct Southern character. In the first four elections a Democrat had been elected governor. In all the years between 1912 and 1952 only three Republicans had been elected to the state's highest office, and only one Republican has been elected to the United States Senate—and that one in the Harding landslide of 1920. During the intervening years most newcomers were advised by friends and business associates to register in the Democrat Party for the very compelling reason that the Republican weakness actually made the Democrat primary the only real contest. Candidates chosen in the Democrat Party primary waltzed through the general election. If a citizen in Arizona wanted to participate in the selection of his local public officials, his only chance to voice a preference was in the Democrat primary. But Arizona had voted for Coolidge in 1924 and for Hoover in 1928 when the percentage of Democrat registration was much higher than the five to one which confronted us in 1952.

The odds were all against a Goldwater victory. We conceded this. Arizona voters were in the habit of electing a Democrat to the United States Senate. To win it would be necessary to persuade ninety per cent of the registered Republicans to vote for Goldwater. This would require effective party action on Election Day. Then, because of the imbalance in registration, we had to persuade at least one of every four Democrats to cross his party line and vote for a Republican candidate. Actually we planned two campaigns—one to reach and inspire the Republicans. Above everything else we must persuade them victory was possible. The second phase of our campaign was aimed squarely at the Indifferents and the Undecideds in the Democrat ranks.

Goldwater was a tiger on the campaign trail. He appeared before Republican-sponsored audiences in every community in the state. But in our television, radio, newspaper and direct mail efforts our appeal was aimed at the nominal Democrats.

In Arizona lists of registered voters by party declaration are available. These lists are divided into precincts, making it possible to plan selected mailings.

One of the devices we used clearly supports the contention that the indifferent voter can be persuaded to reach a decision by a device or technique which rests not at all on the qualifications or philosophy of the candidate.

We purchased over fifty thousand ordinary government-printed post cards. We had these addressed by hand to be mailed to registered Democrats. The message was also handwritten—addressed to the voter by first name.

"Dear Jim, . . . Tuesday is Election Day. I sure hope you'll vote and I hope you will vote for me. Barry."

What a ridiculous, futile exercise! Anyone receiving such a card should know immediately that the candidate could not possibly have taken the time to write the message personally.

Individuals receiving the post cards who didn't know the candidate might very well be offended by the use of the first name. And the message—so obvious, so banal, so undistinguished—"Tuesday is Election Day"—the recipient would have to be dead or in solitary confinement not to know that Tuesday was election day.

"I sure hope that you'll vote." Well, all candidates hope people will vote. The newspapers and the radio and television had been urging and imploring the people to vote.

"I hope you will vote for me." Every candidate hopes the voter will approve his candidacy.

"You're wasting the money," I was told by a member of the old guard Republican leadership in Arizona, "if you think 50,000 or 60,000 people are going to be moved to vote for Goldwater by that post card." "That isn't what I think at all," I replied. We mailed the cards so they would be received on Saturday or Monday preceding election day.

I knew that most of the voters receiving that post card appeal couldn't be moved to cross the party line by a plea from their mother. But I also knew that if I were lucky, perhaps ten per cent of the cards would be received by the Indifferents, by those who had not yet made up their minds, by voters who were not committed emotionally or ideologically to the Democrat candidate.

I was convinced that a personal communication, a post card without any political slogan, just a request for a vote, made on a first-name basis, might be enough of a reason to secure their support.

There was no way to determine accurately the total impact of this post card solicitation. We did get a representative feedback. Our poll watchers reported that in the precincts solicited a number of voters showed up with the post cards in their hands or in their pockets.

After the election, when I was trying to determine why people had voted for Goldwater, the post card was mentioned frequently. Any number of people told us they knew the busy candidate didn't have time to write the post card, but they were pleased to have the request and they responded.

If this device gained even one thousand votes which might otherwise have gone to the Democrat McFarland, it was responsible for two thousand of the seven thousand vote margin by which Goldwater won that election.

I have been privileged to play some role in seventeen different campaigns for the United States Senate. In twelve of these the first step in campaign planning has been to identify the Indifferents. The second step is to devise ways and means of reaching this group with an appeal which can be accepted as a reason for their favorable action on election day.

In 1962 there was a necessary special election for a seat in Congress in the district surrounding San Antonio, Texas. Many factors contributed to the ultimate outcome. The Democrat candidate was Henry Gonzalez, a liberal Democrat of Mexican ancestry, who had previously been elected to the Texas Legislature. His Republican opponent, a bright and attractive candidate, articulated the conservative philosophy.

Texas is a Democrat state. But this district had given a substantial vote to Richard Nixon. John Tower had won there in 1961 as a candidate for the United States Senate.

In the final two weeks the then Vice President of the United States, Lyndon Johnson, entered the district and campaigned vigorously. The burden of the argument offered by the Gonzalez supporters in those final days was this: "We hope you're not going to vote against Henry just because he's a Mexican and a Roman Catholic." Gonzalez won.

Of course no thoughtful voter would permit the fact that Gonzalez was of Mexican origin and a Roman Catholic to decide his vote. But the indifferent voter who is not deeply committed will frequently respond to the careful development of a difference between candidates which has no valid bearing upon their competence.

The numerical strength of the Indifferents is not sufficient to permit them to make the political decision independent of a committed group. Perhaps my years in the political wars have prejudiced my judgment, but it is impossible for me to argue against the proposition that in almost every election superficial considerations influence a sufficient number of the citizen voters to determine the outcome. More often than not political decisions are made by those who respond to a carefully thought out strategy, who act more from emotion than reason, who are the least passionate in their political conviction, who couldn't care less.

# 3 · *The Campaign Manager*

Success in a political contest can be attributed to the personality of the candidate, the vigor and strength of the party organization, or to a domestic or international situation which comes to crisis at a fortuitous time.

The great depression defeated Herbert Hoover. The imminence of World War II elected Franklin Roosevelt to a third term. But these external forces are the exception rather than the rule.

Men have been elected on sheer personality or, as in the case of candidate Eisenhower, as the result of popularity earned in a field apart from politics. But the majority of political contests are won by attractive candidates who conduct skillful, well-timed campaigns.

In baseball the same man cannot be both pitcher and catcher. In politics the candidate cannot successfully manage his own campaign—a truism which was painfully demonstrated when I attempted to manage my own campaign for the Republican nomination for the United States Senate in 1962.

The candidate is on public display twenty-four hours a day. He must keep a schedule of appointments and appearances. He must shake hands with the voters and never appear to be hurried. He must be competent and compelling on television. His speeches must be addressed to subjects which concern the audience and to be effective they must be meaningful.

It is the job of the campaign manager to make the candidate look good, to map the strategy, to command the supporting troops. To do these things successfully, he must enjoy the full confidence and trust of the candidate, and he must be given authority to make all decisions.

Candidates rate the headlines. Campaign managers are shielded from public attention by the shadow of the candidate. This is as it should be. The manager must retain a perspective and objectivity which is denied to the central figures on the political stage.

A proper campaign organization will enlist the special skills and the talents of many people. The manager must direct and inspire. His job is to build an efficient, effective group of specialists who can produce under the terrific pressure and tension of political battle. Unless there is a clear line of authority, the result is likely to be only so much organized wheel spinning.

It is not always easy to find men experienced in the art of running campaigns. In this field there is no substitute for on-the-job training. There are no college courses, no textbooks that deal exclusively with the peculiar, distinctive and usually brutal task of winning an election.

The purpose of this book is to make winning elections easier—not to complicate the process. The ideal campaign manager probably hasn't been born. But a job description will give some idea of the enormity of the problem and at the same time suggest the qualities a manager should possess. Every candidate wrestles with the problem of "What kind of a person should I select as manager?"

The manager must know the constituency—its geography, its people, its commercial interests and those special sectional rivalries that frequently complicate a statewide political contest.

The manager should have some acquaintance with the media that will be employed in the campaign . . . television, radio, newspaper, direct mail. Since no single individual is likely to possess great competence in all of these fields, the problem becomes one of finding a manager who can enlist the right talents for these specialized activities.

The manager should have a strong interest in politics. A technician skilled in the mechanics can perform satisfactorily under almost any situation. But that final extra effort which may make the difference between victory or defeat is more likely to be forthcoming if the manager and the candidate share a common political conviction.

The manager must be able to get along well with people, to control the overly ambitious and to be able to resist the pressures which build up when human egos clash.

The manager must be able to say "no" without giving offense; to say "yes" and stick to it. Frequently he must say "no" to the candidate. And when he makes a commitment it must be kept.

In this regard candidates have much more latitude. They can, by innuendo or suggestion, imply a promise for future delivery. When the manager says something will be done, it must be done—and before the day of election which ends that campaign.

The campaign manager must be cold-blooded and hard-nosed about spending campaign funds. In every political contest there are literally hundreds

of people who come forward with a sure-fire scheme to bring victory. If only—
if only the candidate advertises in their particular program, sponsors their
barbecue, gives financial support to a project being urged by a minority group.

Party leaders will put pressure on the manager to favor their choice for a
campaign itinerary. Important supporters will insist the candidate spend what
may be an unnecessary amount of time in their bailiwick. And to all these
pressures and requests the manager must find a diplomatic refusal.

In addition to all these things, the manager must understand how the voter
is motivated to reach a decision and be able to devise an over-all strategy
which will increase the popularity of his candidate.

I have known lawyers, newsmen, business executives and advertising men
who have made excellent campaign managers—not because of who they were
but *what* they were—intelligent, informed, endowed with administrative ability and committed to the cause they served.

In my own experience each campaign has been slightly different from the
rest, just as each candidate differs from his contemporaries. But the objective in
all was the same—to win. The problems are similar and the solutions which
have been effective in one campaign have also been effective in others.

No one of my acquaintance has ever set out to make a career of managing
political campaigns. The work is spasmodic. At best it offers employment for a
few months every two, four or six years. The wages paid are never enough to
compensate for the labor involved. In my first senatorial campaign I earned
$1,800. In the second one, which required more than six months of concen-
trated effort, I was paid $3,500. But there are other compensations. Politics deal
with the destiny of our society, shape the world of tomorrow in which our
children must live, and each campaign becomes a unique experience.

Lawyers who manage campaigns make valuable contacts in the political
world. Corporate clients who must deal with the government are anxious to be
represented by a lawyer who can claim close relationship with powerful political figures. During the conduct of the campaign the lawyer manager acquires a
knowledge of his constituency which can be put to beneficial use for present
and future clients.

Newspaper men and writers often follow their candidate after election to
serve as administrative assistants, press secretaries, etc. Many of the young men
who now work on Capitol Hill in the office of a congressman or a senator
moved into these important positions after helping win an election.

Managing someone else's campaign is frequently the steppingstone to
becoming a successful candidate and most managers have a more than passing
interest in a public life. Then, there is the excitement. A fierce campaign for
public office generates an atmosphere of competition not to be equalled in any
other endeavor.

For the serious student of politics, managing a campaign provides greater
insight and better understanding than can ever be acquired in a classroom.
Professor Conrad Joyner, who teaches government at the University of Arizona
and recently produced an excellent book entitled *The Republican Dilemma*,

quired his special insight while working on the campaign trail for Governor ark Hatfield of Oregon. Joyner's counterparts can be found on many college mpuses.

I have been privileged to travel more than 100,000 miles on political mis-ns. I have been thrust into almost daily association with the public men of y time. My world has been enlarged with friendships in more than a dozen tes. And the political idiosyncracies of these areas are now my secrets. Every ndidate I have served has given me a new insight, a new understanding of e art and practice of politics.

In 1950, United States Senator Carl Hayden (D-Ariz.) was challenged by vigorous, well-financed opponent. We had good reason to believe that this ndidate had been put in the race by two special interest groups, anxious to essure Hayden into supporting some legislation they desired. Halfway rough the campaign a spokesman for the sponsors of our opponent tried thout success to make an appointment with Hayden to discuss a "mutual oblem."

When the campaign was over and Hayden had won the primary, we met prearrangement on the Wednesday after Election Day to have a victory ink in the Kiva Club—a swank rendezvous located on top of the Hotel estward Ho in Phoenix.

The Hayden campaign had marked my first participation in a United ates Senate contest. I was greatly pleased at Hayden's victory. The world was rs. The voters had just said so.

In this happy frame of mind I casually asked the Senator what he had en doing that Wednesday. His reply is still vivid in my memory:

"Why, I was downtown so I went into such-and-such an office building d paid my respects to Mr. So-and-so. Then I wandered over to such-and-such address and said 'hello' to Mr. So-and-so."

Hayden had named the two men who had sponsored his opponent in the imary. My reaction of incredulous astonishment caused the senator to grin th wry appreciation.

"Let me tell you something, Steve," he said, "never give your enemies any ore reason than they already have to go on hating you."

In this competitive world, where men and ideas constantly clash, I have ver been given better advice.

Most of the opinions expressed in this book are the result of my experience manager and consultant to managers of campaigns for the United States nate. I shall attempt in every instance to offer specific examples of success in pport of these conditions or techniques I advance. It well may be that some my candidates would have been elected without the use of these devices, but t of all the prescriptions for victory offered here there is one I regard as ramount—the manager must command the campaign effort. Any division of thority between the manager and the candidate or between the manager and s assistants will, at some point in the campaign, produce disaster.

I argue this not because I think the campaign manager is in every case or

in any case more competent than the candidate. The campaign must ha
unity. The campaign must move steadily forward from its starting position
its objective of victory. Any delay or deviation from the basic strategic plan w
waste precious time and money.

The manager can be objective; the candidate cannot completely divor
himself from the emotional stress of being the candidate.

The manager who has selected the strategy, after consultation with t
candidate and his crew of experts, must be in a position of authority to impl
ment that strategy.

In my own experience I have found that good candidates are quite willi
to delegate the proper authority. In the 1960 campaigns Senator Curtis told l
working staff in Nebraska that he wanted me to review every piece of literatu
and approve every step proposed to advance the campaign.

In Colorado, United States Senator Gordon Allott's managers accept
every suggestion without question. When I asked Chuck Colson how thin
were going in Massachusetts (Colson was the active manager for Senat
Leverett Saltonstall) he said, "We're running it by the book," referring to t
original campaign outline upon which this more detailed work is based.

I suffered through my first political experience more than thirty years ag
An immensely popular political figure, who was then the elected Secretary
State in Arizona, decided to enter the primary and seek the gubernatori
nomination. His supporters wanted to publish a campaign newspaper. This w
in the depths of the depression and when they offered me $50 a week to ec
their propaganda, I accepted promptly.

Our candidate's two opponents were relatively unknown politically. O
man was backed strongly by the mining and railroad interests in Arizona. V
had a handsome campaign budget. At the outset victory seemed inevitable.

As the campaign progressed, confusion increased. There was no unit
there was no theme. Our man, like Don Quixote, went around the state tilti
at windmills. But for all of this he was still in the lead the night before prima
election day.

The Democrat Party in those days held a final climactic public meeting
the largest outdoor arena in the state. More than 10,000 people gathered
hear the candidates make their final appeals. In addition to the three m
running for governor, there were ten or fifteen candidates for lesser offic
included on the program.

Our man spoke first. He had refused to prepare a written text; he was t
old, experienced campaigner, proud of an ability to deliver stirring orato
extemporaneously. He did. He talked for one hour and eighteen minutes. I
alienated the affection of every Democrat in that stadium. Supporters of oth
candidates resented his usurping all the time. His own supporters were bore
His two opponents spoke for less than ten minutes each.

I watched the agony on the campaign manager's face. He knew and
knew we had lost the election. Our man ran third. If there had been fi
candidates, he would have been fifth. And he lost through an unbridled displ
of that ego which is standard equipment with most candidates.

A poor campaign manager is almost certain to lose the campaign regard-
s of the candidate's qualifications, but even a poor manager who has the
thority to act is better than no manager at all. In my experience I witnessed
ly one campaign which operated without a manager and was successful. This
ndidate won because of his own personal popularity and the weakness of his
ponent, who had been involved in a scandal.

My first opportunity to exercise full command of a campaign came in 1942
en a longtime friend, Ernest Roach, asked me to manage his effort to be-
me sheriff of Maricopa County, Arizona. Our budget was less than $4,000.
e estimated that our opponent spent $25,000. Roach was not a colorful can-
date. His opponent had been a world champion cowboy, was extremely
pular—endowed with an outgoing personality that made friends easily.

We had just one great asset. Roach, a veteran law enforcement officer, had
record of experience which made him, by all odds, the best qualified man for
e job.

It was in this campaign that I first used the Burma-Shave type jingle
litical signs. With $4,000 to spend and the fifth largest county in the nation
cover, a campaign manager has to be cost conscious. We borrowed some steel
nce posts from a friendly rancher. We bought some inexpensive pine lumber,
' x 8" x 6'. We had the signs stenciled on a kind of oil cloth which is
expensive and durable. We tacked and glued the signs to the pine boards and
tached these by bolts to the steel fence posts.

In the West, at least, Burma-Shave signs have produced many smiles for
e traveling motorist. The jingles are impudent and to the point. There were
re lines to our sign. We put them on all the county roads, spaced about 150
et apart for easy reading. This was the jingle:

> "Ain't no cowhand . . .
> Nor politician . . .
> But when crooks pop up . . .
> He's in there pitchin' . . .
> Roach for Sheriff!"

second jingle read:

> "Fourteen years a deputy . . .
> Trained by the F.B.I. . . . .
> His record shows to you and me . . .
> For Sheriff he's the guy . . .
> Roach for Sheriff!"

Our total cost for 120 sets of these jingle signs was less than $200. No one
d ever used this kind of approach in local politics before. Roach was elected.

As the result of this experience with Roach and with his successor in office,
acquired enough confidence to insist that the manager of a campaign be
ven authority to run the campaign.

In this key relationship of any political campaign, when the candidate
rees to accept the ruling of the manager, it is equally important for the

manager to recognize that he is not the candidate. The manager who takes
the hustings with the candidate, who makes all the appearances, who is
much on the go as the candidate himself, really isn't a manager at all. H
nothing more than a functioning political valet. The effective manager, like t
man in charge of a good baseball team, must call the plays and let someo
else run the bases.

The manager-candidate relationship should be one of mutual trust a
divided responsibility. It is not the manager's job to think for the candidate
to manipulate him like a puppet on a string. What the manager must do is he
the candidate to express his ideas, to display his true personality and to avo
mistakes. The manager should have time to think; the candidate has precio
little time for anything. The manager who shares his candidate's conviction a
political faith will coordinate all of the activities of the entire campaign st
into an effective team effort with the special skills of each member addi
strength to the candidate's image.

This is a delicate and precious relationship—one that is not oft
achieved, but one well worth striving for.

Money is necessary for political victory. Before an organization can
built or strategy developed the candidate and the manager must adopt a ten
tive budget, name a campaign treasurer and a campaign finance chairman. T
treasurer will handle the funds raised, pay the bills and keep the records. T
finance chairman should be free to devote all his efforts to fund raising.

A simple and effective method of safeguarding campaign funds is to r
quire a purchase order signed by the manager for every campaign expenditu
This will not be as complicated or as tedious as it might appear. If an advert
ing agency is employed, the amount of money allocated to the various med
can be transferred to the agency on a single purchase order. But unless o
individual has the authority—and the sole authority—to authorize expen
tures, the campaign funds will melt away.

The size of the paid campaign staff will depend upon the amount
money available. In the first Goldwater campaign I had one secretary, a volu
teer publicity man, two college students who erected the Burma Shave jing
signs and a commercial artist. In that campaign we did not use an agency. T
artist made the newspaper layouts and prepared the literature for printing. V
wrote all the copy—speeches, radio, television, newspapers and pamphlets.

An advisory group of knowledgeable experts should be assembled early
the campaign and consulted constantly throughout the campaign. A gro
cannot write a speech, prepare an ad or decide on the copy for TV and rad
but the campaign which does not have available an advisory group will
seriously limited. The members of the group should be chosen for their loyal
to the candidate, for their experience in other campaigns, for their competen
in a particular field or medium and for their acquaintance with the politi
idiosyncracies of the constituency.

Such a group will probably include one or two lawyers who have be
interested in politics, a newspaper writer or editor, one or two experienc

·ty officials who are not at the moment accountable to the regular party
·chinery.

Both the manager and the candidate need this kind of sounding board—a
·ce where ideas and suggestions can be brainstormed—and it is always help-
·to have the critical opinion of a cynical, experienced professional politician.

The campaign manager must prepare a timetable, keeping in mind that
·1stant acceleration is essential. The schedule or itinerary should be placed in
· hands of a gracious, efficient secretary who will keep track of requests,
·ke up the candidate's calendar and be responsible for all the details which
·tribute to the success of the candidate's personal appearances.

When the image and the theme of the campaign have been developed, as
·gested in the chapter on *Image*, the manager will keep the campaign on
·irse, stubbornly refusing to permit any deviation.

If the Cell Groups are to be organized, this is the responsibility of the
·nager. If the Foot Soldier program is selected, the manager will select some-
·e to take charge of this important and vote-producing activity.

The manager need not create all the advertising copy, the television scripts
·1 the candidate's speeches, but he should select the subjects to be covered.
·1ly in this way can he maintain control of the campaign emphasis.

The manager must be ready to encourage the candidate when that is
·eded, and he must prevent the candidate from making mistakes.

From a tactical viewpoint, campaigns are more often lost than won. By
·1t I mean the errors of the opposition offer your candidate the best possibility
· victory. The campaign manager must recognize every blind alley issue and
·ep the campaign from falling into these pitfalls. A blind alley issue is some
·all matter of controversy which does not bear directly on the central con-
·ns of the constituency. At the same time the manager must find ways to lead
· opposition into a blind alley.

In 1958 Goldwater formally opened his campaign for re-election in a radio
·eech delivered from Prescott, the Senator's sentimental point of origin. In
·1t speech Goldwater bitterly condemned his opponent for having voted in
·vor of a particular piece of legislation when his opponent was a member of
· United States Senate.

In developing this speech we had relied upon the research staff of the
·publican Senatorial Campaign Committee. Unfortunately, the researcher
·dn't gone far enough. This particular vote was one of those peculiar parlia-
·entary things which occur in the Senate where a vote of *aye* on the immedi-
· motion was actually a negative vote on the full proposition offered. Gold-
·ter's opponent promptly cried "foul" and then produced the proof of our
·or.

Members of the Goldwater advisory team agreed the Senator should apol-
·ize. I vehemently disagreed. "If we do this," I argued, "it will keep the issue
·ve. If we say nothing, it will die. If we apologize and admit that we were
·mpletely wrong, our opponent can attack everything we say from here on in.
·an hear him now: 'Senator Goldwater claims so-and-so is the truth. I wonder

if he is any more certain of this than when he was finally forced to apolog
for his untruth about my voting record.' "

I could visualize the campaign swinging away from the major issues a
concentrating on this one mistake. Our opponent had made his point. If we c
not respond, either to confirm or deny, there was little more he could say.

We didn't apologize and we won.

The good campaign manager will suffer in every adversity experienced
his candidate. There will come days when he questions his own judgme
Having full authority carries the penalty of being responsible for the errors
well as for the successes.

When the campaign is over, when your candidate wins, he and he alo
will enjoy the spotlight. The manager and the campaign staff must be prepai
to be ignored in victory.

# 4 · The Image of a Candidate

IMAGE is a Madison Avenue term with a not altogether wholesome connotati◄
It suggests a fabricated picture, an artificially contrived impression produc
by the creative skills of the advertising man, a composite, carefully nurtur
profile designed to create a favorable impression upon the beholder.

The image of the candidate is the public appreciation of the candidat
personality, philosophy, intelligence, competence and performance record. T
image is what the public sees, what the public knows, what the public believ
about the man or the woman who is soliciting their approval at the ballot box.

In a political campaign the problem of image does not call for fabricati
or contrivance or distortion. The voters will always penetrate even the small◄
deception. A candidate may win one election by pretending to be something
is not, but when the next judgment day rolls around the voters will expr◄
their anger against the deceiver and against themselves for having been c
ceived.

The problem of image for the candidate and the campaign manager ca
for the wise and considered use of emphasis.

Public figures all labor under a common delusion. They vastly over-es
mate the impact of their own publicity. Politicians, like the stars in the the

l world, feed their egos by reading every word said about them, by listening erly to every spoken comment. The business of government absorbs their ivided attention. In a very real sense they live in a world apart from the ety they seek to serve. Because of their consuming interest in the affairs of ernment and in the actions and statements of other politicians, they believe iout question that all their fellow citizens have this same passionate concern the affairs of government.

At the outset of any campaign—when the candidate and the manager and staff, either paid or volunteer, are gathered together for the first planning ion—this question must be answered:

"Who is this candidate we are asking the voters to support?"

The traditional politician who has won election to public office will dismiss inquiry as a frivolous waste of time. The professionals who have enjoyed a ; association with the candidate will likely agree that everyone knows their lwart champion of morality, wisdom and political leadership."

The reaction to this question which I asked so many times in 1959 and 0 demonstrates the monumental lack of objectivity which contributes to the imon errors of most political campaigns.

United States Senator Carl Curtis from Nebraska is a knowledgeable, intel-nt, effective politician. Curtis is a likeable man with a strict, no nonsense tude. In eighteen months of close association he earned my admiration and affection.

As the first act of that Nebraska campaign Senator Curtis assembled ten or lve of his close political advisers at a meeting in the Cornhusker Hotel in coln, Nebraska. Dick Spelts, who had been chosen by Curtis to manage the e-wide campaign, is a successful lumberman in Grand Island. Dick man, who, with his brother, operates Herman Brothers Trucking Company )maha, is a brilliant, young executive who brought considerable political erience to his assignment as leader of the Curtis forces in populous Douglas inty. Herman and Spelts carried the major Curtis burden in that campaign. when we met in the Cornhusker Hotel both Herman and Spelts completely sed the point of my initial question: "Who is Carl Curtis?"

To them Carl Curtis was an effective congressman, the winner of a very icult campaign for the United States Senate, a champion of conservative )ublican doctrine, an effective member of the McClellan Labor Rackets nmittee. They construed my question as a personal request for background irmation arising from the fact that I was not a resident of Nebraska.

I wasn't at all interested in the description of the Carl Curtis they knew l admired. In a real sense, my question wasn't addressed to them at all. The wer I sought was: "What is the public image of Carl Curtis? How do the ple of Nebraska regard Carl Curtis?" When this was explained, the Senator mptly understood the reason for the question and agreed that we should e steps necessary to find the answer.

If the people who are closest to the candidate don't know who he is, who s? Why, the constituency, of course. And only by combining the opinions of

a representative group of voters is it possible to determine the true imag
candidate brings to a campaign.

Those who are equipped through long acquaintance to know the candid
best can make a contribution to this determination. A practical procedure is
ask everyone on the campaign staff to answer a simple questionnaire. This sa
information should be solicited from those who have great interest in poli*
—editors of newspapers, political writers, party officials.

As a part of this process it is necessary to list all the qualities or positi«
which can be regarded as the assets your candidate brings to the campaign«
comparable list of liabilities must be made.

To determine what the average attitude of the constituency is toward y«
candidate, it will be extremely useful to distribute questionnaires to a w
segment of the voting population. This can be accomplished in many ways.
the Mid-Western states county and state fairs are great gathering places. M«
political parties maintain booths at these fairs, and the citizen is always f
tered then his opinion is solicited. From such an inquiry the campaign mana;
will acquire some startling facts.

In 1959 at the start of the Nebraska campaign we used a questionnaire
determine the public's knowledge of United States Senator Carl Curtis. M«
than thirty per cent of those who responded said they had never seen or he;
of U.S. Senator Carl Curtis. (The type of questionnaires used will be explair
fully in the chapter on polling.)

Impossible! Incredible! There must be something wrong with the figui
Some practical joker had pulled a funny!

No, indeed. The figures were accurate and in some states where the url
population is greater, where in-and-out migration is responsible for a perpe
ally unstable electorate, the percentage will be even higher. Keep in mind th
even in the hotly contested presidential race, less than seventy per cent
those citizens qualified to vote will actually go to the polls.

This kind of "How well do they know me" survey is an effective antid
for the candidate who believes his personality and activities are recognized
every voter in the constituency.

Of course the purpose of the image survey goes far beyond this determi«
tion of how well your candidate is known. If properly conducted, it will g
you a true reflection of how the voters see your candidate and, more imp
tantly, will permit the staff to identify the candidate's liabilities. Once the t
image of the candidate is determined, the full emphasis of the campaign can
devoted to stressing the candidate's assets and to minimizing his liabilities.

Assume for a moment that your candidate shows up as a man of gr
experience in governmen but a poor public speaker, one whose formal addres
either lack color or are too long or fail because of the candidate's manner
delivery. It may develop that your candidate is very good in the famil
question and answer aspect of political meetings. The campaign manager v
immediately schedule fewer and shorter formal addresses and place the «
phasis on the question and answer phase.

In the 1960 presidential campaign Richard Nixon's experience in govern-
ent was a recognized asset. Even those who voted against him readily con-
ded that Nixon's training as Vice President had equipped him to handle the
b as Chief Executive. Nixon's appearance was a liability. The television
mera was particularly unkind to Nixon's face and general appearance.

Kennedy, a relatively unknown Senator from Massachusetts, photographed
ll and projected great charm. Now, certainly, we should not choose our
esidents on the basis of appearance or charm; but, unfortunately, this is the
ciding factor in the minds of many voters. It was a gross error to permit the
ters to view Kennedy and Nixon side by side. Nixon, the logical, forceful
eaker, would have done extremely well on radio. Had his managers empha-
ed the solid, homely appearance of Nixon, had they prevented him from
pearing in competition with the matinee idol exterior of Kennedy, the results
ight have been quite different.

Some candidates, when interviewed by the press, are simply incapable of
ving a direct answer to a direct question. They always insist upon making a
eech and cloaking their opinions in grandiloquent language which is impos-
le to quote and, if quoted, carries a suggestion of insincerity. Other candi-
tes are all too eager to respond with a quick, glib answer. If your candidate
s a tendency to "pop off," to give an opinion which is not based on real
derstanding, the wise manager will minimize the opportunity for such inter-
ews.

In the 1960 South Dakota campaign the voters recognized U.S. Senator
rl Mundt as a tough-minded fighter. Mundt is naturally a soft-spoken, cour-
ous gentleman who devastates his enemies with logic rather than loudness.
is managers discovered they could bring out the fighter in Mundt by report-
g bits of vicious criticism being used by the opposition. Responding to this
nd of stimuli, Mundt would overpower his audiences with the logic and
hemence of his presentation.

The late Senator Henry Dvorshak of Idaho was a likeable, friendly man
ith a tremendous understanding of Idaho's needs. He was an effective sena-
r, but all his years in politics had not conditioned him to accept ingratitude as
e normal payment for a service performed. Dvorshak, who was intensely
yal to the interests of Idaho, expected the people of Idaho to reciprocate that
yalty. It grieved him when they didn't and he made no attempt to conceal his
ief.

Every public servant has a right now and then to complain about the lack
genuine public appreciation for services rendered. But this became almost
obsession with Dvorshak. As a result he found it difficult to make a decision.
he thought that the people wouldn't understand or appreciate what he did
came a stumbling block which might very well have ended in a defeat in
60.

John Martin, Dvorshak's able campaign manager, recognized his boss' pre-
cupation with this single ugly fact of political life was limiting Dvorshak's
ectiveness. Martin deliberately fed the Senator's ego with words of well-

deserved praise from some of Idaho's substantial citizens. He protected his b(
from hearing the critics, and he assumed responsibility for making all of t
vexing decisions.

Martin sent the Senator to a state Republican convention in Twin Fa
armed with the information that factions were threatening party unity and,
permitted to continue unchecked, would probably lead to a Democrat sweep
November. Dvorshak had a cause he loved—the Republican Party. His p(
sonal problems became insignificant, and this great old warrior waded into t
convention. He laid it on the line to his fellow party members. In blu
unmistakable language his words, like a surgeon's scalpel, excised the swol
egos that threatened to produce disaster.

Then he gave the convention a cause—and the cause wasn't Henry Dv(
shak or his re-election to the Senate. The cause was the endurance of t
Republic, the perpetuation of the political faith of the Republican Party. T
image of Henry Dvorshak was preserved—a big, friendly, smiling man w
had given all of his energy and all of his ability in the service of a principle
held more important than personalities.

Keeping in mind that the indifferent voter is the one who must be reach(
it should be obvious that it will be difficult to claim the attention of t
indifferent voter long enough to impress him with all of the virtues or assets
your candidate. It is necessary to make a selection. In making this choi
contrast becomes all-important.

The indifferent citizen will respond favorably when the image of yc
candidate is easily recognizable as something totally different from the ima
of your candidate's opponent. The shades of gray have little significance. It
the black and the white which must be emphasized.

Political billboards are distressingly similar. The voter must choose k
tween two men who wear the same kind of clothes, put their trousers on o
leg at a time, talk about the same things, and are both appearing before t
constituency asking for votes. Really, candidates are monotonously alike.

To assist the indifferent citizen in his task of recognizing your candidate
going to be a difficult assignment, but this is the primary task of the campai
manager. A good place to start is with the campaign photograph.

Most candidates want the photographer to make them look handson
young, well groomed and friendly.

The photographer should be instructed to produce a photograph of yo
candidate which reflects the image you have developed. If the people think
your candidate as young and strong, friendly and informal, the official pho(
graphs can reflect this image. If your candidate is considered experienced, t
cameraman who understands his assignment can capture wisdom and expe
ence in the candidate's photograph. Don't be content with just one pictu
have a different photograph for each facet of the candidate's image and use t
proper picture at the proper time.

The photograph to be used on the outdoor billboard is extremely imp(
tant. Voters whizzing by at 50 mph don't have time to read more than five

words. But if the photograph projects the image you want displayed, the pression of the picture can do the job.

Republican Congressman John Rhodes of Arizona is of something less than rage height. He wears his hair in a crewcut. He is a determined, industri-; worker for the people of his district but no one would accuse him of being natinee idol. One of the most effective campaign photographs I have seen s a full-length figure of John Rhodes carrying a briefcase. He wasn't stand-still, he was moving. (A good cameraman can give action to a still photo.) e billboard said: "He knows your way around Washington."

The impact was tremendous. The picture said it all. Here was a vigorous, ermined man on the job. His opponent in that campaign was a very hand-ne man. His billboards carried what I would call a "collar-ad photograph." e contrast was tremendous. Here was a black and white difference scream-; to be recognized . . . John Rhodes, the worker, busy on the job. His ndsome opponent, almost in repose, was just waiting to be admired.

As the profile of your candidate is developed and the profile of his oppo-nt is developed, it will be easy to discover numerous areas of black and white ntrast and the physical differences are quite as important as political differ-:es.

If your candidate is younger than his opponent, you have the opposites of ing and old. If your candidate is more experienced than his opponent, you ve the black and white contrast of the beginner and the expert just waiting be exploited. Farmer versus city man; professional politician versus con-ned citizen; successful lawyer versus the perennial aspirant for public office; ative of the constituency versus a newcomer—the list of opposites which can emphasized is almost inexhaustible.

The research efforts will keep you supplied with samples of your oppo-nt's printing. Be sure that yours is different. In radio, television and news-per strive to find a format which will identify the cause of your candidate ore a word is spoken or a single line of type is added.

Never attempt to beat the other man at his own game. If the opponent ssesses a great deal more experience in public life, don't argue that your ndidate is experienced. To do so creates a situation comparable to that en a Sunday golfer challenges a touring pro.

In the California campaign which found Helen Gahagan Douglas and hard Nixon contesting for a seat in the United States Senate, Mrs. Douglas s the champion of increased welfare benefits and federal benevolence. Nixon s the toughminded, aggressive anti-communist. Nixon couldn't attempt to mpete with Mrs. Douglas as a champion of public welfare. When Mrs. uglas tried to contend that she was just as anti-communist as her opponent, vas the Sunday golfer challenging the touring pro.

Dick Nixon won that contest and went on to become Vice President of the ited States, but his enemies have never forgiven him for choosing the single ue which put Mrs. Douglas at great disadvantage. Friends of the defeated ndidate still maintain that Nixon smeared his opponent. What he did, according to his campaign manager, Murray Chotiner, was to concentrate on tl issue. In case after case Dick Nixon told audiences: "I have been advised not talk about communism, but I am going to tell the people of California the tru and this is one thing we cannot stop talking about as long as the menace international communism faces us here in the United States."

Nixon led the way in the exposure of Alger Hiss. His knowledge and I competence in this field made the subject a natural one for him and the vote reacted precisely as manager Chotiner hoped they would.

When the voters see the wrong image of the candidate, the campaign headed for disaster. In the Douglas-Nixon California campaign the vote: according to Chotiner, saw Mrs. Douglas as a member of Congress who h voted with Vito Marcantonio more often than any other member. Chotin printed this record on paper with a pinkish tinge and he says: "We had mc requests and demands for this literature than any other." The electorate s Mrs. Douglas not as a brilliant, compassionate member of Congress, but rath as someone who had voted consistently with Vito Marcantonio, a promine left-winger.

In the 1952 race for the Senate seat in Arizona, McFarland saw his opp nent Goldwater as a well-to-do department store owner and a dilettante politics. We made the voters see Goldwater as a serious, determined, you man. McFarland, who was the Majority Leader under Truman, was present to the voters as a henchman and supporter of Harry. We hammered away Truman's Korean war, a conflict which was then dragging into a stalema because the foreign policy makers in Washington refused to permit the milita commanders in the field freedom of action.

Our "Burma-Shave" jingle signs read: "Mac is for Harry. Harry's through. You be for Barry . . . 'Cause Barry's for you."

Goldwater won by 6,727 votes.

In the 1958 gubernatorial race in Arizona, our Republican candidate wa: young, recently retired businessman who had never served in any politic office. His opponent was the successful, incumbent attorney general. The P publican Fannin was presented to the voters as a successful, determined bu nessman eager to bring his knowledge of business administration to bear up the fiscal affairs of Arizona. His opponent saw Fannin as a neophyte, an aw ward, inexperienced politician and we actually capitalized on Fannin's lack political history.

When all the planning has been completed, when the manager and t candidate and the campaign staff are in agreement on the image of the canc date, the next requirement is consistency.

In every campaign the voters try to determine a theme. The theme of t campaign and the image of the candidate govern the selection and creation every piece of printed material, dictate the speeches to be written, and provi the criteria for making a judgment on that perennial question: "Is this acti necessary?"

A candidate can never bring the necessary amount of objectivity to t

templation of those efforts being conducted in his behalf. The candidate is
competent because of his deep personal involvement to make the necessary
l decisions on strategy. The campaign management must make these deci-
ıs. And the campaign management must keep the candidate in character.

Time after time the voters in a particular constituency have elected a man
public office in recognition of his virtues and his faults. Poor public speakers
e often been victorious. Men with little outward polish have been chosen.
ividuals with a narrow viewpoint centered on a concern for the lives and
blems of their neighbors have been chosen. And then what happens? The
nest, dull, poor public speaker begins to conceive of himself as an orator.
humorless student of the constituency's problems tries to be witty. The
in man puts on polish and when he stands before the voters for re-election,
fellow citizens are bewildered—for this is not the man to whom they gave
ir confidence in the first place.

Keep your candidate in character. If he is an incumbent, don't toss away
ninimize those attractive qualities which contributed to his first election.

Members of the Congress of the United States are probably the best
ormed people in the world on a magnificent variety of issues and problems.
eir official responsibilities give them access to a great deal of knowledge
ich is denied to the public. They sit on select committees and benefit from
best brains in the scientific world. They are briefed repeatedly on the
icacies of foreign relations. They are a living, functioning part of the
anism of government. And all of these things can be dangerous.

The candidate who has just returned to his home state after hearing a
efing on some new superior weapons system is almost irresistibly tempted to
re this special knowledge with the first audience he encounters. But if the
lience is not interested in the subject, the candidate's knowledge can back-

When Abraham Lincoln was campaigning for the Presidency of the
ited States he played on a single theme—slavery. Lincoln, as a practicing
ıig, had many strong convictions about the proper role of government.
rtainly he must have been tempted to speak about the subjects which held
at interest for him, but the people were concerned over the slavery question
l Lincoln wisely addressed all of his remarks to what was the major concern
his constituents.

If in our journey into the realities of political campaigning you may have
ned the impression that this political jungle is a world of make-believe
ere the tricks of the trade can produce victory, put aside that misconception.
campaign is deadly serious. What we have discovered here is nothing more
n a collection of complexities. The image of the candidate must be a genu-
image. If the candidate is not possessed of quality, no amount of manipula-
n can give him quality. If the candidate is not concerned with the great
ies of his people, no amount of campaign paraphernalia can cause the elec-
ate to take his candidacy seriously. Serious effort is required to develop an
derstanding of the image of the candidate. Serious effort will also be re-

quired to identify the overriding issues. This assignment will be discussed
the chapter on polls and surveys. There is a logical sequence which must
followed in the development of a successful campaign and image is either
the top or nearly at the top of the list. Once the campaign group has de
mined the image of the candidate, every campaign activity and every indiv
ual connected with the campaign must concentrate on the presentation a
enhancement of that image.

# 5 · *Aspirations and Expectations*

WHAT IS THE IRRESISTIBLE LURE which brings men by the millions to sport
events? Is it merely to see an exhibition of physical power? Or to witness boc
contact between two great athletes? Indeed, this may be a part of it, but onl
small part. Partisan man comes to the sporting event in the expectation and
hope of seeing his team or his champion victorious.

Men cling tenaciously to each rung on the economic ladder. Only a f
dull clods are content with merely holding onto their perch. Most of us
reaching for a higher rung. The devout Christian endures the cruel world
today resting upon God's promise of something better when this life is finish
But even the devout Christian hopes for an improvement in the world
morrow.

Political campaigns which offer no hope of improvement attract few s
porters. The candidate who does not indicate by his words and his actions t
his election will bring measurable improvement to the lot of the body pol
has small chance of success.

We speak with a certain cynicism of campaign promises and this phr
has become synonymous with insincere commitments in every walk of life.

The candidate who out-promises or over-promises runs the risk of hav
his deceit penetrated by the voters, but every campaign platform, indeed, ev
political statement, contains the implicit suggestion that if the author of
statement is given the authority of public office, certain desirable actions v
take place.

The candidate who proclaims loudly that he has made no promises is, in
making a greater promise for he is declaring that he will be independent if
:ed, unhindered by prior pledges bartered for the support of some segment
ιe voting population.

A clear understanding of the part promises play in any political campaign
produce a state of magnificent frustration. Yet, in our recent memory
nhower was elected on his two great promises: "to clean up the mess in
hington," "to go to Korea."

Kennedy was elected on his promise "to get the country moving again."
element which must be understood is the requirement to limit the cam-
n promises of your candidate to the discernible major aspirations of the
ιg public.

In contest for the United States Senate or for the House of Representa-
:, promises are frequently explicit. Candidate Jones will get such-and-such
m for his district. Candidate Smith will bring defense plants to the state.
didate Brown will be an economizer. Candidate Green will fight commu-
ι. The trouble begins when Candidate Black promises to economize in one
th, to bring more federal spending into the state with another; to reduce
expenditures for military hardware while at the same time he plans to
»ort an expansion of the defense capabilities.

The problem of what to promise and what not to promise haunts every
paign manager. Candidates frequently succumb to the irresistible tempta-
of saying what they think the audience wants to hear, and unless the whole
of promise has been carefully defined in advance, even the most experi-
:d politicians will now and then find themselves in boiling hot water.

The changing whims and passions of the people make it virtually impos-
: for any politician to respond affirmatively to every seemingly popular
and. The great strength of the American constitutional system has been its
t-in resistance to the fickle moods of the sovereign voter. All of the repub-
of France have suffered great injury because theirs was a plebiscitery
:m. The English parliamentary procedure bestows upon the ruling adminis-
on a certain advantage in that it is possible for the minister in power to call
:lections at moments most propitious to his cause. The calendar rule of the
:rican Republic makes a certain consistency of position compatible with the
»lems of election.

To be effective your candidate must be consistent. Since on minor matters
specific issues men of good conscience frequently find it necessary to alter a
r opinion, it is important not to permit these questions of passing impor-
:e any room on the schedule of promises your candidate offers.

Every citizen who will vote in the next election, dated from the time you
l these words, hopes to see the tax burden imposed by the government
ened. The more realistic recognize that taxes have always increased and
er substantially decreased, but even these cannot stifle an aspiration for that
when the necessary costs of government will be lessened and the amount
he tax collected reduced.

We can't have it both ways. We can't have increased federal activity and expenditure and reduced taxes at the same time. In every constituency ther a real or imagined need for some new federal operation, be it nothing m than a new and larger post office. What then should be the attitude of y candidate toward this fundamental problem? Before finding an answer it be necessary for the campaign manager and the candidate to become extrem familiar with the budgetary requirements in the area of government candidate aspires to serve. The most adamant pinch-penny among the vo you hope to reach will respond favorably if your candidate can discuss in ligently and with authority the reasons behind the current tax rate.

A study of any governmental budget—school district, county, state federal—will reveal several areas open to question. When these are identi and understood, your candidate can with great consistency discuss these it and recommend sensible reductions in expenditures. If your candidate is b cally oriented toward the philosophy which argues in favor of increased g ernmental spending, his attempt to wear the mantle of an economizer by p ing upon some particularly flagrant wasteful activity will be recognized by voter as mere pretense. Therefore, before the manager and the candidate determine what the campaign promise should be in regard to spending, i necessary for the candidate to adopt without equivocation one or the othe the alternative viewpoints.

If your candidate's conscience requires that he support an increase governmental activities, then his promises can be specific and persuasive w he outlines the benefits that will accrue to the voter if the spending progr are implemented. In the event your candidate makes his decision, you actually gain favor with the voters by admitting that the promised benefits going to cost them additional money.

Nelson Rockefeller, when elected governor of New York State, was mediately pressured to increase certain programs of the state governm Governor Rockefeller found the programs desirable and supported them, he also made it clear that taxes would be increased to pay for the progra The spender who resorts to borrowing or who pretends that additional bene can be obtained without additional government costs is soon branded a hy crite.

In another chapter we will describe a method for determining the m concerns or primary interests of a constituency. The promises made by y candidate should deal in honest and determined fashion with your candida approach to the major concerns of those voters whose support he is seeking.

Since the development of the federal welfare program we have create numerically large group of individuals who are dependent upon the fed program for all or part of their income. These people can be expected to g their vote to the candidate who offers them the best deal in terms of t welfare support.

Some elections have been won with the solid support of groups segrega by economic or geographical situations, but in most campaigns these spe rest voters are not strong enough to determine the outcome. The problem nd always will be, to resist every temptation to try to promise every voter t you think that voter wants.

It does not require the service of a crystal ball to determine the aspirations e American people. The national character reveals that Americans want to ree, hope to be prosperous, long for a world at peace, and want to believe the men they select for public office possess ability, character and integrity.

All of your campaign promises really serve the same end: to convince the r that your candidate has the ability to understand the problems, has a acter strong enough to work for a happy solution, and possesses sufficient grity to be safely entrusted with the power of public office.

There are two kinds of promises, a promise to do something, to perform a ice or to support a particular philosophical position; or a promise *not* to do ething, to oppose a particular concept or philosophical position. The nega- promise is an easier one to make and to keep and because some people are e influenced to vote *against* than to vote *in favor* of the negative promise rves particular study and attention.

Incumbent office holders usually find it more convenient to complement record of their past performance with a promise of future action. Candi- s challenging an incumbent usually find it necessary to criticize the record e incumbent. This criticism becomes more meaningful when the candidate les it with a pledge that if he is successful he will not do what his incum- opponent has done.

Frequently the most effective of the "I will not" promises have to do with ively trivial errors committed by the opposition. From the voting record of opponent, your candidate is able to show that the man he is trying to ace missed a certain number of votes. His promise is coupled with this losure—he maintains that if he is elected to office, he will take care of the e and be there when it is time to vote.

In one Mid-Western state where an incumbent governor was seeking re- tion, about the only real criticism his opponent could make was that the mbent had used the services of a highway patrolman to drive the gover- s official car to and from meetings around the state. At most, there was ing more involved than the highway patrolman's salary, a matter of $500 600 a month. The total budget for that state was well over $250 million rs a year, but the challenging candidate made a great point of the ffeur-driven car and promised that, if elected, he would not force the ayers to hire a chauffeur for him.

All this was a clear appeal to greed and envy, but it was couched in terms ily understandable and the voter who was having a hard time paying his s and living on a small income resented the governor's acceptance of this l luxury. The incumbent was defeated.

In 1911 Henry Fountain Ashurst was elected to the United States Senate Arizona. Ashurst was a florid politician of the old school who affected a low-tailed coat and a string tie. He was a magnificent orator, a good politician; he took scrupulous care of his constituents and they took good care of l at election time.

In 1940, with the clouds of war so visible, Henry Ashurst remained Washington as Chairman of the Senate Judiciary Committee. He had an o gation to the nation which in his mind was more important than a six-mo campaign for re-election in Arizona. Ashurst was confident the people whom had served so well would approve his decision.

An unknown politician, a judge from one of the state's small populat counties, decided to run against Ashurst in the Democrat Party primary. incumbent Senator was not vulnerable to attack for anything he had done failed to do in Washington. His opponent shrewdly exploited the only possi avenue for victory. He traveled the state, appearing as speaker at non-polit meetings and visiting with his fellow Democrats. Invariably he asked: "H long has it been since you've seen Henry Ashurst?" That's all. No criticisms. comment. Just the question which implied that Henry Ashurst was no lon interested in visiting the citizens of his state.

The promise was there—the promise that if the people wanted a sena who cared about them, who was interested enough in their thinking and th welfare to visit with them, then it was time for a change. And change they ( Ashurst was defeated and Ernest McFarland was elected.

*Be leery* of the specific promise. Your candidate can, without fear, com himself to a philosophical promise. He can say that the federal governm should demand an hour's work for every hour of wages paid. But if you let l suggest that federal wages are too high and should be reduced, all those on federal payroll will oppose him; and should he be elected, the chances are t at some point in the future your candidate will have to reverse himself on t position. The spiraling economy argues against such specific commitments.

Goldwater, elected in '52 as a candidate who opposed increased fed< expenditures, drew strong critical fire when, shortly after his election, he vo for a raise in postal rates.

The platform is a general collection of promises, specific and impl When your candidate's platform is being prepared, ask him if he means to k< the promises—if it is within his power to keep the promises.

Since the wide-spread development of membership in the John Bi Society, we have had numerous candidates whose political beliefs embrace the actions of the Blue Book. "We must take the United States out of United Nations." Ah! This statement is a promise, a promise that, if elected, Birch candidate can be expected to work toward the withdrawal of the Uni States from that world-peace organization.

It is obvious that one senator could not take the United States out of United Nations. One senator demanding our withdrawal from the U.N. wo find very little support in the Senate as that body is constituted in 1964. 1 kind of promise reveals the maker as either an immature, impractical drea or a faker of the first order. John Birch-thinking candidates could take much the curse off their extremist position if they would confine themselves to sp soring objectives within the realm of practical achievement.

Senators have been elected on "share-the-wealth" platforms and "every-
-a-king" platitudes, but they are not often re-elected on such obviously
ird promises.

Someone will object that no politician is in a position to guarantee delivery
ss he be elected President of the United States—and even in that office
e are limitations on personal power. Yet there are, indeed, many promises
:h will satisfy the aspirations and expectations of the electorate and are
within the area of delivery. A candidate who espouses a particular legisla-
solution to a particular problem can promise to introduce a measure in the
gress aimed at accomplishing that objective.

At one time the question of whether or not to repeal the Connally reserva-
had political significance in a number of areas. Candidates on either side of
question were provided with an opportunity to make a promise which they
d keep: "I will vote against the removal of the Connally reservation," or "I
vote for the removal of the Connally reservation."

In many Western states, the so-called right-to-work laws which are state
er than federal legislation have enlisted violent support and violent criti-
. Partisans were eager to have all candidates for public office commit
iselves on the right-to-work issue. In such an area, no promise should be
icted or made by a candidate for the Congress or a candidate for governor
e the matter is specifically within the province of the state legislators.

Every candidate can make certain promises of a personal nature that will
e him more acceptable to the voters. Promises having to do with the
lidate's intentions toward the voters after election are extremely important
commitments to love them as deeply in December as he did in October
e paved the way to office for numerous public figures.

Promises have to do with honor, and honor is a moral state. A candidate
promises to benefit one segment of the constituency at the expense of
her is making an immoral promise and, even if the obligation is never
, such a course of action leads to disillusionment for the voters.

In many areas it is impossible to out-promise the opposition. The old way:
do everything he'll do for you, only I'll do it better" has not produced many
ries on election day. Promises that only announce a moral commitment
every American implicitly or explicitly makes by virtue of being an Ameri-
citizen are dangerous. A politician who says: "I'll tell you the truth" may
ying to imply that his opponent is a liar. But we expect our public figures
eak the truth and such a promise cannot be exchanged for votes at the
it box.

Be sure your candidate can keep the promises he makes.

Be sure the promises relate to the major concerns of the constituency.

Be sure the promises are consistent with the character and image of your
lidate.

Be sure the promises deal realistically with the anticipations and the ex-
ations of the voters.

# 6 · *Timing*

POLITICAL CONTESTS capture the public interest because they offer the cit
an opportunity to be both spectator and participant. The rival candidates
the acknowledged competitors. But as the campaign progresses and the te
increases, partisan supporters become in a large measure personal combata
These citizen supporters carry the fight to the enemy. They defend the ca
date who enjoys their affections and on election day their vote helps to de
the issue.

The season of politics extends by tradition from Labor Day to the
Tuesday after the first Monday in November. In any contest where there
primary to determine the candidate, the season may be extended by anyw
from four to six months. Successful campaigns are usually set in motion at l
a year in advance of the decision date, and many candidates establish t
organizations eighteen to twenty months in advance of that day.

Because the struggle for victory at the polls lacks that splendid u
which distinguishes a championship prize fight or a championship foot
game, the timing of the effort is all important.

For the candidate and his manager each contest—no matter how hur
the office sought—is a championship affair. The candidate isn't required to
so many preliminary bouts to go after the grand prize. He is not judged or
season's average. The shadow of defeat will last for at least two years an
some areas it may be four or six years before the defeated candidate h
chance to go after the prize he lost.

In many aspects of the conduct of a political campaign the manage
required to do the best with the tools he is given. Only so much mone
available—never quite enough to do all the things a manager would like to
Candidates can't be selected the way beauty queens are chosen—for
appearance, grace, personality, talent, etc. The manager must take what
qualities the candidate possesses and exploit them.

The area of conflict where the victory must be won is frequently dict
by forces over which the manager has no control. In some elections an et
group holds the key to victory, or sectional interest may make the final deci
Bad weather can keep enough voters at home to make the difference. Bu
the matter of timing the manager is a free agent.

Timing alone cannot win every campaign. Too many other factors i
ence the final outcome. But in my experience poor timing must be named as
major cause of most political defeats.

Public enthusiasm is a fragile, ephermeral thing. No amount of pu

nion sampling can prove conclusively "what might have been." Many quali-
political analysts believe that if the 1948 presidential election had been
1 in early October instead of November, Tom Dewey would have been the
or instead of Harry Truman. In that effort the Dewey managers allowed
ir candidate to peak too early.

Dewey began the campaign well in the lead. Truman, who had inherited
Presidency upon the death of Franklin D. Roosevelt, was regarded as a
itical accident and there was every indication to believe the people wanted
1ange. Truman in his forthright and sometimes profane way began to attack
record of the 80th Congress. Dewey refused to defend the Congress, ap-
ently believing that he might offend some section of the electorate. The
ls put Dewey way in front. One commentator has said that Dewey cam-
5ned as though he were already President. Truman, the acknowledged un-
dog, probably benefited from a sympathy vote. At any rate, he confounded
he pollsters and won re-election.

The key to timing a major political contest successfully is acceleration. It
sn't really matter where the candidate stands in the public affection at the
t of a campaign. What does matter is that the candidate gain some new
porters every day.

To understand the importance of timing we must keep in mind constantly
t if the candidate is to win, he must reach and persuade no more than
nty or twenty-five per cent of the electorate. These are the Indifferents who
oftentimes select one candidate over another just because they want to be
h the winner.

The indifferent voter lives on the periphery of our real world. He may be,
very frequently is, a solid citizen—law abiding, productive, but apathetic
iis attitude toward political decision. Many of the voters in this class have
fessions or jobs which absorb all of their interest. Until the past few years
st doctors felt they were too busy to be interested in politics. Professional
ers who follow the tournament tours must devote all of their energy and
ention to playing golf and very few of them have any time at all to give to
other interest. Men whose jobs keep them constantly traveling find it
icult to identify with local issues and local candidates. This group of in-
erent voters will remain untouched and uninfluenced by the clamor of a
itical campaign until moments before it is necessary to make a decision.

Political campaigns generate their most strident sounds as the climactic
of decision approaches. No matter when the campaign is formally opened,
manager must plan his maximum efforts for the final two weeks.

In the 1952 Arizona Goldwater-McFarland contest the poll takers never
e indicated that Goldwater was in the lead. The final sampling was taken
and a half weeks before election day. Goldwater won that election in those
and a half weeks.

In 1960 in South Dakota, Karl Mundt defeated his Democrat opponent,
rge McGovern, in the final days of that contest.

This necessity for acceleration has a great bearing on the allocation of

campaign funds. As a general rule one-half of the campaign funds availa
should be allocated for expenditure during the first three-quarters of the t
available, with the second half of the campaign money being spent in the
one-quarter of the available time. Frequently, commitments must be mad
advance and this will be discussed in detail in the chapter on Mass Media.

The candidate's schedule of personal appearances should be arranged
that he will be seen by the largest audiences in the final weeks. This can rea
be accomplished by sending your candidate to the less populous areas of
constituency during the early days of the campaign, bringing him into the
urban centers in the final weeks. (A device for increasing the effectivenes
these final appearances will be discussed in the chapter devoted to the pro
use of television and radio.)

If elections were always decided on rational issues or upon the compete
of the candidates or as an expression of an allegiance to a profound polit
philosophy, timing would undoubtedly be less important.

Frequently the methods employed by an astute campaign manage:
accelerate the campaign are not apparent to the voters. In one campaign
strategy for increasing the pace was misunderstood by some and bitterly
demned by others.

Most candidates distribute bumper strips or windshield stickers to t
followers. A moving automobile provides an excellent place for the displa
the candidate's name. It can be assumed that if a citizen plasters his car
the candidate's name, he intends to vote for that candidate. The distributio
these stickers will give the activists in the citizen groups supporting your ca
date a chance to satisfy their desire for physical participation.

I have been experimenting with various types of car stickers since 1
Bumper strips are more popular now than they were when I first commen
my political activities. The quality of printing is better and the adhesive
been improved. Bumper strips available today will defy the elements and f
trate anyone who deliberately attempts to remove them. But bumper strips
expensive.

A colorful gummed sticker with the printing on the gummed side of
paper can be installed on the inside of an automobile rear window. (In m
states it is illegal to put them on the windshield.) Protected by the glass,
sticker becomes an eye-level miniature billboard. The ones I have used h
been about two inches high by eight inches long.

Traditional politicians will object to this size on the ground that it is
big enough to carry the candidate's full name. This is true. But the manag
job is to make his candidate a first-name friend of every voter. I believe the
of first names on the window stickers gives the candidate a real advantage.
first time I used this was for a candidate running for sheriff whose first na
was Cal. The sticker said: "I'm for Cal."

In 1958 I decided to use a white gummed sticker printed with blue let
carrying the legend: "I'm for Barry." The *for* was very small type and *B*
covered about two-thirds of the surface. We had estimated that at least 325,

₂rs would go to the polls in that election so I ordered 250,000 of the blue
. white stickers printed, to be delivered to me the first day of September.
₂ printer kept his promise but I didn't distribute the stickers until the first
₂k in October. My refusal to depart from the timing schedule brought the
th of the gods down on my head.

Goldwater had announced his candidacy for re-election in the early spring.
was unopposed in the primary and so we decided to start the major public
₂t the week following Labor Day. In July and August Goldwater covered
outlying communities in the state, went to coffees in small towns, appeared
₂re luncheon clubs in out-of-the-way communities. But our billboards, our
₂or television, our radio and our newspaper efforts were all scheduled for
₂tember, October and the first week in November.

Early in the summer the Goldwater supporters began asking for bumper
₂s. At first I was able to put aside these requests merely by saying we would
₂e them later. But when we officially opened the campaign the clamor for
₂per strips or stickers increased.

Mrs. Emery Johnson, a very talented and wonderful woman who was
₂ing as an elected member of the Republican National Committee from
₂ona, made a trip from Tucson to my office in Phoenix to demand a supply
₂umper stickers.

I explained to Mrs. Johnson that bumper strips and car window stickers
₂ct a maximum of attention when they first appear. After a few days or a
₂ weeks they become just another part of the automobile—like the radio
₂al or the bumper guard or the license plate.

"Did you read every license plate on the cars you passed or met coming up
₂?" I asked.

"Of course not," she said.

"Did you see any cars without a license plate?"

After a moment's reflection, she said, "Yes, just as I was coming into
₂ndler, but it was a new car."

She had proved my point. She had seen all the license plates on all the cars
₂ause she was accustomed to seeing license plates. She had seen them with-
₂ really giving them any attention. The unusual situation of a car without a
₂e had attracted her interest.

"We're going to distribute window stickers," I told her, "the first week in
₂ober. They will be on the cars for less than five weeks and nobody will have
₂ugh time to become accustomed to them.

"I'm going to try to have these on all the cars within the time span of five
₂s. We believe this will heighten the impact tremendously."

My plan for distribution was rather simple. I mailed two stickers, together
₂ a letter from Barry Goldwater, to every registered Republican in the state.
₂ letter thanked them for everything they had done and then asked one
₂itional favor: "Would you please put one of these stickers on your car and
₂ a friend to use the second sticker? It will be most helpful if you will do it
₂re October 4."

Bumper strips cost about $40 a thousand. The gummed stickers cost us than $5 per thousand. We would not have been able to finance such a wi spread distribution of bumper strips. They are too big to be mailed in ordinary envelope. Our total cost for the window stickers, the letter, the en lope and the postage was about $35 a thousand.

The results were extremely satisfactory. Five days after the stickers w mailed, anyone observing the flow of traffic, anywhere in the state of Arizc must have believed that Goldwater supporters were in the majority. The eff of the appearance of the car stickers on our opponent and his suppor exceeded my most optimistic anticipation. Gloom and despair spread throu his campaign office. One individual in the opposition camp must have b driving in a real nest of "I'm for Barry" cars. He came to work one morning report that six out of every ten automobile owners in Arizona intended to v for Goldwater. As far as he was concerned, the election was lost.

Ten days after we distributed the stickers I had a count made of the in parking lots and shopping centers in the greater Phoenix area. In some of locations the "I'm for Barry" greatly outnumbered the McFarland cars. when the reports for the day were totaled, we found that twenty-eight per c of the cars had McFarland stickers, twenty-nine per cent of the cars had Gc water stickers and forty-three per cent of the cars didn't have any stickers at

The McFarland stickers had been out for at least eight weeks at the t the count was made. It was the timing of our distribution which gave impac our use of the stickers. The appearance of the Goldwater signs within one w created an impression of strength out of all proportion to the actual number stickers used.

The campaign manager should gear his efforts to reach maximum ef tiveness in the forty-eight hour period before election day. This is a narrow difficult target. It is much better to be twenty-four or forty-eight hours ea than to be even twelve hours too late. But a campaign which reaches its pea week to ten days ahead of election can bring disaster. Public affection is ne static. *A candidate is always gaining or losing.* A campaign manager can lear great deal about the fickle public by attending any top-notch sporting event.

World Series fans are usually extremely partisan. Thousands of people come to the baseball park to cheer "their Dodgers" will actually boo and jee the performance of the Dodgers is lackluster or marked with error. The "fa in a political contest, like the fans in the stadium, want to won. They wan see action.

A political candidate must hit home runs in the eighth and ninth inning he is to retain the enthusiastic support of the indifferent voters until the ment the winner is determined. Since there are no umpires, no scorebo nothing but a final total to determine the winner, it becomes the responsib of the campaign manager to plan the home runs.

Proper scheduling of the advertising media and the candidate appearar will give the mechanical acceleration required. Developing the "home-run is a task for the manager.

In the 1962 congressional elections President Kennedy and his advisers illfully exploited the presence of Russian missiles in Cuba. Kennedy hit a eritable barrage of over-the-fence home runs when he established the naval ockade and ordered Khrushchev to remove the weapons.

The Cuban type of made-to-order international situation which can be everly exploited is not always present toward the end of a political campaign.

In 1952 Dwight Eisenhower was battling for the finish line when his anagers provided him with a real home-run statement. The war in Korea had een dragging, casualties were increasing, the American public was clearly :pressing its impatience with this no-decision war.

Candidate Eisenhower did not condemn our entry into the Korean conflict. e didn't challenge President Truman's judgment. To be openly critical of an merican military effort would have been extremely offensive to the parents .d relatives of the men who were dying in battle. His managers skillfully voided all of the possible liability. Their candidate simply said: "If I am ected, I will go to Korea."

This magnificent home-run statement, coming from a highly respected ilitary leader, captured the imagination and the loyalty of thousands of iters. It implied action, it aroused the nation's hopes and it was unanswerable ✓ the opposition.

On that final day in November we all put our "X" in the square beside a an's name. Outwardly our act is an evidence of choice or decision between /o human beings. Frequently a clever campaign effort avoids a head-on clash etween the two candidates and instead permits the winner to run against an ea or a concept or a situation. In 1932 the Democrats made President Herbert oover personally responsible for the great depression. Roosevelt ran as much ;ainst the economic distress which then existed as he did against Hoover. In 6 and again in '40 Roosevelt's campaign strategists recalled the horror of the :pression and made it synonomous with the Republican Party.

In the Goldwater-Arizona campaign of 1952 we identified our opponent as close confidant and associate of President Harry Truman. We campaigned ;ainst the "Truman scandals," the "Truman profanity" and "Truman's Korean 'ar."

In the Goldwater 1958 campaign we emphasized the irrefutable fact that it-of-state labor leaders wanted to see Goldwater defeated, coupled our op- ment with these out-of-state labor leaders and then aimed our big guns at the .st and present misdeeds of monopoly labor unions.

Our research division paid close attention to the activities of all union ficials in Arizona. We were particularly interested in finding and identifying yone who might be properly described as an emissary of out-of-state labor terests.

Arizona is not a labor state. Most of the union members in Goldwater's mstituency work at the construction trades. These are the craft unions— urpenters, bricklayers, electrical workers, stationary engineers and teamsters.

Arizona's great industrial development has been in the area of electronics and aircraft components—products that utilize a highly skilled, technical trained labor force. (The vertical unionism of the Auto Workers type has nev really caught on in Arizona.) A very high percentage of these people a college graduates whose training in technical skills would find them emplo ment anywhere. We believed if Goldwater could be presented as a candida who was championing the freedom of the individual worker and challengir the dictatorial orders of the union bosses, we could arouse sympathetic suppo

In May of 1958 our research people advised us that a West Coast lab leader had established headquarters in a Tucson hotel. This man, the region representative for the Political Action group of the AFL-CIO, immediate contacted labor officials in Arizona who introduced him to a number of labc endorsed political candidates.

When the AFL-CIO COPE organization met in Miami, Florida, in tl spring of 1958, the newspapers reported that organized labor would mal Goldwater its number one target. COPE would provide the brains, the musc and the money to defeat this Senator whose constant questions were a co tinual embarrassment to the leaders of the labor movement.

Most Americans resent being told what to do. Orders coming from out state are deeply resented. If the voters in any constituency somehow come believe that an out-of-state expert or a representative of out-of-state interests intruding in their political quarrels by telling them how to vote, an angr negative response is predictable.

The resentment we provoked in response to the labor leaders' declaratic against Goldwater was not based on any general antipathy toward the leade personally. We would have been just as successful had their statement con from the President of the United States Steel Company or from the Chairmɛ of Americans for Democratic Action.

Because organized labor traditionally supports candidates of the Democr Party, Republicans throughout the country have tried to make this union su port a bogey man. The CIO, which is very resourceful in political matters, h developed an extremely effective technique for getting out the friendly vot They even made a documentary training film called "The Wisconsin Story" be used in instructing members enlisted for political action.

With the over-all strategy of our campaign in mind, the appearance of tl regional union political officer in Arizona provided an opportunity to demo. strate the truth of our claim that out-of-state union bosses were organizing the resources to defeat Goldwater. But May of 1958 was not the time to do this. Hɛ we exposed the presence of the out-of-state union official when we first di covered him, the exposure would have been ignored by many of the Indifferen who were not interested in politics in May. The effect would have been fo gotten by November.

To make the most of this situation we had to time the disclosure—to key in with the last few weeks of the campaign when the public's interest wou peak. We kept our mouths shut and the research division began to expand i file on the activities of this non-resident union official.

By mid-summer we had developed quite a portrait of our visitor. He was a
ran of union organizational warfare with a record for violence which
uded at least one arrest by California police. Someone provided us with an
cial arrest photograph showing the identification numbers pinned on the
pect's chest.

During the summer months our visitor increased his activities—apparently
he belief that his presence in Arizona had gone completely unnoticed. He
ved back and forth between Phoenix and Tucson and visited the labor
ples in both cities with great regularity. A parade of political lesser-fry made
ir pilgrimages to this man's hotel room. Our research division heard that the
pose of these calls was to get union support. We had a real home run
cker—if we could prevent premature disclosure.

About the middle of October a member of our research team informed me
t an alert newspaperman had been asking questions in the hotel where the
on leader made his headquarters.

From my standpoint it was still too early to break the story. A campaign
nager must deal constantly with reporters. It is his job to know the ones who
be trusted to keep a story confidential . . . he must also know the reporters
o would sell their mother for a news beat.

The newsman who had been asking questions was extremely competent. I
w he would keep digging. The danger from our standpoint was that his
uiry would produce only such information as could be found in Arizona. If
union leader became aware of the newspaper's interest in his activities he
ht disappear. To give our planned exposé its maximum impact it was very
ortant to keep the out-of-state union man with us until the day the story
scheduled to break.

I had no choice. I aproached the reporter who had been asking questions.
ld him he was on the trail of a really hot story and offered to make a
gain. "If you will wait one week, we will be able to give you the full
y—the man's pedigree, his police photograph and a documented history of
of his activities as a political agent in California and in Arizona. I will give
a list of the local candidates who have been to see him. I'll give you the
es and the times when he has consulted with labor officials in Arizona. And,
ou want it, you can have it on an exclusive basis."

The reporter's response was: "You sonofabitch. You've had this story all
ng and been sitting on it."

"Not exactly sitting on it," I told him, "we've been developing it. Each day
produced some new information. And I thought it would be better to give
the full story than to break it too early and let our friend leave town before
had the real dope."

The reporter said he would have to consult with his editor and added,
u'd better come along with me."

In the editor's office I spelled out the whole story. I didn't have the photo-
phs or the list of contacts or the day-by-day account of the visitor's travels in
zona with me, but I could recite most of these from memory. The story was

so big the editor didn't want it exclusively. I think he was afraid his pap
might be all alone. He knew the unions and the Democrat Party officials w
had been connected with this effort would be extremely angry. He want
every paper in the state to have the story on an equal basis.

"If you have the facts to back up what you've told me," he said, "this th
alone could swing the election. It'll push in the Republican gubernatorial c
didate right along with your Senator. And it might carry two or three otl
Republicans with him."

We all recognized the possibility that some other enterprising repor
might stumble on a lead to the story. It was agreed that I would call a pr
conference in Phoenix at the end of the following week. I would make all of t
information available to all of the state's daily newspapers and I would ha
pictures and fact sheets and supporting detail for distribution at that time.

The story broke on Saturday—two weeks before election Tuesday, a
only three days in advance of the ideal release date I had first established wl
the possibility of such exposure had first come to my attention.

An enterprising candid camera enthusiast had provided us with pho
graphs of the union organizer in the company of Democrat Party state offici
These became front page art on every important newspaper in Arizona.

There was absolutely nothing illegal or immoral in the labor union's pol
cal activity. They had every right to send an expert in to assist the lo
officials. National political parties commonly engage in this kind of activi
Special interest groups other than the labor unions have their traveling expe
constantly engaged in attempting to influence the outcome of an election. I
in this case the union boss had moved with great secrecy. Democrat officials
Arizona had constantly denied they were receiving any help from organiz
labor and a number of opposition spokesmen had emphatically denied t
charge that out-of-state political experts had been sent into Arizona by t
unions to assist the Democrat candidates.

The story was a real shocker. The police record for an act of violence, t
police photograph, the long history of political activity on behalf of lak
unions, suddenly and dramatically illustrated one of our principal campai
themes.

We had said that out-of-state labor bosses would project themselves i
the Arizona political contest to defeat Goldwater. The newspapers printed t
truth of that prediction and the union aspect became almost incidental—t
obvious resentment was against an "outsider" trying to tell the people of A
zona how to vote.

This experience made a lasting impression on me. When I became a co
sultant to the United States Senators running for re-election in 1960, my fi
resolve was to remain anonymous. I had remarked that other employees of t
Republican Senatorial Campaign Committee often received publicity. It
absolutely legitimate for the campaign committees of the House and the Sena
to send their agents anywhere in the nation to assist a national candidate. Bo
parties do this with great regularity. But no amount of legitimate authoriy c
make an out-of-state expert an acceptable participant in a local election.

# 7 · Researching the Opposition

NOW THINE ENEMY" is good advice any time. In a political contest it bees an imperative. Professional football teams spend almost as much money
energy scouting the opponents as they do on developing their own game.
1 while we frequently think of our candidate as a member of the party's
tical team, the voters who will make the decision look upon the contest as a
d-to-head battle.

No campaign manager, no candidate, can wage an intelligent offensive
il he has equipped himself with every shred of available information about
opponent. The facts, collected and carefully catalogued, fall easily into four
gories: 1. Personal information about the candidate and his associates; 2.
candidate's voting record or other public actions; 3. The voting habits or
istical summary of the constituency, precinct by precinct; 4. The issues.

In every political contest there is a semblance of effort to scout the opposi-
. In my experience most research is under-financed, poorly organized, and
lly lacking in the depth of detail necessary to make the effort worthwhile.

The research organization should be set up under the direct command of
campaign manager. Since a variety of information is desired, it is necessary
mploy a research staff with highly specialized competence.

A librarian with the ability to organize the information so that it will be
antly available should be placed in charge of the files. A lawyer, news-
erman or someone skilled in investigating, who is capable of going behind
public information, should be selected to develop the personal history of
opposing candidate. A student of public affairs or a political scientist is best
ipped to develop the voting records and the position papers. As issues arise
ing the campaign, the manager and the candidate will need intellectual
port for their position and similarly they must know what authority sup-
ts the position taken by the opposition.

The investigator who is to build the file on the opposing candidate should
be assigned to a similar task in regard to everyone who is prominently
ciated with the opposition candidate.

A campaign manager who has available a complete dossier on all of the
ple in the opposition will frequently be able to predict accurately the kind
ampaign that will be waged against his candidate.

"Know thine enemy" suggests that it is necessary to understand the psycho-
cal, economic and emotional forces that will be arrayed against your candi-
e.

The research task begins with newspaper and magazine clippings doesn't end there. If the man you are trying to beat is an incumbent hold high office, it may take several weeks to gather the available newspaper magazine items.

Most newspapers keep a morgue—a reference file on individuals who h made news in the past. It is often difficult for an outsider to gain access to information, particularly if the newspaper happens to be supporting your ponent. But it is always possible to find a friendly staffer who will prov photo copies of all the clips on file in his paper's morgue.

If no other source is available, search the public libraries. Bound copie the state's newspapers will provide a day-to-day history of your oppone activities. Some libraries will permit you to make a photo copy from the file this cannot be done, equip your researcher with dictating equipment and h the material transcribed.

Unknowns don't very often aspire to public office. It is always possibl find a record of your opponent's past in the daily press. This gathering newspaper clippings is commonplace. Unfortunately, too many managers s digging when they have exhausted the public sources of information.

How has your opponent made his living in the past? How much of world's goods has he acquired? What are his family connections? What was record in school? Business associates can provide valuable information if y opponent is in business. If he is a lawyer, your investigator should search past clients, review the prominent cases in which your opponent has part pated, gather the opinions of your opponent's contemporaries.

In one campaign we developed enough information to fill three standa size filing cabinets. This collection of newspaper clippings, photographs confidential memos on our opponent and his close associates was indexed cross-indexed. When the campaign was over and we were ready to dispos the material, I had it weighed—123 pounds. I estimated that we had used i specific way only seven items. But because of that mass of information, were never taken off guard, and in two areas I could forecast accurately bei the event the strategy our opponent would employ against us.

In one campaign research developed the information that a Mr. X, one our opponent's most active supporters, had a political history in the Midw As the campaign developed, Mr. X became a particular thorn in our flesh—t is, he was an effective operator on behalf of our opponent. We sent an inve gator to the man's former home and learned that he had at one time b publicly identified with a socialist newspaper. This information was pas along to a friendly reporter. As a result of the stories which appeared, Mi resigned his position as an official member of the opposition campaign staff left town.

The possibility of a candidate being punished because of the sins of associates is an ever-present angle. Our opponent didn't know about Mr. X his socialist background. He should have checked Mr. X before accepting I as a volunteer member of his staff.

Most campaign groups are recruited from the close associates of the can-
date. Long acquaintance makes it unnecessary to examine the qualifications
the loyalties of these people. In a state-wide campaign where a large organi-
tion is needed the wise manager will have his research people dig into the
ckground of any unknown who offers to help the campaign in an official
pacity.

The campaign manager must be extremely careful not to offend the voting
blic by allowing his candidate to appear to be aligned with any of the
ried, semi-political organizations which have been formed in the past few
ars. If a member of Americans for Democratic Action becomes identified
ith your candidate, those in the body politic who disapprove of the ADA will
ansfer their disapproval to your candidate. Since 1960 the John Birch Society
s stimulated a great many people to political action. The inclusion of a John
irch member in an official campaign organization would adversely affect those
ho disapprove of the society. A known communist, a professional labor agi-
tor, an individual who has been prominently identified with some highly
motional public question such as segregation or integration, right to work, anti-
pital punishment or any controversial cause, will be a definite liability to any
ndidate.

In political contests there is no clearly recognized code of ethics. Candi-
tes have been stripped of their privacy time after time. Old sins for which
onement has long since been made are dredged up and put on display before
e electorate.

Most successful campaign managers of my acquaintance adhere rigidly to
e following rule: All aspects of your opponent's public actions and public
atements are fair game. No matter when the action was taken or where a
atement was made, you are well within your rights in bringing it to the
tention of the voters. A candidate's voting record is public property no matter
hat sound logic might have provoked the vote at that particular time. *But a
an's personal life, the personal life of his family and friends, should never be
ed.*

If your opponent has been arrested on a drunk driving charge, the arrest is
blic and the electorate is entitled to know about it. If your opponent has
en accused of taking advantage of a partner in a business deal and ultimately
as the defendant in a law suit arising from this situation, the electorate is
titled to hear about it. But if your opponent or his wife is a secret alcoholic, if
ur opponent has a more than platonic relationship with a woman other than
s wife, or once associated with disreputable friends, this information is off
nits.

There are politicians whose specialty is the ugly rumor, the derogatory
nuendo. Sometimes the electorate is fooled and rewards this kind of filthy
tion. More often than not such tactics will produce a reaction against the
thor.

In one California campaign which pitted Will Rogers, Jr. against Bill
nowland for a seat in the United States Senate the Rogers' supporters cried

"foul." They said it was a smear when the Knowland camp released proof tha
Will Rogers, Jr. had written articles for a socialist paper, "The People's Dail
World."

But the Democrat candidate had performed a public act; he had at th
time of writing been quite willing to have anyone who read the paper see h
by-line. When the Knowland forces produced evidence of his one-time associa
tion, Mr. Rogers had no legitimate complaint.

Any attack against your opponent which offends the public's sense o
fairness will lose votes for your candidate. But when the action or situatio
exposed has become public property, the cry of "smear" is phony and you
candidate will benefit.

If only the public actions of an opponent are fair game for criticism, wha
then is the purpose of digging into the non-public history? There are tw
answers: 1. To protect your own group from making a serious error, and 2. T
arm yourself with a real understanding of your opponent's true character.

In one campaign my candidate was running against an entrenched offic
holder of the opposite party. This man had spent most of his lifetime on th
public payroll. His enemies whispered that he had used his political position t
acquire three or four thousand acres of valuable farmland.

We hired an aggressive young lawyer and sent him to the title companie
His task was to search out every real estate transaction in which our opponer
had figured either as a buyer or a seller. It took him seven weeks to finish th
job. His written report was thirty-seven pages long and covered more than tha
number of separate real estate transfers.

One aspect of the rumor was true—our opponent did hold title to a millio
dollars worth of land—and it had all been acquired since his first election t
public office. But every transaction had been legitimate.

The eager young researcher who brought in the information was confiden
he had produced the basis for asking some serious questions. "If we go afte
him on this," he said, "it won't make any difference whether we can prov
wrong doing. Just the fact that he owns all this land is enough to make lots o
people believe he got it through political deals."

"Yes, they might react in that fashion," I agreed, "but what if they say tha
just proves that our opponent has sound business judgment?"

So we wasted seven weeks and the thousand dollars it cost us for th
agent? Not at all. Later on in that campaign a disgruntled one-time associate o
our opponent tried to sell us information which he claimed would insure m
candidate's victory. What was the information? A completely false account o
how our opponent had connived and cheated to acquire his land holdings. I
we had fallen for this tempting offer and made such claims, the reaction woul
certainly have turned the tide of public support against us. Our painstakin
research prevented us from making this error.

It is almost as important to know your true friends as it is to know you
enemies. In every campaign there are individuals who want to be with th
winner. These people will tell your candidate they are all for him. Ten minute

later they are whispering the same promises of support to your opponent. Special interest groups expect to prosper as the result of political connections. Sometimes they make identical contributions to both candidates. When a contest is close, this class of support is extremely non-committal. But if research has done its job, the manager will not count on support which doesn't exist and will not be trapped into giving his confidence to individuals who are actually more sympathetic to the opposition. Candidates who like to believe and accept all offers of support as genuine are in desperate need of knowing who their real friends are.

In South Dakota the Rural Electrification Administration publishes the state's most lavish newspaper. The headquarters is knee deep in staff. Many of these executives are capable in the political field. This work is called "Community Relations." It is perfectly legitimate but it does make the REA a real power at election time. Shortly after United States Senator Karl Mundt was elected in 1954 spokesmen for the REA began urging Mundt to soften his opposition toward the expanding bureaucracy of these public power groups.

The second important political factor in South Dakota is the Farmers' Union. Mundt, who had been a severe critic of the federal farm program, a subsidy operation dear to the hearts of the Farmers' Union executives, was courted by representatives of this group.

Every politician wants peace at home. These overtures carried the implication that if Mundt would tone down his criticism—compromise his opposition to an expansion of the REA and the continued farm subsidy—these groups were willing to let bygones be bygones, would offer only a token opposition to his re-election in 1960. The Senator was suspicious of their sincerity, but did not choose to deepen their antagonism. He stood on his record.

The Mundt research organization was slow getting started in 1959. When they finally came in with solid information that the REA and the Farmers' Union had lined up behind Mundt's 1960 opponent, George McGovern, a college professor, the Senator came out swinging. This sudden re-emergence of the old Senator Mundt—a tough-minded, conservative, free enterprise American—so encouraged his followers in South Dakota that he won re-election. But his victory was not certain until twenty-four hours after the polls had closed.

In the 1952 Goldwater Arizona campaign our research revealed that one of the state's most brilliant and successful criminal lawyers was helping to guide the opposition strategy. Our research studies of this individual disclosed a familiar pattern—Attack! Attack! Attack! . . . Challenge a judge . . . Challenge the indictment . . . Challenge the jury. I concluded we could expect a last minute assault on Goldwater.

I couldn't prevent such an attack but I could anticipate it. We bought an additional time segment on the state's only television station for the Monday evening preceding election day. Whatever happened, we would have the last word.

The attack came on the final weekend in a full page newspaper ad and a thirty minute speech on radio. "Goldwater was the spoiled child of a wealthy family. He spent most of his time in La Jolla, California, an exclusive South Coast resort.

"Goldwater was an ingrate. He had in the past solicited and accepted substantial favors from the man he was now trying to defeat."

It was alleged in the attack, although it was untrue, that "Goldwater's war record was pure fabrication."

True or untrue, such charges carry some weight. Goldwater did own a house in California; Goldwater had solicited a favor from his opponent—he had asked the Senator's help in getting a transfer from the Reserves to active duty before the Japs struck at Pearl Harbor.

Goldwater had no combat record. Over-age for such duty at the start of the war, he had out-maneuvered the red tape to get pilot status. Assigned to the Air Transport Command, he had flown in every theatre but the European, but never in combat.

We had twenty-four hours to consider the charges and decide upon a proper course of action. There was a temptation to make an angry answer, to offer overwhelming evidence and refutation of the distorted allegations. We wrote several speeches in this vein. Then we re-read the research report on the man who had made the attack. It was true he had brilliantly defended some notorious offenders. Most of his clients had escaped punishment. He had a small circle of close friends who admired him tremendously. But most of the voters had never seen his name except in connection with some rather notorious evil doer. On the television program Goldwater reviewed the charges without any display of anger or other emotion. Then he said: "I can't understand why this man would say these things about me. I have never shown him anything but kindness."

The job of researching the personalities of the opposition cannot be completed in the normal season of politics. Sometimes the identity of your opponent will not be determined until after mid-summer or early fall primary contests in the opposition party. In such cases facts must be gathered about all the potential opponents, their supporters and probable advisers.

If your candidate is running against an incumbent who is of the opposite party, the Senatorial Campaign Committee and the Congressional Campaign Committee can provide the voting record and a great deal of background information.

In times past purely local elections have taken on national significance. This usually occurs when one of the candidates is the special champion of a nationwide interest or group. Political units of the AFL-CIO are sometimes sent into a state to assist a candidate who is especially friendly to labor. The public vs. private power controversy has provoked outside participation in what otherwise would be a purely local election. These outside interests frequently contribute significant information to the research file.

In a senatorial contest some years ago industrial interests combined with oil money from Texas to finance a super-duper espionage effort aimed at defeating a candidate who enjoyed the all-out support of organized labor. An out-of-state detective agency, operated by former FBI agents, was hired to produce evidence that out-of-state labor men and money were being used to defeat an incumbent senator. A crew of operators moved into the state. Some of them checked into the hotel where the labor agent was living. They even managed to take the room next door. Everyone who came to see the labor agent was identified.When the agent left his room he was followed and photographed. In some mysterious fashion these sleuths came into possession of a list of telephone calls made by the labor man. They rented the top floor of a downtown office building and a cameraman with a telephoto lens photographed every politician who entered the labor man's hotel.

Such elaborate operations are not always necessary or desirable and they are extremely expensive. The treasurer of this campaign estimated the cost of this one research effort at $37,500. The operation must have been a particularly nervewracking one for the manager of that campaign. The presence of out-of-state spies, if disclosed and documented by the opposition, would have been extremely harmful to his candidate. The spies weren't discovered and the shocking disclosures made possible as the result of their efforts helped the candidate to win a resounding victory.

The voting or administrative record of your opponent, depending upon the type of office involved, can always be gathered from public records. But the staff member doing the research must be someone who understands the habits of either the legislative body involved or the administrative office in question.

A "yes" vote on a proposition in the United States House of Representatives or Senate is not always an indication of support for the measure. Parliamentary maneuvers employed sometimes create a situation where "yes" means "no" and "no" means "yes." We discovered this in the '58 Goldwater campaign.

We had been advised that our opponent—one-time Senator Ernest Mc-Farland—had voted "yes" on a particular issue. Goldwater opened that campaign with sharp criticism of McFarland for his "yes" vote. It was a mistake. The Senator had voted "yes" but his affirmative vote was against the bill, not in favor of it. After that experience I personally verified the facts in advance before advising Goldwater to mention any of the McFarland votes.

Such indexes as those prepared by COPE, ADA and the Americans for Constitutional Action are tempting traps for the inexperienced. All of these groups seek to document a particular point of view. Their ratings are based upon selected legislative issues. The total voting record is more informative and a failure to vote, a pair*, or an absence from the chamber can be just as useful as an affirmative or negative action on some measures.

Voters expect their senators and their congressmen to be on hand and to express an opinion on every legislative question. If your opponent is an incumbent, the charge that the senator or the congressman wasn't there when the chips were counted will cost the absent member dearly at election time.

Issues change, the needs of a constituency change, the state of the econ-

---

* *Members of Congress who find it impossible to be present for an actual vote frequently arrange a 'pair' which links their vote in favor of or against a measure with some other Member of Congress who wishes to vote the opposite way, the result being that each vote is cancelled.*

omy is never quite the same. Consequently, a position which might have been applauded ten years ago can be a liability today.

In the 1958 campaign Goldwater was challenged by the same Democrat he had defeated in 1952. This man had served two terms in the United States Senate and had a voting record.

Beginning in mid-1957 the national economy entered a period of recession. By campaign time the domestic copper mining industry was in serious trouble. Unable to produce at a profit, the mines in Arizona were operating on a part-time basis. Hundreds of miners were out of work. Those fortunate still to have a job were working shortened hours. Three counties were affected—Cochise, Gila and Graham.

Our opponent's itinerary called for personal appearances in Bisbee and Douglas, mining towns where the reduction of the world price of copper had thrown Arizonans out of work.

McFarland had raised the pocketbook issue by claiming the cost of living had gone up under Republicans and that people in Arizona had been better off when he was in the Senate.

We asked our research division to give us what they had on McFarland and copper. There were numerous speeches in the file. In every one our opponent had spoken glowingly about the importance of the copper industry to the economy of Arizona. He was four square in favor of a prosperous mining industry—any other position would have been stupid. Our opponent was not a stupid man.

In 1950, when our opponent had been a member of the United States Senate, there had been a measure before that body calling for the establishment of a four cent protective copper tariff. Democrats don't like protective tariffs and the Truman administration was opposed to this one. Moreover, the copper industry was booming in 1950. Arizona's mines didn't need the four cent advantage. McFarland had voted against establishing peril point protection. At the time there had been no great public criticism of the Senator's position. But if that legislation had been in effect in 1958, it was reasonable to suggest the miners in Bisbee and Douglas would not have been out of work.

We bought all the available radio time we could afford—two minute, three minute and five minute segments. The message was always the same:

"Former Senator McFarland is going to be in Bisbee and Douglas today asking you to vote for him. When McFarland was in the Senate he voted against a four cent peril point protective tariff for copper. If that tariff were in force today, you would probably be on the job instead of being out of work. When the former Senator asks you to vote for him today, why don't you ask him why he didn't vote to protect your job when he had the chance?"

Dirty pool? Not at all. The one-time Senator's vote was a matter of public record. Had the bill passed, the miners would have been working. The fact that the legislation wasn't needed when it was offered had nothing to do with the situation. Its sponsors in that long ago time had urged passage of the measure, not on the grounds that it was needed then, but rather that it might be needed some day and needed desperately.

Was this tactic effective? Goldwater carried Cochise county by 185 votes in 1958. He had lost Cochise County by 2,397 votes in 1952.

When a campaign actually starts it is necessary to have daily information on the activities of the opposition. Someone in research should be assigned to the task of making tape recordings of every radio and television appearance of your opponent. Newspaper statements, stories and advertising must be clipped and kept. Your opponent's itinerary deserves a place on your bulletin board, if for no other reason than to let you know when and where your candidate may come face to face with the opposition. We have found it is best to follow and not to lead. Let the opponent enter the community first but be sure your candidate is not far behind.

Most newspapers have a limit on the space they can devote to politics. When two candidates are in the area the space is divided. When your man comes in after the opposition, he has the upper hand. He can refute any harmful charges made by the opponent. He can raise questions which require an answer, an answer which will be difficult to deliver because it will be physically difficult for the opponent to revisit the scene in time to be effective.

I have heard of spies being planted in an opposition headquarters and I have had people working for the opposition offer to sell me information. A man who will sell out his boss is, in my viewpoint, capable of a double sell-out.

There are many ways of finding out what is going on without employing spies or buying from traitors. One campaign manager of my acquaintance actually made arrangements to receive the contents of the waste baskets from the office of the opposition. He came into possession of carbon copies of letters, envelopes which betrayed the identity of individuals and organizations who had written letters to the opposition, memos in the handwriting of his opponent's manager, telegrams, instructions to the advertising agency and many totally useless items. It took a lot of digging through the trash to come up with the nuggets. But he told me that daily planning produced some very fine gold.

## THE ISSUES

Candidates are expected to know the answers. Voters demand that an individual seeking public office be able to discuss and give a reasonable opinion on every subject from grain storage to the conflict over the seals on the Pribilof Islands. No candidate should be expected to know all these things. The world of politics is not a reasonable world.

Every candidate can be rehearsed and be knowledgeable on the principal issues. The method for determining the principal issues is explained in the chapter on Public Opinion Surveys.

Beyond the major questions the candidate is at the mercy of his research organization. If the necessary staff work has been performed efficiently, the candidate can shine in any situation.

This phase of research begins with the compilation of a bibliography. Seek out the authoritative publications on every conceivable subject. Let some staffer make a two or three page digest of what the authors have said. Give two or three opinions if necessary. If the issue is particularly controversial, document opposing positions. This may appear a monumental assignment. In practice we have never found it necessary to build a fact book covering more than 200 issues or situations. By situation I mean such things as the state tax rate over a period of years or federal budget figures or appropriations for government projects in particular categories.

A candidate won't have time to memorize the fact book but he can take it with him. When someone in the audience raises a particular question, the candidate can gracefully acknowledge that he is unwilling to trust his memory on this particular subject, produce the fact book and either read the information or paraphrase it.

I have been present time after time when this kind of a performance earns real Brownie points for the candidate who says: "I just happen to have some information in my brief case on that subject. If you will allow me, I'd like to refresh my memory so that I'll give you accurate information and won't make any mistakes."

It will be helpful when there is a real controversy between your candidate and his opponent to put a few opposition quotes in the fact book. Your candidate can usually give an accurate account of what he has said on a subject. When he then produces and reads what the opposition has said on the very same subject, the differences between the two positions are underscored.

It is in the nature of politics that candidates make statements which they afterward regret. Quote your enemy when you can but be sure you quote him accurately.

The staff members who work daily with the research material can usually provide a manager with what he needs at a particular time. But don't rely on memory, yours or theirs—insist that all of the material be indexed and cross-indexed. A box of three-by-five cards will serve nicely and any librarian can put this information together in such a way as to give the campaign manager the kind of devastating ammunition which will rock the opposition.

Don't use all your fire power at any one time; save some of it for the counterattack and remember that the final two weeks of the campaign are critical. That brave commander at Breed's Hill wasn't thinking of politics when he said: "Don't fire until you see the whites of their eyes." But he might have been.

### VOTING HABITS

The fourth general area of research is in the field of the Voting Habits of the Constituency. It is a pure statistical study based upon the history of the past two or three election contests. Because the information developed by this study bears heavily on the problem of where to look for votes, we will deal with it in the next chapter.

# 8 · *Where the Ducks Are*

PRACTICAL POLITICS is often described as the art of winning elections. Among those who attempt to practice this art there is no greater general misunderstanding than the one which surrounds the title of this chapter.

Over the years I have chosen to describe what will be outlined here as "going where the ducks are." To do this, it is necessary to understand where the ducks will be found. Since all managers and all candidates labor mightily for victory, it would seem the practical necessity of determining the area of greatest probable return would invite the most careful consideration. More often than not candidates devote a great deal of energy and spend substantial sums of money in those areas of the constituency least likely to produce victory.

In the business world a super-salesman is described as one who "can sell fur coats to a South Sea Islander," or "refrigerators to an Eskimo." What is implied in this kind of compliment is a situation where the most unlikely buyer purchases a product he doesn't want and doesn't need.

All too often in the traditional political campaign the candidate expends his energy trying to convince those who are already convinced or to persuade those who are least likely to be persuaded.

In every constituency there are identifiable segments of the population that by tradition consistently favor either the Republican or the Democrat candidate. In recent years big city voters have favored the Democrat candidate. Outside the solid South, rural voters and residents of smaller cities have favored the Republican candidate.

The Democrats have done an extremely effective job of identifying their party as the political instrument which best serves the poor. They have branded the Republicans as the party of the rich and the well to do. This strategem of dividing the electorate on an economic line contains an element of truth. Since the days of Franklin D. Roosevelt, Democrats have invariably supported the welfare state concept. The beneficiaries of the welfare state are at the bottom of the economic ladder. A precinct populated with citizens who are living on unemployment benefits, old age pensions or Aid to Dependent Children checks is not going to be receptive to a Republican candidate whose conscience requires him to suggest that "when the government makes a man dependent, it also robs him of a certain amount of freedom."

There is good evidence to indicate that college graduates earn more money than do those who only graduate from high school. One of the great arguments for higher education is that better schooling leads to better income. The Republican philosophy, which stresses opportunity and responsibility, has a better chance of being understood by college graduates than it does by those with an inadequate education.

Geographical origin has a great deal to do with the voting habits of the population. Southerners are traditionally in the Democrat Party. The War between the States is ancient history but the South has not forgotten about it. The Irish Catholic is apt to vote Democrat. The population in the Mid-West tends to be Republican.

All of these generalizations can be borne out by a study of past voting habits. Yet time after time the green, inexperienced candidate is urged to enter the opposition's strong territory and fight out the election.

I have heard candidates of some experience point to a district or a group of precincts which has traditionally favored the opposition and then declare with great conviction: "I'm going to work those precincts twice as hard as I did in the last campaign."

A precinct that has traditionally given 65 per cent of its vote to a Democrat candidate is obviously composed of voters who either can't hear what the Republican candidates are saying or don't want to hear because of their immutable antagonisms to the Republican Party. A precinct or district that gives 65 per cent of its vote to the Republican Party is obviously composed of Republican-inclined voters who won't or can't listen to the arguments advanced by Democrat candidates. To determine where the ducks are, a candidate must first equip himself with an understanding of where the ducks have been in the past.

The area of greatest probable return will be found in those precincts which your party candidates have carried or lost by five per cent. The fact that in the past a Republican candidate has been able to gather 45 per cent of the vote in a precinct is clear indication that at least 45 per cent of the voters are capable of aligning themselves with the philosophy of a Republican candidate. In such a precinct there will be no traditional or economic barrier to prevent an additional five or six or even ten per cent of the voters from giving their approval to a Republican Party candidate.

In areas where a Republican Party candidate has carried a precinct by five per cent or received 55 per cent of the votes cast, there is good reason to believe that an active campaign will persuade an additional four or five per cent of the voters to give their approval to a Republican Party candidate.

The area of least likely return is to be found in those precincts where in election after election the voters have been almost unanimous in their choice. If 70 per cent or 65 per cent of the votes have gone to a Republican in the past, your Republican candidate will probably be unable to increase that percentage significantly. If 65 per cent or more of the votes have gone to a Democrat candidate in the past, your Republican candidate may persuade an additional two or three per cent to come with him, but the gain will not be substantial.

The season of politics is short. There isn't enough time for every candidate to make a maximum effort in every precinct. But there is always enough time or the candidate to make a maximum effort in the area of greatest probable eturn.

At the start of any campaign one of the tasks to be assigned to the research lepartment is the compilation of a precinct-by-precinct voting history of the tate or constituency. These figures will tell the manager in no uncertain terms vhere to find the ducks. And the ducks are not flying in the precincts which lave overwhelmingly supported your party's candidate in the past or the oppo- ition party's candidate.

In the 1958 Goldwater Arizona election the Senator attended a coffee or a neeting in every precinct which qualified as belonging in the area of greatest possible return. There were many precincts where the Senator didn't make a ingle appearance. Some of these were predominantly Republican.

Once the manager has determined where the ducks are, he must be pre- pared to take some abuse in the pursuit of this strategy. There is a fine Repub- ican Legislative District Chairman in Arizona who still cherishes considerable animosity toward me because I insisted Goldwater go after the ducks.

In the final two weeks of the campaign the Senator was scheduled to pend two days in Tucson attending precinct coffees. The evenings were re- served for larger gatherings in legislative districts. Every chairman of a legisla- ive district in the area wanted Goldwater for an evening meeting. One charm- ng lady who was the leader in an area which Republicans traditionally carried by about 65 per cent of the vote insisted she was entitled to the Senator. In an adjacent district candidates in the Republican Party had traditionally lost by about five per cent of the vote. We scheduled the Senator for an appearance in this area.

In 1962, this wonderful partisan chairman of the good district was still criticizing me for my decision. But Goldwater carried that district which other Republicans had lost. The final vote was 51 and a fraction per cent for Gold- water.

In the good Republican district the Senator received precisely the same percentage he and other Republican candidates had enjoyed in the past. We didn't lose anything by not sending him to the good district. We gained six per cent by sending him to what was clearly an area of the greatest probable return.

In the 1960 Curtis election in Nebraska, Dick Spelts and Dick Herman scrupulously followed the practice of sending the Senator into those areas where he could logically expect to make the greatest gains. The Curtis victory in these precincts adds an additional endorsement to the practice of "going where the ducks are."

In the 1960 presidential election, Richard Nixon carried his campaign into every one of the 50 states. He worked just as hard, perhaps harder, in those areas which every knowledgeable Republican recognized as hopeless as he did in those areas which in the past have been favorable to Republican candidates. In the final week of that effort he visited Alaska—an area which could not possibly affect the outcome of the presidential race.

In making the precinct analysis to determine where the ducks are, consideration must be given to the peculiar circumstances of the contest chosen for the index. A more accurate reflection of the voting habits of a precinct will come from a study of two or three contests. Don't choose the stars of any particular year; select some average-to-good candidates in both parties and when the votes have been tabulated, calculate the percentage. The sample on page 281 can be followed as a guide.

In the three precincts shown here for purpose of illustration, we have a four-year history covering three elections and five offices—governor, member of Congress, attorney general, state auditor and state representative.

In 1956, the Republican running for Congress carried Chandler No. 1 precinct. The Republican running for governor lost by a little more than six per cent. The Republican candidate for attorney general lost by 3.39 per cent. The Republican running for auditor lost by 12.93 per cent, but the Republican running for state representative won by 4.89 per cent. This is clearly a potentially profitable precinct for Republican candidates. The 1958 figures demonstrate this conclusively. The Republican candidates for governor, congress, attorney general and state representative all carried the precinct. In 1958, based on the 1956 performance, this precinct was worth concentrated effort. In 1960, it had forfeited this classification because of the overwhelming '58 Republican vote.

Emerson, the second precinct, shows a steady swing to the Republican candidate; the ducks were here in '56, the hunting was good in '58; and, in 1960, every Republican candidate except the state auditor got more than the limit of birds.

Fowler precinct demonstrates conclusively how the same precinct can switch from party to party. In 1956, the Republican for governor lost, the Republican for the House of Representatives won and the Republicans for attorney general and state auditor were badly defeated. In 1958, the Republican for governor won picking up 9.9 percentage points. The Republican for congress picked up 3.24 points, but the Republicans for attorney general and auditor both lost ground. In 1960, the Republican for governor again gained, the Republican for congress lost and the Republican for attorney general gained but not quite enough. It is clear from a statistical point of view, in 1960 the Republican candidate for congress failed to work the precinct.

When the statisticians have determined the precincts which hold the greatest possibility for your candidate, these should be identified on the voting maps. In most cases a geographical pattern will emerge. The next step is to determine how many votes your candidate must gain or retain in order to win. This becomes your target. If victory can be had by increasing the vote for your party candidate in 50 precincts, concentrate on the 50 which, from your study, offer the greatest possibilities.

The precinct habits can be extremely helpful in determining where the foot soldiers should work, but the best vote-getter on your campaign team is the candidate himself. Schedule coffees, rallies, luncheon club speeches and concentrate them all in the area where past history indicates your candidate will find the audience he needs most.

It would be obvious nonsense to waste your candidate's time in the smaller precincts where a pickup of 10 per cent of the vote might mean a numerical

## PRECINCT VOTE ANALYSIS

Maricopa County, Chandler No. 1 Precinct (Chandler East Precinct Divided in 1958)

| YEAR | GOVERNOR | | | CONGRESS | | | ATTORNEY GENERAL | | | AUDITOR | | | STATE REPRESENTATIVE | | |
|---|---|---|---|---|---|---|---|---|---|---|---|---|---|---|---|
| | *Dem.* | *Rep.* | *% Rep.* | *Dem.* | *Rep.* | *% Rep.* | *Dem.* | *Rep.* | *% Rep.* | *Dem.* | *Rep.* | *% Rep.* | *Dem.* | *Rep.* | *% Rep.* |
| 1956 | 582 | 457 | 43.98 | 444 | 562 | 55.86 | 520 | 454 | 46.61 | 628 | 370 | 37.07 | 452 | 550 | 54.89 |
| 1958 | 245 | 610 | 71.35 | 271 | 568 | 67.70 | 380 | 427 | 52.91 | 485 | 320 | 39.75 | 245 | 601 | 71.04 |
| 1960 | 407 | 866 | 68.03 | 419 | 798 | 65.57 | 433 | 812 | 65.22 | 669 | 539 | 44.62 | 516 | 739 | 58.88 |

## PRECINCT VOTE ANALYSIS

Maricopa County, Emerson Precinct

| YEAR | GOVERNOR | | | CONGRESS | | | ATTORNEY GENERAL | | | AUDITOR | | | STATE REPRESENTATIVE | | |
|---|---|---|---|---|---|---|---|---|---|---|---|---|---|---|---|
| | *Dem.* | *Rep.* | *% Rep.* | *Dem.* | *Rep.* | *% Rep.* | *Dem.* | *Rep.* | *% Rep.* | *Dem.* | *Rep.* | *% Rep.* | *Dem.* | *Rep.* | *% Rep.* |
| 1956 | 487 | 498 | 50.55 | 383 | 597 | 60.91 | 469 | 497 | 51.44 | 556 | 418 | 42.91 | 468 | 504 | 51.85 |
| 1958 | 327 | 533 | 61.98 | 343 | 497 | 59.17 | 383 | 443 | 53.63 | 489 | 329 | 40.22 | 432 | 397 | 47.88 |
| 1960 | 300 | 623 | 67.50 | 352 | 536 | 60.36 | 352 | 548 | 60.89 | 485 | 403 | 45.38 | 369 | 495 | 57.29 |

## PRECINCT VOTE ANALYSIS

Maricopa County, Fowler Precinct

| YEAR | GOVERNOR | | | CONGRESS | | | ATTORNEY GENERAL | | | AUDITOR | | | STATE REPRESENTATIVE | | |
|---|---|---|---|---|---|---|---|---|---|---|---|---|---|---|---|
| | *Dem.* | *Rep.* | *% Rep.* | *Dem.* | *Rep.* | *% Rep.* | *Dem.* | *Rep.* | *% Rep.* | *Dem.* | *Rep.* | *% Rep.* | *Dem.* | *Rep.* | *% Rep.* |
| 1956 | 141 | 111 | 44.04 | 126 | 128 | 50.39 | 147 | 96 | 39.50 | 181 | 82 | 31.17 | 168 | NC | |
| 1958 | 120 | 136 | 53.13 | 115 | 133 | 53.63 | 153 | 91 | 37.30 | 179 | 67 | 27.24 | 176 | 77 | 30.43 |
| 1960 | 152 | 190 | 55.56 | 174 | 147 | 45.79 | 171 | 160 | 48.34 | 238 | 94 | 28.31 | 244 | 92 | 27.38 |

gain of 10 or 20 at the most. Don't ever be tempted to give in to those who urge you to send the candidate into those areas which historically have given 65 or 70 per cent of their votes to the candidate of the opposition party.

There are some strategems that can be employed and that will only be productive when aimed at those who are nominally in the opposition party. But your candidate's time is far too precious to be spent before predominantly hostile audiences. The decision to concentrate on the potentially good areas and neglect the poor ones requires considerable courage on the part of the campaign management. Such a decision will draw the accusation that you are giving up without a fight, that you are conceding certain areas to your opponent; but it isn't rational to try to sell expensive electric refrigerators to impoverished Eskimos when you could be aiming your sales efforts at residents of a warmer climate who are financially able to buy your product.

When the bad or non-productive areas have been identified they should not be abandoned before you ask yourself why. Why is it that these people seem unable to accept your party's candidate? In most cases it will be worthwhile to make a serious effort to understand the thinking of this segment of the voting population. A properly conducted public opinion survey may provide the key to your party's lack of popularity and, in some cases, this animosity can be conquered; if not in this election, perhaps in the next one. Managers are concerned with the present election and its outcome, and good managers will "go where the ducks are."

# 9 · *The Cell Group*

THE MILITARY COMMANDER who sends his soldiers into battle without having first developed detailed plans for the attack is almost certain to be defeated. The plan of battle must include, among other things, the proper use of specially trained forces as well as the deployment of conventional units.

The troops available in a political campaign are for the most part volunteers. The recruitment, instruction and deployment of volunteer forces is the task of the campaign manager. If he is skillful, his organization will bring sufficient pressure to bear upon public sentiment to produce victory on election day.

The measurable strength of a political party is to be found in its precinct committeemen. In the big urban centers precinct officials frequently benefit from a patronage job. They devote their full time to political work and are paid for it. But outside the big cities the party functionaries are individuals who enjoy the excitement of politics, who derive satisfaction from the recognition they receive as an elected party official. Precinct committeemen choose their own captains, elect legislative district leaders and have a voice in the selection of county and state chairmen. With these people politics is a hobby to which they eagerly devote their leisure time.

Candidates, particularly those for lesser offices, must depend upon the party organization. But a man running for the office of governor, for the U.S. Senate or for Congress needs to establish a private organization. To be successful he must recruit an army of supporters who will give him their first loyalty and devote all of their efforts to advancing his cause.

Precinct organizations get out the party vote. But except in those areas where one party enjoys an overwhelming majority registration, this is not enough to insure victory.

In Arizona, where Democrats outnumber Republicans—the ratio was five to one in 1952 and about three and one half to one in 1958—it would be folly for a Republican candidate to pin his hopes on the regular Republican vote.

Mao Tse-tung, the communist revolutionary general, has written a valuable book on the tactics of infiltration. In it he says: "Give me just two or three men in a village and I will take the village." In the Goldwater campaigns of 1952 and 1958 and in all other campaigns where I have served as a consultant I have followed the advice of Mao Tse-tung.

Almost all candidates try valiantly in one way or another to consolidate their supporters. Politicians steeped in the old tradition frequently organize clubs. Voters are asked to sign up, perhaps contribute a dollar or so, and become a charter member of the "Smith for Senate Club." Frequently these groups are identified by a lapel pin or are given special stickers to put on their cars. The strategy we used is totally different.

For easy identification we called our operation the "Cell Group," because the title suggests precisely what we hoped to create—enthusiastic, knowledgeable Goldwater supporters who would not be labeled or identified as members of any special organization.

The individuals we enlisted became a secret weapon possessing strength, mobility and real impact. They were able to infiltrate centers of opposition support, keep us informed of opposition tactics, disseminate information, enlist other supporters and to do all these things completely unnoticed by the opposition.

As the program is outlined here, it will appear to be simple and the usefulness of such a group will be obvious. My understanding of how to develop such strength and how to use it is the result of trial and error in numerous campaigns. Over the years I have abandoned those techniques which do not produce results.

In those years when I was serving as a special consultant for the Republican Senatorial Campaign committee I discovered the very simplicity of the plan sometimes made it difficult for the traditional politician to understand the dynamic upon which it operates.

Mao Tse-tung might have been able to take a village with just two or three men. I have learned that to guarantee success in the political effort it is desirable to have three to five per cent of the voting population enlisted in the Cell Group.

In 1958 we finally had about thirty-two hundred Cell Group members in Arizona. In Nebraska in 1960 we had almost one hundred thousand. In this instance the program actually got a little out of hand. In Massachusetts, Chuck Colson, a director of the 1960 campaign for Senator Saltonstall, kept the membership in his Cell Group within manageable limits.

Before we examine the mechanics of enlisting Cell Group members, it will be helpful to review the considerations that prompt individuals to volunteer for any service outside the narrow orbit of their everyday lives.

Volunteers in a political effort do not expect to receive any direct financial or material return from their work. The appeal to them must be essentially an emotional one. To be successful it must contain something more than the oft repeated request of a candidate for a voter's support. The plan outlined in this chapter suggests involvement, an entering into the inner circle, with access to information not available to the general public.

The foundation of a successful Cell Group organization requires a wide acquaintance with the individuals in the constituency. It isn't at all necessary that the individuals selected be close friends of the candidate.

As the first step the candidate is asked to list the names of important or competent individuals with whom he is acquainted. It is helpful to indicate the actual relationship by establishing three categories: close personal friends, close political associates, individuals who are known to the candidate but not necessarily on a personal basis.

In setting up the file we used three different colored cards to indicate the categories. On a large list the use of IBM equipment is almost mandatory. To gain the maximum return from the Cell Group operation it is necessary to be able to identify the Cell Group members by occupation, economic status and geographical location.

An incumbent politician will have no difficulty providing an adequate number of names in all three groups. Men in public office have a wide circle of personal friends. The practicing politician establishes contacts with people who are not necessarily close friends on the basis of mutual interest.

The incumbent's correspondence file can provide the names of individuals in every community who have been sufficiently interested in the problems of government to write him one or more letters during his tenure in office.

An individual who is a candidate for the first time may have more difficulty with the names. But if a man can be considered a serious candidate for a public office, he must enjoy a wide acquaintance. The first-timer will probably fill his list with the names of business associates, service club or church contacts, or members of the party if he has been active in politics.

The candidate's manager and those who are to be closely associated with the campaign effort can very likely contribute as many useful names as the candidate himself. The manager must give balance to the list. I dislike the odious term "little people" but that phrase best illustrates what I mean by

alance. A candidate will know the big shots; the managers must add names to
*ake the total list representative as nearly as possible of the total constituency.

When the list has been compiled, the research division—an activity dis-
ussed in another chapter—should provide as much additional information as
ossible. It will be helpful to know the financial situation of the respective Cell
Group member, his banking connection, his relationship with the home town
ewspaper, his church or lodge identification, his occupation or profession, and
is family connections throughout the state. If the individual has been active in
olitics, this information will be extremely important. The quality of the indi-
iduals suggested is much more important than the quantity. As the campaign
rogresses the list will grow.

The initial approach should be made with a personal letter—from the
andidate if the candidate supplied the name or from the manager or associate
ho put the name on the list.

The whole problem of the use of mail in a political campaign will be
iscussed in depth in another chapter. For our purpose at this moment, how-
ver, it is necessary to understand the kind of first letter that will produce a
avorable response.

The objective is to cement the relationship between the recipient of the
tter and the candidate. Ultimately we want to establish a mutual interest and
develop this interest to such a degree that the member of the Cell Group will
e strongly identified with the candidate's fortunes, will actually come to con-
ider the threat of defeat as menacing him personally.

The approach must be on a first-name basis. If no one in the campaign
roup knows the individual well enough to call him by his first name, put that
ard aside for future development. The letter must be personally typed, not
eproduced—robotyped letters have the appearance of being individually
yped but the uniformity or similarity of the contents of such letters makes it
angerous to take this short-cut in the initial approach. It can be assumed that
number of the individuals selected for enlistment in this Cell Group will share
ome mutual interest; they might be close friends. Since anyone approached
ith the kind of letter we have in mind will be both pleased and flattered, the
anger that one of the recipients might show his letter to someone who has
lso been approached is a risk that must not be taken at this time.

The content of all the letters—whether written by the candidate or by his
ssociates—is basically an appeal for the opinion or the judgment of the indi-
idual addressed. NOTHING IS SAID WHICH WOULD INDICATE THAT THE REAL
NTENT OF THE LETTER IS TO INVOLVE THE RECIPIENT IN A POLITICAL CAMPAIGN.

The reason for the letter must be clear in the very first paragraph. Assum-
g the candidate's name is Robert Maxwell:

Dear Jim:
The Banking and Insurance Committee of the Senate is considering
HB-146. The sponsors of this bill claim it will give more protection to a
bank's depositors. If you could take time to read the enclosed copy of

this proposed legislation and let me have the benefit of your thinking, would be most grateful.

Some of our staff members will work up information on the propos but I feel the need of your knowledge and your understanding. A lon time ago, Jim, I learned that the people back here don't always think th same way as the people in Arizona.

Gratefully yours,
Bob

Why does the letter lead off with the discussion of legislation affectin banking? Because the research division has provided the information that Ji is a stockholder in a bank or a board member or an attorney in a firm whic represents banking interests.

In each session the Congress considers a wide variety of proposed nev legislation. It is never difficult to find a particular bill which will lie in th special area of competence belonging to the individual to whom the letter being written.

If the letter is to be written by someone other than the candidate, it migl go like this:

Dear Jim:

When Bob was here last week, (if the Senator hadn't been in th state, the letter might begin: "I was talking with Bob on the telephon last week.") he mentioned he was concerned with some legislation whic is being considered by the Banking and Currency Committee. It has t do with new regulations being offered as additional protection for ban depositors.

Bob would be very interested in having your opinion on the subjec

I am enclosing a copy of the proposed legislation. If you want to sen your opinion direct to me, I will forward it on to Bob. But better still, jus address your letter to him at the Senate Office Building in Washingtor D. C.

At this point, if the author of the letter is someone other than the candi date, there is an opportunity for a comment on the local political situatior For example:

We hear that a good deal of Eastern labor money will come into th state to beat Bob Maxwell next year. It's going to be a real battle.

Gratefully yours,
Steve

A request for advice or an opinion on proposed legislation provides a incumbent with a logical and legitimate reason for the letter. The resourcefu campaign manager can find dozens of other reasons for writing just as valid— an editorial from a newspaper, a reprint from a magazine which the Senato believes the constituent would enjoy reading, an inpending action by the ad ministration.

In December of 1963 Secretary of Defense McNamara announced the
osing of a great many military installations throughout the country. In those
eas affected there was an immediate editorial reaction. A candidate seeking
ection to the Congress would find this an ideal springboard for the first letter.
he communication would contain a reproduction of the editorial and then
licit the individual's opinion as to the effect the proposed action would have
1 the community.

There are a number of very sound reasons why the initial approach should
ek an opinion from the recipient. Anyone is flattered when a U.S. Senator or
man of sufficient stature to be a logical candidate for the U.S. Senate asks his
lvice. When the form of advice solicited calls on the individual's special field
competence, the implication of respect is even stronger.

The candidate may find some very useful opinions in the responses. The
al benefit from the request is that it requires the individual to act. This action
the forerunner of a real commitment. In this trade of managing campaigns
hich I have followed for so many years, we call it accountability. Ask some-
dy to do something for you. Make the request flattering if possible. Provide
e necessity for positive action. And wherever practical put a deadline on the
sponse.

In those letters that have as their subject proposed legislative action, there
an implicit deadline. The committee is holding hearings, therefore the Sena-
r needs a response before the legislation is brought before the Senate for
tion. If the excuse for the letter is a proposed governmental action, a re-
onse is required before the action becomes final.

The recruitment of Cell Group members is a gradual process. At the outset
e tempo will be limited by the clerical help available to the candidate or his
anager. Because the letters are personalized and suited to fit the special
terest or ability of the recipient, it will be difficult to send out more than a
ndred a day. The manager must keep enough clerical help in reserve to
spond promptly to the answers as they come in. An immediate reply to the
turn letter is essential to the ultimate organization of an effective Cell Group.

The acknowledgment must be a personal letter. It must be directly respon-
ve to the suggestions made by the citizen, but it should do much more than
press thanks or gratitude. The tone of the second letter assumes a continuing
lationship.

This original approach and first response, requiring individually typed
tters and first class postage, is the most expensive part of the Cell Group
eration. The exchange of letters on a personal basis is continued for only a
ry short time. In some campaigns we have moved names to a general bulk
ailing list after the first exchange. Sometimes, owing to the nature of the
sponse or the prominence of the individual involved, this correspondence has
en continued on a personal basis for some little time. But the objective is to
ve all the names on a single bulk mailing list, receiving duplicated letters as
on as possible.

If the approach has been carried out with some skill and sensitivity, the
nsition to bulk mailing will not be resented. A high degree of skill is required

in the preparation and wording of the mass communications. Mailings must n
be sent with any kind of calendar regularity. The letter or other material in th
communication must document and explain the reason for the letter. Never
any time should there be an indication that the recipient is a member of a
organized group.

In all my experience I have had only one angry objection to the use
duplicated letters sent to a Cell Group. This came about because the recipie
resented the fact that my name was signed to the letter rather than the cand
date's.

In developing this technique I made a serious effort to interview Ce
Group members after election day. I learned their interest was in the content
the communication. The form went almost unnoticed. Some of them told n
they realized others were getting the same information or, as they put it,
knew Barry was sending this stuff to some of his good friends but most of th
people I talked to weren't getting it and I was real pleased to be a part of th
inner circle."

Once the initial contact has been established, the campaign manager w
have no difficulty in finding a valid reason for further letters. Editorials from a
out of state newspaper, reprints from the Congressional Record, a copy of
letter the candidate has sent to someone setting forth his position on an issu
and finally, advance information on the candidate's plans.

Many individuals enlisted in the Cell Group will respond by asking
"What can I do to help?" At this point the manager is in a delightful positio
It is a real advantage to have someone ask: "What can I do?" Because the su
gestions made in response to that request rarely arouse any antagonism. None
us really like to be told what to do. When a manager sends out a suggestic
cold he can be sure someone will make an angry response.

The list of things Cell Group members can do for a candidate is almo
inexhaustible. They can provide an accurate index to public sentiment as pa
ticipants in the continuous survey—a technique fully described in the chapt
on public opinion polls. They can and will keep the manager constantly ad
vised on activities of the opposition.

In 1958 we had Cell Group members working for most of the radio ar
television outlets in Arizona. We were informed immediately when the oppos
tion tripled its request for time on the Saturday, Sunday and Monday immed
ately preceding election day. This told us in advance the opposition was co
ing up with some new tactic, some new appeal, and we were able to turn th
sudden flood of buy orders into an ultimate liability for our opponent.

The most important service performed by the Cell Group members is
mention the name of your candidate favorably to everyone they meet.

In 1948 the University of Chicago sponsored an investigation into th
voting habits of the people of Elmira, New York. This city was selected, aft
careful study, as being typical. Information was developed through a series
interviews commencing in June and concluding after election day. The samp
selected was carefully weighted to represent a true cross section of the soci

conomic divisions of the population. In discussing the August to November oting changes, the authors reveal that nine per cent of one group changed to e opposite party candidate sometime before election day. This nine per cent ho intended to vote for Dewey in June but switched to Truman in November, r vice versa, made the change because they had a majority of friends who ere opposed to their June decision. A nine per cent switch can change the utcome of any election.

The surveys in Elmira also revealed that twenty-five per cent of those who ad family members in the opposite party switched from their intended choice June to their family's choice in November. For the purpose of understanding nd then exploiting those voters whose minds can be changed, it is important to mphasize that this substantial switch was brought about through personal ontact and family pressures.

The members of a "Smith for Senate Club" of the old tradition were all dentified partisans. Their endorsement of Smith loses much of its strength ecause of their identification with an organized group pushing Smith.

The members of the Cell Groups are not publicly identified as partisans in e same sense prominent party members or members of a candidate club are dentified. The opinions of the Cell Group members are more readily accepted ecause their endorsement does not carry the same implication of self-service hich is attached to a party official, or to a publicly identified member of a artisan club. Cell Group members can be recruited from both major parties nd when a man who is nominally Democrat, who in past elections has publicly pported candidates on the Democrat ticket, advances the cause of a Repub- can candidate, his words carry real conviction.

The Cell Groups have a second advantage over the traditional clubs, for ich clubs draw together like-minded people and members of such clubs are clined to associate with each other rather than spreading out. A Cell Group ember, on the contrary, frequently finds himself in company with members of e opposition. His social activity is not limited to individuals with strong olitical convictions.

Of course a citizen who wanders about saying: "Senator Smith's a wonder- l guy. I hope you'll vote for him" will immediately be identified as a partisan nd soon rejected as a bore with a one-track mind. It is up to the manager to se his Cell Group members effectively. He must keep them from being robot artisans. The campaign manager must use his mass mailings to keep the dividuals in this group supplied with a valid reason for injecting the candi- ate's name into every conversation. His job is to supply the Cell Group with side information which will in turn become a natural point of departure for jecting the candidate's name into every conversation.

We all like to talk about things in our particular field of special knowledge special competency. If we read a book or see a new play, the book or the play comes our topic of conversation for a few days. If we know something about public figure that is not general knowledge, we are eager to display the fact at we have access to inside information.

If the candidate is going to make a speech on an important subject, the speech should be duplicated well in advance in order that it may be distributed in advance. The first page should be marked: "Not for release until . . . (the date the speech is to be delivered)." Copies are mailed to members of the Cell Group together with a letter something like this:

> Bob is going to speak on Federal Aid to Education in Lincoln on such and such a date. He thought you would like to know in advance what he is going to say. Please keep this matter confidential until after the release date.

Now the members of the Cell Group are really on the inside. They have the speech ahead of the newspapers; the candidate has trusted them with this confidential information. They will find it impossible to resist the temptation to talk about it.

Some members of the Cell Group will quote directly from the speech. But most of them, mindful of the situation, will confine their remarks to something like this: "The Senator is going to make a speech two weeks from now. He's got a lot to say and it's about time someone said it."

With that kind of a starter the conversation is really opened. It is centered on the candidate. The Cell Group member has been provided with the most logical reason to talk about his favorite politician.

I have learned that just sending the candidate's itinerary to members of the Cell Group is beneficial. If the candidate is going to make a speech or is appearing in some section of the state three hundred miles away, the Cell Group member knows it. He can and will inject the candidate's name into the conversation quite naturally by mentioning where the candidate is going to be.

The utility of the Cell Group does not end with its ability to spread the word about the candidate. It can be used to counterattack the opposition in a dozen different ways.

In the election described in an earlier chapter, Senator————was defeated in part through the circulation of a derogatory rumor. Had his manager established a Cell Group in that state, they might very well have destroyed the effectiveness of that slander.

The campaign manager is required to develop an intimate knowledge of his opposition. This is discussed at length in the chapter entitled *Researching the Opposition* but to understand how the Cell Group organization can protect a candidate, the subject must be mentioned briefly here.

The security surrounding campaign headquarters can be penetrated. Knowing in advance what the opposition proposes is very useful information indeed. Acquaintance with the habits of the men leading the opposition will permit the campaign manager to prepare a defensive counterattack—something to be held in readiness until it is needed.

In 1958 in Arizona, at the outset of the campaign, I learned that among our opponent's camp followers was an individual whose forte was the circulation of harmful rumors.

Armed with this information, I immediately sent a communiqué to all Cell Group members. In it I explained the probability that someone, somewhere, would start an ugly rumor about Goldwater. To give them an idea of what I anticipated, I recited the history of the————campaign. Then I asked the Cell Group members to report by telephone the moment they encountered this tactic in their community.

From certain sources extremely antagonistic to Goldwater, we heard the charge that his department store paid substandard wages. Our intelligence produced the information that an employee in the Goldwater store had been approached and questioned about her salary. The conversations had culminated with the Goldwater clerk selling her paycheck to those who made the inquiry. It seemed necessary to anticipate a rumor attacking Goldwater as a rich man who paid substandard wages.

In preparing to combat this possibility, we decided the best testimony to refute such a charge would be a statement from Goldwater employees and we prepared a full page newspaper ad. [Note: This kind of appeal will be discussed in detail in the chapter on Mass Media.] The burden of the message was: "We, the undersigned employees of the Goldwater store, receive wages above average for department stores in the Phoenix area. We enjoy the benefits not available from other managements. We deeply resent any suggestion that we are to be pitied or that the Goldwater management in any way mistreats us."

Such an ad could not be used in the ordinary course of the campaign because it would appear too self-serving. We believed it would be most effective in response to a rumor alleging Goldwater paid substandard wages. We intended to time the response to the appearance of the rumor.

On a particular day in August we received more than thirty telephone reports from members of the Cell Group residing in every geographical area in the state. The rumor that Goldwater paid low wages was heard almost simultaneously in Yuma and Douglas. These communities are almost three hundred miles apart. The rumor was documented or based on the experience of a supposed relative and quoted the net amount of a paycheck after deductions. And the language of the rumor started in Douglas was identical with the language employed in Yuma:

"My brother's wife works at the Goldwater store. I just couldn't believe it when she told us her paycheck for two weeks work was only XXX dollars."

Having anticipated this attack in advance, I was able to quote the gross amount paid by the Goldwater store to employees in several categories. I told the Cell Group members who called to ask the rumor spreaders if they were talking about gross or net pay and to suggest if their brother's wife received only XXX dollars, she must be a part-time employee.

Seventy-two hours after the story was started our full page advertisement appeared in the state's major newspapers. The message of the ad was strengthened by the fact that space for its display was purchased and paid for by Goldwater employees, not by the Goldwater campaign group.

In that '58 campaign the officials of organized labor were all out to beat Goldwater. They refused to sell us space in the labor publication; they refused to give Goldwater an audience at labor meetings. Our strategy was to try to reach the men who worked with the tools.

One Tuesday afternoon in the middle of that campaign summer I received a telephone call from a Cell Group member. This man, a registered Democrat, was a member of an important union. He called to report that his group was holding a regional meeting in a community one hundred and fifty miles from Phoenix. He said the official agenda was a short one. He had asked union officials if Goldwater could appear and had been refused but he had an idea:

"There's a vacant storeroom next to our union hall. If we could get that storeroom and have Barry there making a speech, I think most of the boys would drift in to hear him."

It was a good suggestion. Could we implement it? In the card file we had about sixty-five names of Cell Group members in this community.

Thanks to the background material supplied by the research division we were able to locate a member who was a real estate man. It developed this member represented the owner of the vacant storeroom.

I didn't have to leave Phoenix. I called each member of the Cell Group in that city and explained our problem. In less than twenty-four hours they were able to do these things: secure the use of the vacant store building without charge; borrow and install portable air conditioning equipment; borrow and install one hundred and fifty folding chairs. They painted signs on the window advertising the meeting. They put spot announcements on their radio station inviting people to come to the meeting. They organized a refreshment committee to provide lemonade, soft drinks, cookies, and I am told there was beer in the back room—but I never asked about that. They produced a nucleus of the audience. That night, by actual count, Goldwater spoke to seventy-six members of the labor union.

Tucson, Arizona, is a delightful, sophisticated, winter resort city, home of the University of Arizona. Its buildings are reminiscent of the Spanish occupation, but the barber shop conversations are typical of the rest of America—sports, politics, the day's news.

The owner of one barbershop in Tucson was a most enthusiastic and effective member of our Cell Group. We didn't find him—he found us. Many months before the actual campaign commenced, he had written me asking for a photograph of the Senator.

In the spring of 1958, the Congress was going through its perennial hassle over foreign aid. As one of our bits of inside information, we had sent to all Cell Group members a brief résumé of committee action on the foreign aid bill together with Goldwater's remarks on the subject.

The week our barber friend received this information he entertained as his customer a prominent citizen long identified with the Democrat cause. This man had been a major contributor to Governor McFarland's Democrat campaign in 1956. He had just returned from a trip around the world—a trip which

ad taken him into Southeast Asia. He was in the process of being shaved when
e mentioned that he had landed at an airport in some far away little country
with so many magnificent buildings and so many runways it made the Los
Angeles Municipal Airport look like a cow pasture operation.

Our barber friend responded by saying, "Did you read what Barry Goldwater has to say about the waste in foreign aid?"

The traveler expressed interest.

"He sent me a copy of his speech along with some other information on
what they are proposing to do about foreign aid," the barber said.

"Where is it?"

"I've got it right here."

"Let me see it."

The traveler sat up in the chair and while the lather dried on his face he
carefully read Goldwater's comments. Then he said, "Well, I never voted for a
Republican before, but I'll be damned if I'm going to do it this time."

He did more than vote. He contributed over $3500 to Goldwater's cam-
paign and was probably personally responsible for the votes of at least one
hundred Democrats who followed him across the party line.

All of this might have happened anyway because the individual involved
was intelligent, was offended by the foreign aid situation, and took more than a
passing interest in politics. We think the fact that a barber came up with the
right supporting information at exactly the right time was the key in this
switching of support.

Members of a Cell Group can be useful in many other ways. They can
prepare a climate of disbelief by suggesting in their everyday conversations
that "your opponent will probably follow a certain course of action or make
certain declarations." By predicting the future action of the opposition, it is
possible to turn what might be a liability into an asset.

In the early spring of 1962 prospects for a Republican victory in a number
of congressional races were bright indeed. The Kennedy administration was
suffering because people were blaming the President for his failure to take
decisive action in regard to communist Cuba.

By mid-summer it seemed obvious the administration would have to take
some positive act to quiet the criticism and to rehabilitate Kennedy's position in
this regard. A few candidates in races across the country timidly advised the
voters to expect some such action. But to my knowledge there was no well
organized effort to attack in advance the credibility of any dramatic last-minute
gesture in regard to Cuba.

In Oregon, where a good Republican candidate, Sig Unander, was challenging Wayne Morse, the polls showed Unander gaining in October and gaining at a rate which, if continued to election day, would bring about a defeat of
Morse.

When President Kennedy dramatically challenged Premier Khrushchev
and ordered the removal of missiles from Cuba, Unander started to slide and
Morse began to gain.

The Kennedy managers had timed their operation perfectly. Senator Keating and others had been warning of the Russian build-up in Cuba since early in the spring of 1962. It is difficult to believe that a single Senator had access to more reliable information than was available to the administration. But a move to halt the build-up of Russian strength in Cuba in May or June would have lost some of its impact by November.

It is my opinion that if Sig Unander had developed a well organized Cell Group in Oregon, he could have disseminated Senator Keating's warning coupled with a prediction to expect dramatic action and taken the edge off the administration's last-minute maneuver.

In that election contest the voters in Oregon supported a Republican for governor but sent Democrat Morse back to the United States Senate. This demonstrates that enough voters in Oregon crossed the party line in 1962 to have made victory possible for Unander. The Oregon voters simply responded to a magnificent political maneuver, to the kind of stimulation that a campaign manager cannot generate completely independent of events, but a stimulus that can be cleverly exploited.

# 10 · *The Foot Soldiers*

THE COMPLEXION of the electorate will vary slightly from state to state but the difference is never more than one of degree. There may be more committed voters in one constituency than in another—there are always enough Indifferents and Undecideds to turn the tide in an election contest.

The campaign manager who understands the make-up of the electorate and what is required to motivate a favorable action will always attempt to arouse the Indifferents.

The candidate must inspire the party faithful; he must radiate confidence he must challenge the opposition; he must please his audience. All this is quite an undertaking. The voter who has seen him personally or heard him speak is more likely to be influenced by that brief personal contact than he is by advertising or literature. But in most constituencies it is physically impossible for a candidate to appear in person before, or to be seen by, more than an insignificant number of the voting population.

Television has increased the opportunities for personal confrontation

Skillful use of this new medium may one day revolutionize the whole field of politics. The candidate may be charming on TV. He may be extremely persuasive. But the members of the indifferent group will most likely be watching "Rawhide" or "Perry Mason" when the candidate is on the channel discussing those issues that will affect the direction of the world.

The mathematics of majority decision are irrefutable. The Indifferents and the Undecideds must be reached; they must be persuaded to vote for your candidate.

When I began managing political campaigns in Arizona in 1938 it was possible for a candidate to meet and shake hands with a high percentage of those who would be qualified to vote for him. Traditional politicians still put great faith in the personal handshake, the quick greeting, the plea: "I hope you'll vote for me."

The candidate's personal appeal for support can be multiplied effectively through the proper use of an especially enlisted group of supporters. These are the foot soldiers. They walk the streets in their own neighborhoods and ask for votes. They do this on a person-to-person basis. They become the candidate's private army, mobilized to do a particular job at a certain time. In my experience a candidate with a properly enlisted group of foot soldiers has never failed to win election.

The purpose of a political campaign can be summed up in one sentence—to address a persuasive request to every registered voter to support your candidate at the polls.

The foot-soldier program is designed to implement that sentence. Because the Indifferents *are* indifferent, the approach to them must be made on a personal basis if that is possible. Some campaign devices or strategies gain their maximum effect by being widely publicized. Having an overflow crowd on hand when the candidate appears indicates popularity and strength. Prominent citizens who declare their support for your candidate attract those who like to follow the leader.

The foot-soldier campaign is particularly effective because it can be organized and used quietly. Usually when the opposition does discover what is going on, it is too late to make an effective counterthrust.

The program permits the enlistment and deployment of a substantial number of workers for an extremely modest allocation of campaign funds. The foot-soldier campaign exerts its maximum influence just before decision day. A similar effort by the opposition might minimize the effect of your foot soldiers; it cannot cancel out their efforts.

The concept is simple; the results obtained are magnificent. It is difficult to understand why the foot-soldier program outlined here or some variation on this theme is not employed by every candidate. The only comparable operation I have ever observed is the almost traditional use of precinct workers to get out the vote on election day.

Many voters complain of the ho-hum deadly similarity between all political campaigns. As the day of decision approaches the differences between the candidates have been clearly defined. The superior virtues of candidate Jones have been spelled out in the newspapers. Jones has been on the radio and on the television asking his fellow citizens to vote for him.

Jones can't knock on every door. It is physically impossible for him to say in person to every voter: "Please vote for me." The next best thing is to send someone to knock on that door on behalf of Jones. If the emissary selected carries the credentials of a neighbor who believes in Jones, who because of this belief is asking *his* neighbor to vote for Jones, the response will be amazing.

"Such a request wouldn't influence me," says a committed member of the Democrat Party, "I know who I'm going to vote for."

"My own mother couldn't change my mind," says the active Republican.

The foot-soldier program isn't calculated to influence anyone who has a firm political conviction. Great caution must be exerted not to stir up political arguments. The foot soldiers are not commissioned to try to convince by logic. Their single assignment is to say: "Mr. Jones is a good man. Please vote for Mr. Jones."

In our complex urbanized society we may not know the name of the man who lives four houses down the street. But if he comes to our door and identifies himself as the man *who lives four houses down the street*, there is an immediate bond between us because we are neighbors. This is the key to the success of the program—the man asking you to vote for Mr. Jones is your neighbor. It is impossible to treat him as a stranger.

In most residential areas such a call would be made under more favorable conditions. If the householders have children in the same school, the chances are good the caller's name will be known. In most cases the caller will not be a stranger. The common concern and mutual interests of people who live in the same neighborhood argues in favor of the foot-soldier program.

Voters living in the same geographical area shop at the same neighborhood grocery store, patronize the same cleaner, buy milk from the same dairy. They may go to the same church or have youngsters in the same Boy Scout troop.

In our lonely society all of us hunger for identification. Most of us instinctively resist the impersonal association. In any crowd we seek to find a familiar face. We want to belong to the group. We feel closest to our own family members. Next we cling to early friendships. But with the exception of the completely dehumanized, stratified society, we respond warmly to the claims of our neighbors.

The foot-soldier program has other aspects to recommend it. People who can be solicited to work for a political candidate are more apt to be extrovert than introvert. The shy and the retiring cannot be drawn into an activist political effort. Usually the people who respond to an appeal for campaign workers are the same people who have been enlisted to make calls for United Fund or the Cancer Society or the Red Cross or the Boy Scouts. This increases the likelihood of their names being known and enhances their credentials as neighbors.

If the solicitor has been instructed properly, he cannot possibly arouse any antagonism. If the person called upon is not strongly committed to one candidate, this personal plea for his vote from a neighbor may be the only truly compelling reason he will have to make a choice between the candidates on election day.

Every successful sales manager instructs his new recruits in this fashion: if you work hard and make enough calls, if you ask enough people to buy, you won't have to worry about making enough sales.

The foot-soldier program, properly organized, will completely blanket a residential area. The plea on behalf of your candidate will be delivered in person to every qualified voter in the precinct or the district.

The size of the task force required for this personal solicitation will vary with the population of the constituency. In the Arizona Goldwater campaign of 1958 we had a few more than 7,000 foot soldiers working their neighborhoods on behalf of Goldwater. In Douglas County, Nebraska, in the Curtis campaign of 1960, Dick Herman had about 3,400 foot soldiers calling for Senator Carl Curtis. In the 1962 Senatorial campaign in Utah, Tom Judd had about 8,000 asking neighbors to support Senator Wallace F. Bennett.

Canvassers are asked to cover the houses on their side of the street in their block. They are instructed not to engage in arguments; not to discuss their candidate in contrast to his opponent. Their task is to knock on the door of their neighbor's home, hand out a peice of especially prepared literature and as *neighbor* ask their *neighbor* to vote for the candidate.

People who respond to an appeal for volunteer workers always intend to carry out their commitment. The campaign manager must help them avoid the great temptation to procrastinate. The instructions are to make the calls sometime in the five-day period before election day. This deadline is helpful but to inject a still further element of accountability, we have always included a postal report card in the packet of literature distributed to the workers.

The number of houses to a block will vary. In the 1958 Goldwater campaign we estimated that our 7,000 neighbors made an average of eight calls each. 56,000 pieces of literature were distributed in the five-day period before election Tuesday. If 70 per cent of those contacted were committed voters, we still reached 16,800 who might have been undecided or indifferent.

If each canvasser secured an average of only one favorable vote, the total is still impressive: 7,000 neighbors votes, plus the certain vote of the worker, amounts to 14,000 votes for Goldwater in an election which was won by a majority of only 35,000. Almost one-half of this victory could have been produced by this single volunteer effort.

When the project was first started I questioned seriously our ability to enlist enough volunteers to make the house calls. When the volunteers had actually been enlisted and the literature was being prepared for distribution, I was still skeptical. The instruction sheet with each packet suggested that when the canvassing had been completed, the worker should estimate whether the response was favorable or unfavorable and forward to us his opinion on the postal report card. But I was impatient.

The third day after the packets of literature had been delivered I selected a list of volunteers at random. I limited my choice to those precincts which by tradition had gone overwhelmingly to the Democrat Party candidate. One of these precincts surrounds the State Capitol. The homes are modest but well cared for. Many of the people in the neighborhood work for the state government in various capacities. Goldwater's opponent was the incumbent Democrat governor.

When I set out to call on the volunteers to get their personal reaction, I was still unconvinced the device would be successful. At my first stop I introduced myself to an extremely articulate member of a minority group. I told him I wasn't trying to find out which of his neighbors were going to vote for Goldwater. I just wanted to know what the general reaction had been.

"Very good, very good," he said, "most of the people I talked to on this block are going to vote for Barry."

Partisans are frequently incapable of objective judgment. Obviously this man wanted Goldwater to win. The thought flashed through my mind that perhaps I was being told something the volunteer thought I wanted to hear.

I made seven more calls before lunch. In every case the reaction was the same. One dear lady responded to my question in a whisper: "Oh, I can't tell you how my neighbors are going to vote. They all work down there for Mr McFarland," she said, nodding toward the Capitol, "but you tell Mr. Goldwater it's all right."

It was all right. We carried a number of very doubtful precincts and got a much higher vote in the rest of them than any Republican had ever enjoyed before. I was convinced.

The foot soldiers are all recruited on the telephone. To implement this neighbor-calling-on-neighbor campaign the first step is to get an accurate map of the area to be covered. Count the blocks. This will give you the number of volunteers needed and will determine the number of telephones required. I use the word *telephones* rather than *telephone callers* because it is impossible for one girl to work constantly eight hours a day.

If the map reveals there are 5,000 blocks to be covered, 5,000 canvassers will be required. One telephone can solicit approximately thirty canvassers per day. Thirty divided into 5,000 is 166.6—the number of days it would take to solicit the needed workers with one telephone.

If the manager elects to allocate twenty calling days to enlist his workers he will need 8.3 telephones. To be safe he should order ten and then man the telephone room with fifteen experienced operators and at least three supervisors. Working twenty or thirty minute shifts, the girls will retain their charm and poise no matter how many "not at homes" or wrong numbers they encounter. And your telephone girl's voice must be warm, friendly and cheerful. We have always used professional operators and paid them for the work.

Volunteers can look up names and telephone numbers, bring coffee and assemble and deliver packets. Preparing the list of names to be called will usually take longer then the actual calling and this work can be commenced thirty or forty days before the telephones are put to work.

The operators must be carefully trained—cautioned never to depart from the established solicitation speech. Professional operators will complete their calls in the time allotted. They will refrain from engaging in any conversation not indicated. They can be counted upon to retreat gracefully without offending if the request for help is refused.

The request, to be successful, must be made in the name of the candidate.

"Mrs. Jones, this is Mary Brown. (The telephone operator should use her correct name.) I'm calling for Senator Robert Maxwell. Would you be willing to help in his campaign for re-election?"

Another form which has worked well for us:

"Mrs. Jones, this is Nina Gleeson. I'm calling for Senator Robert Maxwell. He asked me to *ask you* to help him in his campaign. Would you be willing to do that for him?"

If the person called expresses annoyance, reluctance, or indicates a non-receptive attitude, the call is terminated. If the person called indicates a desire to comply with the Senator's request but expresses inability to do so, the operator says: "Mrs. Jones, I know Senator Maxwell will understand. Thank you very much."

The type of response from each person called should be recorded on the name and number list. If it is hostile, there is a chance the party precinct worker might be able to iron out the difficulty. If it is warm and friendly but for some valid reason a non-volunteer, the name should go to the precinct organization or to whoever is responsible for getting out the favorable votes.

If the person called is receptive and asks what he or she can do to help the candidate, the operator replies: "Bob wants you to call on your neighbors . . . just the people who live in your block on your side of the street . . . and ask them to vote for him. Could you do that, Mrs. Jones?"

If the response is affirmative, further instructions are given: "Thank you very much, Mrs. Jones. We will deliver a packet of literature to your house on such-and-such a date. (This should be the Tuesday before election day.) Your packet will contain your identification, a letter of instruction and a little pamphlet about Maxwell. What he wants you to do is to visit the neighbors in your block. Bob knows that when you tell your neighbors you are going to vote for him and ask them to vote for him, it will really help."

There may be another thirty seconds of conversation before the operator can conclude with: "Bob will be very pleased and very grateful when I tell him you are going to help us, Mrs. Jones. Thank you."

In some cases it may be impossible to enlist a recruit in every block. When this happens it is necessary to ask someone to travel a block or two from his own home to make the calls. But the volunteers must be recruited from an adjacent street if they are to achieve the desired identification with the people whom they will solicit.

In 1960 Dick Herman thought the foot soldier program might be particularly beneficial in South Omaha—a territory which so far as anyone could remember had never voted Republican.

We anticipated there might be difficulty in enlisting enough volunteers to carry out the project. Registered Democrats outnumbered the Republicans in this area by about three to one.

Herman established his headquarters for the telephone lines in a downtown hotel. He employed professional operators with telephone experience. In the first two weeks Herman's girls called every registered Republican in the target area. The results were encouraging but we were still far short of full recruitment.

The contribution Dick Herman made to this procedure came about after he had exhausted his list of Republicans in the area of solicitation.

"I still need about five hundred workers," Dick told me on the telephone, "and I want to try random calls to the people who live in the neighborhoods where we do not now have a volunteer."

"But they will all be Democrats," I protested.

"I know they will," he told me, "but let's try it for one day. If we get a bad reaction, we'll stop. If the reaction isn't too antagonistic and we pick up some workers, we'll continue."

The results amazed both of us. The number of antagonistic responses was about the same as he had experienced when calling selected Republicans. The number of workers enlisted was about the same.

To confirm the telephone commitment requires prompt action. The volunteer's name and address, with the acceptance verified by the initials of the telephone operator, must move immediately to the mail room. Here a letter of confirmation ending with the personal signature of the candidate is prepared and mailed immediately. The letter should strive to enhance the personal relationship between the cause of the candidate and the volunteer.

"Dear Mrs. Jones: Nina Gleeson has told me that you are going to help us. I am truly grateful and greatly encouraged by your willingness to be an active worker in my campaign.

"The packet of literature Nina told you about will be delivered on such-and-such a date. Mrs. Brunson, who lives not too far from you, will bring it to your house . . . Gratefully yours, Bob."

"Nina Gleeson has told me you are going to help" . . . this is confirmation of a personal commitment on a personal basis. "Mrs. Brunson will bring the packet. She lives not too far from you" . . . you are really joining your neighbors in this effort, Mrs. Jones, and don't worry—if you still have some questions, Mrs. Brunson can answer them when she calls.

Now someone is going to make a personal contact, someone who knows that you, Mrs. Jones, told Nina Gleeson that you would work for Bob. Nina told Bob that you said you would work for him. Bob has told Mrs. Brunson that you said you were going to work for him. If you were just trying to be nice to that girl on the telephone and don't really want to help in the campaign, it's too late now, isn't it?

If funds are available, enthusiasm can be further stimulated by including an autographed photograph of the candidate with the letter of confirmation. High quality photographs, complete with signature, can be reproduced by various printing processes quite inexpensively.

On the wall at telephone headquarters there should be a detailed map, one that shows all the streets in the area to be covered. Colored pins on the map will indicate where the volunteers have been solicited. The area should be divided into a comfortable geographical section for the distribution of the packets. A volunteer captain is assigned to each district.

The name of the volunteer solicited is printed or typed on the packet. We have found commercial nine by twelve envelopes suitable for this purpose.

The packet must contain an identification badge or name tag. This strengthens the volunteer's sense of commitment. A printed instruction sheet to inform Mrs. Jones precisely what she is expected to do and enough pamphlets to cover the estimated number of houses in the block are included.

*Don't* put in a few extra pamphlets. Your volunteers will probably fail to connect with two or three of the householders assigned to their area, and two or three unused pamphlets in each packet can result in a lot of wasted printing.

The instruction sheet is a review of everything we have discussed here. The volunteer is admonished not to engage in any arguments—never to mention the name of the opposition candidate or to speak critically of anyone in the opposition. Then a sample solicitation is outlined:

1. To be used if you know your neighbors on a first-name basis:

"Good morning, Helen, I'm out working for United States Senator Robert Maxwell. He's a good man and I think we need him in the Senate. I hope you and Bill will vote for him. Please read this pamphlet and show it to Bill when he comes home."

2. If the neighbor's name is not known:

"Good morning, I'm Mary Jones. I live at 1012 Elm Street. I'm a volunteer out working for United States Senator Robert Maxwell. He's a good man and I think we need him in the Senate. I'm going to vote for him and I hope you and your husband will, too. Won't you please read this pamphlet? It tells all about Senator Maxwell."

I have explained the neighbors' organization to a dozen different campaign managers. Someone always says: "Why should they vote for a candidate just because their neighbor is voting that way? What kind of a reason is that to choose a United States Senator?"

It is a very good reason indeed—for someone who is not firmly committed to either candidate. If they don't have any strong convictions, the fact that their neighbor has volunteered to solicit votes for Robert Maxwell will provide them with a sort of second-hand personal identification with the candidate himself. If they know the neighbor who is doing the soliciting, their regard and respect for the neighbor becomes an additional reason. If they don't know the neighbor, the fact of their geographical nearness lends strength to the request.

And what about the pamphlet, what does it say? That Senator Maxwell is an expert on atomic energy or has served with distinction on a foreign relations committee or is a member of the Republican Policy Committee? Not by a jugful.

The pamphlet is titled *Neighbors for Maxwell*. The layout is simple. There are pictures of the candidate in a homey atmosphere, pictures of the candidate's wife, pictures of the candidate's children. If the candidate had a humble beginning, it is probable the pictures were taken with the candidate standing on the front porch of his old home. The text emphasizes that neighbors should be for Robert Maxwell because he is a good man who believes in the American family, puts his faith in Almighty God, loves his country and works hard. Corny? Emotional? Yes, indeed.

The great issues of our time absorb the interest of those who are politically sophisticated. Traditional party loyalty will prompt a majority of voters to stay within their own lines. But the undecided voter, the citizen who pays scant attention to the political wars, who is inclined to think that "his vote doesn't count very much anyway," can be motivated to respond to the kind of appeal we are discussing here by an emphasis on those qualities which would make the candidate a good and desirable resident of the neighborhood.

Results which can be readily verified from a foot soldier operation in campaign after campaign argue that when the issues are complex and the competition between candidates is bitter, there is room for simplicity, for neighbor-to-neighbor appeal.

# 11 · *Public Opinion Polls*

PUBLIC OPINION SAMPLINGS that attempt to predict the winner in an election contest are utterly useless to a candidate and an unnecessary waste of money. Unfortunately, most candidates are suckers for the crystal ball gazers. There is no real way to tell what impact they are making upon the public so they seek solace in the popularity poll.

Practitioners of the polling art have built a great temple of socio-scientific logic. The only poll that counts is the one taken in the voting booth on election day.

The elaborate apparatus that surrounds the scientific counting of the public pulse demands weighted samples, geographical distribution and expert computation of the results. Those of us old enough to remember the Literary Digest poll will have good reason to question the infallibility of Dr. Gallup and his legion of imitators.

The poll takers don't guarantee their predictions will come true. They frequently claim an accuracy of two or three per cent. But there is a sophistry in this claim. If they predict 52 per cent of the vote and candidate Jones only gets 49½ per cent of the vote, the error is described as being 2½ per cent and, from one viewpoint, this is a logical and honest contention. But if the 2½ per cent Jones didn't get is given to Smith, Jones' opponent, the total error comes to five per cent of the voting population and many elections are decided by less than five per cent. Witness the less than 200,000 vote difference in the popular support between candidate Nixon and candidate Kennedy.

The position polls are usually announced by the candidate who is ahead, the theory being that some of the undecided voters will want to join the winner. Numerous imponderables defy prediction. How many citizens will go to the polls? Will bad weather keep a substantial percentage of the people from voting? What about the calculated, last-minute charge of one candidate or the other? Will a national crisis such as the announcement that Russian missiles had been established in Cuba affect the outcome?

Assume the polls are accurate, your candidate is behind and is going to lose the election. Will this permit you to abandon your efforts and concede victory? Of course not.

Newspapers, radio stations and other organizations that derive profit from probing the public mind will, in most cases, sponsor the popularity polls. It is hoped publishing or announcing the results will increase circulation or enlarge an audience. A candidate, his manager and the campaign staff will find more productive ways to spend the money at their disposal.

The position polls, if the sampling is accurate, reflect relative strength and reveal any change that has occurred in the public mind during the weeks of the campaign. So far as the outcome of the election is concerned, it doesn't matter what percentage of popularity your candidate enjoys at the start of the campaign. Such a flat statement must be qualified, of course. If your candidate has no popularity, he shouldn't be in the contest to begin with. The information that will be useful to the campaign management team is to be found in the improvement or deterioration of your candidate's popularity. The candidate who is gaining in public favor always has the possibility of victory. The candidate who is losing public favor will probably be defeated. In any case, both candidates will campaign as vigorously as possible right up to election day. And the advance reports predicting triumph or disaster must be regarded as nothing more than a kind of crystal ball gazing.

The campaign manager with victory on his mind will solicit the public's opinion of his candidate. But the questions asked will be calculated to provide answers helpful to the conduct of the campaign.

In the 1960 presidential contest the pollsters working for candidate Kennedy brought in the information that Kennedy's youthful appearance was a liability. JFK immediately changed the style of his haircut, adopted a more conservative dress and deliberately attempted to appear older and more mature.

The kind of public opinion sampling that enables a candidate to change his attack or alter his strategy or aim at the principal concern of his constituent will pay off on election day.

There are two general areas where, in my experience, public opinion sampling should be an essential part of campaign planning:

Question One has to do with the image of the candidate.

Question Two has to do with identifying the major concerns of the constituency.

Sampling public opinion of the voters to determine the profile of your candidate as he is seen by those who will vote for or against him can be completed during the first few weeks of the campaign.

Professional poll takers interpret the results of their interviews in accordance with a formula based upon the population of the constituency, the occupation, economic status, education, age and residence of the person interviewed. If there are ten times as many brick layers in the constituency as there are doctors, the opinion of one brick layer will count ten times as much as the opinion of one doctor.

The allocation of values in taking a weighted sample requires the service of an expert. In performing their work, most of these professional groups actually sample only a very few opinions and then, by projection, formulate their report. But the divisions of society which do very well to provide a weighted sample for determining, let us say, the public's attitude toward Plymouth automobiles, do not operate with such inexorable force when the question is political. For the purpose of determining the candidate's image, a mass sampling, which can be done quite inexpensively, will produce satisfactory results. I have used the professional poll takers in some cases; I have a great respect for their ability. But a simple questionnaire such as the one illustrated on these pages, widely distributed, will provide an accurate reflection of the public's attitude toward your candidate.

The questionnaire can be printed on inexpensive paper with ample room for the respondent to answer those questions which are not multiple choice. The method for distributing and collecting this sample must guarantee the respondent's anonymity.

The type of questionnaire we are examining is one that I have used in numerous campaigns with only slight alteration to fit a particular candidate. The answer part of the sheet is always folded inside and if locked ballot boxes are provided for deposit of the completed questionnaire, the problem of maintaining anonymity is resolved.

## GOOD GOVERNMENT SURVEY

You are being asked to help with this survey because your opinions are vital to good government. As a voter you are a participant in every political decision. Your viewpoint on matters of public interest, on national and local issues, on the selection and performance of a public official, is important.

As a knowledgeable citizen you are being asked to register your judgment, to give your opinion of _____ (name of candidate) _____ . Please be frank. Your opinions will be correlated with those expressed by other thoughtful citizens of our state. PLEASE DO NOT PUT YOUR NAME AND ADDRESS ON THIS SHEET.

### OCCUPATION

Those who will eventually evaluate these reports do not want to know your name and address. It will be helpful if they can have some information about you.

Employed in trade or business _____

Owner or manager of business _____

Employed in industry _____

Owner or manager of industrial operation _____

Professional _____

Wheat farmer _____

Livestock farmer _____

Farm owner _____

Farm operator _____

Farm worker _____

#### RESIDENCE

If you live in town or city, please put the population _____

Live on farm _____ Home owner _____ Home renter_____

#### AGE BRACKET

20–30_____30–40_____40–50_____50–60_____

When you have finished filling out this form, will you please deposit the completed form in the locked ballot box?

1. Do you know Senator_____(last name)_____?

    a. Do you know him personally? _____

    b. Have you met him once or twice? _____

    c. Have you seen him but never met him? _____

    d. Have you never seen or met him? _____

    e. Have you never heard of him? _____

2. Would you please write on the following lines either a ten word description or the adjectives which you feel best illustrate Senator_____(last name)_____'s performance as a member of the United States Senate?

3. Which of the following words would you select as most descriptive of Sen ator_____ (last name)_____ ?

    Friendly _____ Intelligent _____ Considerate _____
    Young _____ Vigorous _____ Courageous _____ Skillful _____ Cautiou[s]
    _____ Determined _____ Experienced _____ Conservative _____ Lib eral _____

4. If you were asked to put five words together to describe Senator (las[t] name)_____ 's outstanding characteristics or abilities, which five would yo[u] use?

5. Which particular phase of (name)_____ 's service in the Congress, is, to you[r] mind, the most valuable and appealing to the people of (name of state) ?[*]

    a. His work in behalf of _(name of state)_____ in securing projects etc. _____
    b. The prompt attention he gives to every problem presented to him b[y] the people of (name of state)_____
    c. His work in the Foreign Relations Committee _____
    d. His work on the Senate Labor Rackets Committee _____
    e. His constant defense of the freedom of the individual and the preserva[-] tion of those moral standards which we have inherited from our re ligious background. _____

6. Do you believe the people of (name of state)_____ associate Senato[r] (last name)_____ most closely with:

    Wheat farmers _____ Beef farmers _____ Dairy farmers _____ Busines[s] groups _____ RTA Co-operatives _____ School teachers _____?[*2]

7. Do you believe the people of (name of state) regard (first and last name as a:

    Strong advocate of economy _____ As a spender _____ As a middle-of-the roader _____ As a conservative defender of constitutional rights _____?

8. Do you believe the people of (name of state) would rate (first & last name as:

    Pro-labor union bosses _____ Anti-labor union bosses _____ One who de mands justice for all segments and individuals _____?

9. Do you believe the people of (name of state) would rate Senator _____ as:

---

[*1] *Name the committee assignments which have earned the Senator recognition.*
[*2] *These categories illustrate what might be used in a farm state. Forms should be altered to satisf[y]* *the population-occupational demands of the Senator's state.*

A representative of a special segment of the state population ____?

0. Would you describe the qualities which you believe are (first and last ame) 's greatest assets?

_____

_____

1. Would you put down the qualities which you believe are (first & last name) _____'s greatest liabilities?

_____

_____

The questionnaire may be headed *Good Government Survey, Citizenhip Opinion,* or *Voters' Viewpoint.*

Please note the first paragraphs:

You are being asked to help with this survey because your opinions are vital to good government. As a voter you are a participant in every political decision. Your viewpoint on matters of public interest, on national and local issues, on the selection and performance of a public official, is important.

As a knowledgeable citizen you are being asked to register your judgment, to give your opinion of _____ (Insert name of candidate.) Please be frank. Your opinions will be correlated with those expressed by other thoughtful citizens of our state. PLEASE DO NOT PUT YOUR NAME AND ADDRESS ON THIS SHEET.

Now what have we done? We have expressed our admiration for the hinking and opinions of the respondent; we have suggested it is his duty as a itizen to register his opinion. We have guaranteed that he will remain anonyous.

Under the heading *Occupation* we have asked some questions about the nan whose opinions we are going to consider, but nothing on this part of the orm could lead to identification of the individual. "Those who will eventually valuate these reports do not want to know your name and address. It will be elpful if they can have some information about you."

Question One with its five subdivisions is designed to permit the campaign nanager to discover what percentage of the general public is acquainted with he candidate. It was Section E of this question which produced the shocking nformation that more than 30 per cent of the people in Nebraska who filled ut the questionnaire had never even heard of their present United States enator Carl Curtis.

Questions Two and Three are probably a little unfair. Question Three uggests words which might be included in the answers to Question Two. But nyone opposed to your candidate will choose his own words. If you can prod he Undecided to associate good words with your candidate, so much the etter.

Question Five can prompt some particularly revealing answers. Sub-question C is a plant—the Senator was not a member of the Senate Foreign Relations Committee. Anyone who picked this as his most valuable work was revealed as someone who didn't know much about the Senator.

Questions Ten and Eleven are particularly important. If Ten is answered and Eleven ignored, chances are good the respondent is a stalwart supporter of your candidate. Conversely, if Eleven is answered and Ten is ignored, the questionnaire was probably filled out by a member of the opposition. When both questions are answered and the qualities mentioned can be recognized as being among the assets or liabilities of your candidate, you are probably considering the opinions of a thoughtful, well informed voter.

What the campaign management is striving for with this type of questionnaire is a mass reflection from a mass audience. There is, however, an additional benefit. If the voters can be prompted to consider the good qualities of your candidate and his past performance, the impression gained will probably be a favorable one.

Similar questionnaires should be prepared and distributed to solicit an evaluation of your candidate's opponent. When the results of these two surveys are placed side by side, the task of finding the major differences, identifying the blacks and the whites, becomes an easy one.

In rural communities it is often possible to enlist the assistance of the editor of a weekly newspaper. Americans like to answer questions, particularly questions about politics. If your questionnaire is fair, if both candidates are treated impartially, widespread circulation can be obtained.

In several campaigns we have had as many as 20 per cent of the voting population respond to this type of questionnaire. A man or woman who is willing to spend five minutes recording his or her opinions of a candidate has moved several steps closer to commitment.

Each respondent is required to give some thought to the questions and more thought to formulating the answers. If the answers are favorable to your candidate, this is beneficial. A voter who has expressed a favorable opinion on the questionnaire will be inclined to vote for your candidate.

The questionnaires may reveal that your man is better known in one area of the constituency than in another. This provides the campaign management with an opportunity to correct the situation well in advance of election day. It may be that your candidate is better known to one class or group of respondents than to another—better known let us say to the farmers than to the city people. And again this information can help the management guide the candidate to victory.

One more benefit from this type of poll deserves to be mentioned. The average American is flattered when asked to give his opinion on any subject. Many people are skeptical of the Gallup poll because they have never met anyone who was interviewed by a Gallup pollster. The mass distribution of the profile questionnaire will enhance any statement your candidate wants to make at a later date. On controversial issues where the electorate is genuinely di-ded, your candidate can strengthen his position by the argument that the ajority of the voters support his position. How does he know this? He has en sampling voter opinion.

The second phase of public opinion sampling concerns the identification of portant issues. Experience in a number of campaigns indicates that this ngle function is perhaps the most important of all aspects of campaign man-ement. If carried out successfully, the results of such a survey will enable ur candidate to speak directly to the issues of greatest concern in the minds the people he is trying to reach.

The purpose of this type of survey is not to find out whether a majority of e people favor one side or the other of an issue. Such a determination would quire a very accurate polling apparatus. No candidate can hope to be on the pular side of every issue although many try to do so. And their antics of mping frantically back and forth invariably convict them of insincerity.

The problem is a simple one. The eople in County X are concerned about e Cuban crisis. Some think we should invade Cuba and depose Castro by rce. Others think we should avoid war but recognize the danger in the ntinuation of Castro's government. Your candidate has an understanding of e Cuban situation. The people may not agree with the solution he offers but ey will retain a favorable impression; they will listen to what he has to say cause of their concern over Cuba.

Let's assume that the major industry in one large area is growing peanuts. another area the major concern is for a deep water harbor. If your candidate scusses the prospects of a deep water harbor before a penaut-minded audi-ce, they won't be interested or impressed by what he says. If your candidate scusses peanuts before a deep water harbor-minded audience, no one will me away from the meeting with a conviction that your candidate is fit aterial to hold public office.

Now let's reverse the situation. Your candidate comes to the peanut-inded county, discusses the problems of growing peanuts, exhibits an under-anding, and then suggests there is a grave danger in becoming a single onomy community, that perhaps the difficulties the peanut growers have en experiencing indicates they might better grow alfalfa or potatoes. His ews may be contrary to the popular concept but the fact that he addressed s remarks to the major concern of the community will qualify him in the inds of many voters as a candidate who is on his toes, who has taken the ouble to be informed. And this impression will persist long after the actual ntent of the speech is forgotten.

Voters do not require that candidates agree with them. They do insist at candidates recognize and appreciate their fears and their problems and dicate some understanding of those problems and fears.

In one of the many campaigns I have helped to manage, the candidate and s staff stubbornly denied there was anything to be gained by what I call the ssue Questionnaire." The candidate was an ardent golfer and I knew it. After minutes discussing other subjects, I switched the conversation to golf. I

happened to have my putter with me. Clubs can be rented at almost any go
golf course but a putter is a purely personal weapon. I engaged the candida
in a discussion of the problems of putting. I had him show me his stance, ther
deliberately picked it to pieces—he was too erect, his grip was wrong, l
stance was awkward—and with each critical suggestion I cited some gre
golfing authority. Then I dropped a couple of golf balls on the hotel roc
carpet, suggested the candidate try putting my way. He spent five minut
absolutely absorbed with the problems attendant on trying to knock that g
ball into a glass at the other edge of the carpet. After this exercise we return
to politics and sometime later I deliberately switched the conversation to
discussion of the fine points of quarter horses. The candidate had spent most
his life in a city and while he could recognize a horse as being different from
Mercedes-Benz, this was about the extent of his knowledge. He very prompt
lost interest in the conversation and turned to something else. Then I made n
point.

"When we were talking about golf," I said, "you were eager to listen. Y
didn't agree with anything I said but you listened because your were inte
ested. When I started talking about horses, you refused even to carry on tl
conversation. When you are touring this state, you'd better talk about som
thing in which the voters are interested or they'll give up on you the way y
gave up on the horses."

The suggestion that there is a need to seek assistance in determining tl
major issues in a campaign will invariably be rejected by the old pros. Th
will argue, and with some measure of authority, that the real issues are tho
matters under discussion in the public press. This may be valid from a coi
pletely national point of view. But elections are won in the precincts and tl
districts and concerns do vary.

In the 1958 Arizona campaign the nation was suffering from widespre:
unemployment. The news magazines and even the local press were filled wi
stories concerning this problem. But with the exception of three localitie
unemployment was not an issue in Arizona.

The candidate who wants to be heard by the voter must speak of tl
issues which concern the voter. To do this he must, in the vernacular, "kno
what it is that's bugging the voters."

The kind of public opinion sampling necessary to determining the issu
must be conducted on a continuing basis. The public passion is constant
changing and in a well-organized campaign effort the Cell Group organizatio:
is a made-to-order apparatus for this kind of survey.

The procedure is not complicated or expensive and it works. Two copies
the issue questionnaire are sent to each member to solicit the opinions of som
one who is not a member of the Cell Group with instructions to register h
opinions of his social or economic circle on the second form.

The letter requesting this assistance can strengthen the sense of impo
tance which the manager has given to the Cell Group member. Soliciting tl

cond opinion provides the Cell Group member with a project which makes
m an active participant in the campaign.

* The sample used in this chapter is from the 1958 Arizona campaign. We
inted the questionnaires two-up on an 8½" x 14" sheet of paper. The cost of
uplication either by mimeograph or multilith is almost negligible, and the
ed-back was extremely valuable.

Over the fifteen months of that campaign effort, in every issue list we sent
it we included "more water for Arizona." Arizona is a reclamation state. In a
ery real sense, the economic well-being of all the residents is dependent upon
1 adequate supply of stored water.

ARIZONA'S WATER PROBLEMS WERE NEVER SELECTED AS
HE PARAMOUNT ISSUE BY THOSE WE POLLED.

Our advertising experts estimated Goldwater's opponent in that campaign
ent at least $25,000 on magnificent television spots which identified him as
e champion who had helped bring water to Arizona. The segments were
eautifully prepared, convincing and informative. That money was wasted.
he people of Arizona in 1958 were not concerned about water.

Nebraska is a farm state. Corps under the programs of the Agricultural
tabilization Act provide a major share of the state's income. It would be en-
rely reasonable to anticipate that the voters in Nebraska would indicate great
oncern over the various proposals lumped together as the "farm program."

In 1960 this issue was never number one in the minds of the people in
ebraska. The issue survey clearly indicated the voters of that state were more
iterested in other problems. The knowledge permitted U.S. Senator Carl
urtis to concentrate on those issues which were the primary concerns of his
onstituency. There was no need either to attack or defend the many compli-
ated aspects of the federal agricultural legislation.

This type of public opinion sampling is obviously not as accurate as one
onducted by personal interview and then computed on the basis of a weighted
imple. If the questionnaire had been sent only to members of the Cell Group,
e answers might have been distorted. The use of the second questionnaire
revented this. And for the purposes of a campaign, the method described is
itisfactory.

The interpretation of a survey can be done by any clerical worker. The
sues are rated in order of importance as the respondent views the questions.
he ratings are transferred to a master sheet; then it is necessary only to total
e figures to determine the number one issue. The lowest total would be
Jumber One, the next Number Two, etc.

After three or four samplings have been made, a consistent pattern will
merge. It is usually possible to find an impressive black and white difference
etween the position of your candidate and the position of the opposition on
hese issues which are of greatest concern to the voter.

The importance of candidate identification with the over-riding issues can

* See page 313.

easily be illustrated by a review of the Roosevelt campaign, the Eisenhowe
campaign and the Kennedy campaign.

The issue of the great depression was given to Roosevelt, but he exploite
it. In almost every speech, every statement, every news conference, both a
candidate and President, FDR promised action to alleviate the symptoms o
the depression—"freedom from fear," "freedom from want." His constant a
tack on economic royalists, his numerous alphabetical agencies all made Roose
velt the solid champion of the poor working man and the unemployed.

The war issue in 1940 and again in '44 were handed to Roosevelt but h
exploited them beautifully.

In 1952, the Korean War was the over-riding issue. Stevenson's beautifu
speeches dealing with an abstract political philosophy lacked the sharp cuttin
edge of Eisenhower's statement: "I will go to Korea."

The Nixon-Kennedy contest provides a particularly productive subject fo
study. Senator Kennedy was a regional candidate. He was not a giant in th
Senate. Except for those few moments at the '56 convention in Chicago whe
he was mentioned for Vice President, Kennedy was unknown nationally.

Theodore White's book: "The Making of a President" reveals that follow
ing that convention in 1956, Kennedy recruited a staff of able, political techn
cians and set out to capture the 1960 nomination. The Democrats had fou
possibilities—Stevenson, Humphrey, Johnson and Kennedy. Humphrey wa
better known than Kennedy. Johnson had powerful support as the Majorit
Leader of the Senate and Stevenson was still the darling of Mrs. Eleano
Roosevelt and the controlling wing of the existing Democrat Party.

The Kennedy strategy was geared, first, to "going where the ducks are
and, second, to building an image—youth and vigor—which would place th
other aspirants at a great disadvantage.

The Kennedy campaign was almost silent and by its silence gained effec
tiveness. Kennedy won Wisconsin with organization, money, charm and a bet
ter understanding of the concerns of the Wisconsin constituency.

Kennedy's victory in West Virginia was a foregone conclusion. His publi
cists deliberately built it up into a major contest knowing their candidate woul
win. And what did Kennedy talk about in West Virginia? The problem o
unemployment. He pre-empted the subject. Everything Humphrey sai
sounded like an echo. The Kennedy team out-smarted all the rest.

In 1960 there was great public concern over the emergence of Castro i
Cuba. Kennedy had described Castro in one of his books as a patriot compar
able to Simon Bolivar. The liberals had supported Castro's revolution an
helped to finance Batista's downfall. Kennedy was extremely vulnerable on th
Cuban issue. He turned this into an asset by challenging Nixon; the Republica
candidate was forced to make a rather weak defense of the Eisenhower policy.

When Nixon, during the debates, conceded that as a Republican presi
dential candidate he would endorse all the goals enunciated by Kennedy, h
virtually removed the issues and reduced the 1960 election to a personalit
contest.

The kindest thing which can be said about the Nixon campaign is that it
.cked direction. There was no recognizable head. When Nixon met with Rock-
feller in New York to discuss the Republican platform, his campaign manager,
.en Hall, didn't even know the meeting was scheduled. When the first reports
ame to Chicago, Hall was furious. It is difficult to say who really managed the
Iixon campaign. Bob Finch had some limited authority. Len Hall had to
ccept public responsibility for the fiasco. But Arthur Flemming and Attorney
-eneral Rogers are credited by insiders with Nixon's endorsement of welfare
ate proposals.

To those of us who were trying desperately to win the election for Nixon,
 was painfully apparent that our candidate did not have an overriding strat-
gy and had not selected the issues upon which to build a continuing theme.

When Nixon's advance man came to Arizona he met with 30 or 40 party
.aders to arrange for the Vice President's visit. At one point he asked: "What
o you think Mr. Nixon should talk about? The Arizona water problem?"

When someone suggested the people of Arizona would be more interested
 hearing Nixon's proposals for defeating communism, remedying the Cuban
ituation and correcting our deficit balance of payments, Nixon's man said:
They care about those things way out here?!"

Nixon did come to Arizona and he made a fighting speech. Many of us
.ho heard it believe that if he had spoken in the same manner before audi-
nces in every section of the country, he would have been an easy winner.

In the '60 election it was so difficult for the voters to find any clear black
nd white differences between Kennedy and Nixon, they were almost com-
·elled to rest their decision on such unimportant things as the candidate's
·elatives' appearance on television.

It has been argued that Nixon's illness at the start of the campaign was a
'ability from which he never quite recovered. The truth is that the lack of a
.entral theme, the campaign's refusal to concentrate on the really important
:sues, coupled with Nixon's quixotic promise to visit every state, made it im-
·ossible to bring the campaign to a peak before election day.

Both private and public polls indicated that Nixon was gaining. Numerous
·rojections indicate that, had the election been held the *third* Tuesday in that
November, Nixon would have been the victor.

The Indifferents and the Undecideds who determine the outcome of every
·lection are fickle. The winning candidate must conduct a campaign which will
·ut him *first* in the affections of this group on election day, not 10 days before,
.ot 10 days after.

## Sample *ISSUE QUESTIONNAIRE*

You and I as responsible citizens are required to think about the
future. We are concerned with the great problems of our day. On this
sheet we have listed six of those concerns. Will you help me determine
which is most important in your mind and in the minds of your fellow
citizens by rating these issues in their order of importance?

Please study the list. Ask the advice of a trusted friend if you lik▎ Then number the list from "1" to "6" giving a rating of "1" to the issu▎ which you believe to be most important and "6" to the least importan▎ Please try to make your ratings reflect the thinking of your community.

Gratefully your▎

s/    Bob

☐ Unemployment and the recession.

☐ Federal aid to education.

☐ National defense and the Russian activities in space.

☐ Additional water for Arizona.

☐ The threat of world communism.

☐ The right-to-work law.

# 12 · Direct Mail

IT IS GENERALLY AGREED the most effective solicitation for votes takes plac▎ when a candidate grasps the voter's hand with a warm and friendly grip an▎ says "Please vote for me." Because it is impossible today for any candidate t▎ shake the hand of every constituent, political campaigns must utilize ever▎ advertising medium known to man.

The only legitimate objective of political advertising is to extend the im▎ pact of the candidate's personality and political philosophy. Virtually ever▎ candidate for political office uses some kind of direct mailing piece to solic▎ votes. In the season of politics the average householder will receive from two t▎ twenty pieces of such mail—political circulars, letters, post cards, stickers, but▎ tons and pot-holders. Most of this sizable effort is wasted.

Direct mail is effective only when it can be an extension of the candidate▎ Unless your mailing piece carries something of the impact of a personal solic▎ tation, it will probably be overlooked between a beautiful and almost irresisti▎

e appeal to join the book-of-the-month club and a four-color brochure extol-
ıg the virtues of the latest Detroit product.

The businesses of this nation that sell millions of dollars worth of mer-
ıandise through the use of direct mail are satisfied when three out of every 100
tters produce a sale. The politicians of my acquaintance naively expect every
ıter eagerly to read their mailing pieces and unanimously accept and approve
ıe claims made for the candidates.

Newspapers, television and radio are truly mass media. Some slight selec-
vity can be found as to audience in specialized publications such as the
urnals that are house organs for the well organized minorities. But for the
ost part, the political ad on television or radio or in a metropolitan newspaper
ınnot be aimed at any particular segment of the voting population. Presenta-
ın in the mass media calls for the shotgun approach. Direct mail can be
med like a rifle at a specific target. Because of this selectivity, direct mail in a
ılitical campaign can be far more productive. Planning and preparing politi-
ıl direct mail is no job for an amateur. But even the most experienced profes-
ınal in the field will require a thorough political orientation.

Because of its many commercial uses, the mail order business has become
ınost a craft apart from all other advertising. The uninitiated will be immedi-
ely bewildered by the number of mailing lists available. In most constitu-
ıcies you can find:

1. Lists of all registered voters.
2. Lists of registered voters segregated as to parties.
3. Lists of registered voters segregated by geographical location of resi-
ence.
4. Lists of new voters who have registered in the previous year.

These are the obvious targets for political mail and the only ones most
ıliticians use. The real political gold is to be found in a proper exploitation of
ıe selective lists, such as

1. Lists by income bracket.
2. Lists by occupation:
        Doctors
        Lawyers
        Dentists
        Independent businessmen
        Service station owners
        Printers
        Farmers
        Bankers. . . .

The direct mail expert working on a political campaign should first assem-
ıle detailed information on every available mailing list. When this has been
ıne the campaign manager can select the targets, much in the same manner as
ı determined the area of greatest probable return. What kind of people are
ıost likely to respond to the qualities of your candidate? Where is there a
ıcognizable mutuality of interest existing between your candidate and one of

the categories of mailing lists? Is your candidate a prominent farmer? Then b
all means the mailing should be sent to farmers. Is your candidate an activ
churchman? Then the mailing piece should be sent to all of his fellow churc
members. Does your candidate have a point of view particularly appealing t
doctors? Then the doctors' list should be mailed.

We are all familiar with the mechanical typewriters which will mass pro
duce what appears to be a personalized letter, but this type of mailing piece
far too expensive to be used as a general rule. However, effective ways of per
sonalizing the mailing piece can be found once the general profile of the ad
dressee has been determined.

There is a place for the Robo-type or Hooven letter in politics, particularl
if your candidate is an incumbent. Members of Congress receive many letter
from their constituents. A voter who has demonstrated his interest in politics b
writing a letter to his senator or congressman is a likely target for a machine
type letter with personal salutation and signature. Community leaders usuall
deserve this kind of personalization, but most campaign budgets simply canno
stand the expense required to make large scale mailings of this kind of letter.

How can large scale mailings achieve the effectiveness of personal solicita
tion? By addressing themselves to the particular interest or situation of th
addressee and this can be determined quite accurately by a review of th
categories of mailing lists available.

Residents of a generally rural area should be approached with a letter an
a special pamphlet addressed to the common concerns of rural residents. In th
great cities an entirely different approach will be required and a differer
pamphlet should be enclosed, one that identifies your candidate with the prob
lems of urban living.

Is your candidate trying to persuade the residents of an industrial distric
to support his election? Is unionism a problem? If so, a letter that speak
directly to the interests of union members, together with a pamphlet that deal
exclusively with your candidate's position on unions, will be read and remem
bered.

The voters who are registered in the political party of your candidat
should receive a letter aimed at exploiting their party interest. But, here agair
area of residence will dictate a special letter for party members who live in th
country with perhaps an entirely different kind of letter for the party member
who live in the city.

No single letter, no single enclosure can be devised that will effectivel
present your candidate's appeal through every mailbox in the constituency
Newly registered voters, for example, should receive a letter exploiting thi
situation. The possibilities are infinite.

Members of the campaign staff should be required to list the name o
every person in the constituency with whom they have ever had any persona
contact. In such correspondence signed by the candidate himself, the relation
ship should be established in the first paragraph: "Dear Mr. Smith: . . . Bil
Jones of Grand Island, who is helping on my campaign, has told me of . . .

ice the entree or bridge is established, the candidate's message becomes mpelling and personal.

All direct mail letters should attempt to create a mutual objective between e writer and the reader. *You* and *we* are the magic words that help to create e feeling of mutual interest.

If the letter is printed or duplicated by any of the usual processes, no :empt should be made to conceal this fact, but this does not mean that it is possible to create the suggestion of personal communication. In one cam- ign in which we mailed a letter to every member of our candidate's political rty and requested a particular action, the letter began as follows:

Dear Fellow Republican: . . . This is an age of miracles. I am not referring satellites and guided missiles and such mysterious things as television. This ter is in itself a miracle. It has been reproduced by a camera, printed on an tomatic machine—even the address on the envelope was put there by an tomatic process. Yet, this is truly a personal message.

You and I are enlisted in the same cause. We serve the same principles of vernment. We believe in the same future for America. . . .

Every piece of direct mail—pamphlet, letter, post card—must be prepared r a specific target. Each piece should contain an offer of benefit. The need for tion must be stressed. And, if possible, it should be a personal appeal for a ecific kind of assistance—please give this pamphlet to your neighbor—please it my sticker on the windshield of your car—please watch the television at ch a date and time.

Because direct mail can be aimed at a specific target area, it lends itself to ilization in the last two weeks of the campaign. At this point the major ncerns will have been identified. Research will have developed the blacks id whites of the differences between your candidate and his opponent and rect mail can exploit these to good advantage.

There must be a logical reason for every mailing. The more pertinent or nely, the greater the reception will be. If your letter can deal with a specific ue which has been raised, reader interest will be heightened. The develop- ent of the issues and of the differences between your candidate and his ›ponent will probably dictate your selection of the most productive mailing t.

Assume for a moment that in the campaign the issue of a method of xation has been developed. I recall one state campaign where our opponent as strongly opposed to a sales tax and argued instead for an increase of the come tax. Our candidate opposed an increase to the income tax and argued e sales tax as being more equitable. We exploited this natural division by ailing a letter and a pamphlet of our candidate's position to those voters who ould suffer most if the income tax were raised.

In every state-wide campaign there are overriding issues and the state- ide candidate in his mass advertising must confine himself to these issues. Not frequently there will also develop local issues which so far as the voters of at particular locality are concerned become of first importance.

In recent years the planners of federal superhighways have insisted on b
passing small communities. In Arizona and a number of other Western stat
communities have developed along the old highway routes which are depen
ent upon the highway traveler for their economic life. The problem of b
passing is vital to the residents of these communities. Residents of larger citi
are frequently eager to have the highways by-pass. Thus, we have a conflict
interest between the voters in a single constituency. In the small highw
towns the motels, gasoline stations, garages, restaurants and curio stores a
threatened with a serious loss of trade if the proposed new highway carries t
traffic around the town.

In 1958 Senator Goldwater was in favor of reasonable by-pass provisioi
arguing that existing towns which were dependent upon highway traffic shou
be protected by planning the new highways to pass within sight of the tov
and by providing easy access from the highway to the town.

Direct mail addressed to the residents of these small communities was
perfect vehicle for expressing the Senator's views. It was a rifle approach th
hit the target in the bull's-eye.

In another chapter we discussed how direct mail was used to distribute t
candidate's car stickers, how direct mail assists in the enlistment of the C
Group. The postcard last-minute appeal is an example of direct mail. T
letters and other mailing pieces need not be elaborate, but they must be sp
cific. Don't attempt to disguise a mass-produced letter as a personal cor
munication. Don't begin your letter with "I"; the reader is far more importa
than the writer. Don't fail to request a specific act of cooperation. Don't stan
ardize on long letters or short letters. Use enough copy to get the messa
across—and not one extra word. Don't entrust the creation of your direct ma
to an amateur.

In one campaign the use of direct mail permitted us to approach th
special group we were most eager to reach—the Indifferents. How does som
one demonstrate that he or she is not very interested in a political decisioi
Simply by not voting.

I once had a Republican candidate in a state where registered Democra
outnumbered registered Republicans by a ratio of about three to one. In ord
for my man to win it was necessary to persuade more than one-third of tho
voters who were nominally registered in the Democrat Party to cross the lii
and vote for a Republican. Almost fifty per cent of the population of this sta
lived in one county, and we were convinced the outcome of the election wou
be decided by how this county voted.

Immediately following the party primaries I contacted the election of
cials. The law did not permit anyone to take the great registers away from th
courthouse, but these voting records were public property and as such wei
open for inspection.

Through the cooperation of a county election official I was able to secui
permission to have the names copied. We put ten girls to work addressir
envelopes. There was no printing on the envelopes and, fortunately for us, r

mocrat official got wind of what we were doing. The girls copied the name
every registered Democrat who had failed to vote in the primary. On Friday
l Saturday before election Tuesday we mailed a few more than 40,000 letters
hese Indifferents. The letters were sponsored by a group of Democrats who
re supporting my Republican candidate. The letterhead was non-committal,
. the letter was strictly hard-sell, strongly in favor of my candidate, strongly
posed to the Democrat nominee. It bore the typewritten signature of twelve
minent members of the Democrat Party.

By the time the opposition discovered the letter it was too late for them to
anything about it; the polls were closed. The Republican candidate had
n, his victory made possible because a great many Democrats crossed the
ty line. We are confident that the last minute letter convinced a substantial
aber of nominal Democrats to follow the example of the men who signed
t letter and cross the line to vote for a Republican.

# 13 · *Mass Media*

NG BEFORE THE SEASON of politics reaches its climax on election day the
lic will begin to manifest resentment against the overdose of political adver-
ag. In every election candidates monopolize television screens, overcrowd
radio channels, fill the newspapers with their pleas for votes. In addition to
paid advertising, the public must put up with newscasts and news columns
oted almost exclusively to the great battles for public office. Producing any
l of an advertisement which will claim the public's attention in the midst of
his competition requires great ingenuity. Advertising agencies can be help-
to the campaign manager but the political product is unique . . . totally
ike the soap and the subdivisions, the automobiles and the air travel which
m the attention of advertising men most of the year.

In planning successful political advertisements the qualities and abilities
he candidate must be considered. Any political advertising that fails to deal
h those concerns uppermost in the minds of the electorate is wasted effort.

TELEVISION

Television is the most personal of the mass media. Through the magic television the candidate enters the living room to be seen and to be heard a: to be judged.

The candidate who can put himself across on TV enjoys a tremendo advantage, but the electronic camera can be cruel as well as kind. Ma students of the 1960 election will argue with stubborn persistence that it w Mr. Nixon's failure to match Mr. Kennedy's performance in the great deba1 which produced defeat for the Republican candidate.

The politician on television must not only outdo his opponent on the sar medium; he must also be more appealing and more entertaining and mc commanding than the great stars in the world of entertainment, news a sports whose domain he has invaded.

The conventional time segments of television are against the candidate. may be that an incumbent President of the United States can hold the attenti of a TV audience while he delivers a 30-minute speech, but even this is open question. Certainly the lesser candidates cannot hope to capture any substant audience for such a lengthy period with a program consisting of nothing mc than a camera focused upon a speaker at a rostrum.

The majority of all prime television time is available only in 30-minu segments. Some stations will sell a 15-minute period during the peak audier hour. But these stations are the exception rather than the rule.

The normal reaction to this dilemma is a decision to buy the one minu 40, 30, and 20-second commercial spots between existing programs. For ma candidates this is a wise decision. But the rate structure of television is su that most stations charge almost as much for a spot between two 30-minu segments as they charge for the 30-minute program time.

Daytime television is more flexible. In these off-peak hours the candid; can frequently find 5-minute availabilities. The rates are less because the au ence is smaller. But the politician intent on carrying his message to every vo cannot accomplish this objective with daytime TV alone.

In my experience most advertising agencies think in terms of spot ad cencies to highly rated programs and completely overlook the possibility content. The television audience demands entertainment, amusement and formation. Imaginative programs, with exciting content and dramatic presen tion, can make a political program on TV just as attractive as a "Bonanza" o who-dunnit. Political contests possess the same inherent drama that is found a championship sporting event. Political television which reflects the true mensions of the contest for public office will claim the audience attention a enlist the loyalty of the viewer in behalf of the candidate.

The advertising agency experts are best equipped to schedule the TV I the campaign team must provide the imagination to employ the time effective

Keeping in mind the need for acceleration, it is wise to concentrate at le 50 per cent of the TV budget in the last two weeks before election day. Ot!

ndidates will recognize this same necessity. The result may well be an almost
ady diet of political programming on the TV channels that serve the major
pulation centers of the constituency.

Ten years ago the number of channels available to any particular viewer
re limited. Now, set owners in most communities can choose between a
mber of stations.

Spot announcements, with good adjacencies, present your candidate to
at segment of the audience which is attracted by the adjacent program. The
ly other way to guarantee audience attention is to arrange a simulcast—that
have your candidate appear in program time on all of the available television
annels. In some areas this is impossible. In all areas it takes careful advance
heduling. In 1958 and again in 1960 a number of the candidates whom I was
rving as a consultant were able to buy identical time segments on several TV
annels. There is of course some danger of generating animosity on the part of
few viewers who are more devoted at the same time present your candidate
direct contrast to the opposition. If the script is adequate, it will magnify
ur candidate's assets and at the same time reflect the opposition's liabilities.

I once knew a successful candidate who could not make a speech, who had
shy and retiring personality, who had no particular training for the technical
sition he sought. But this man was the world's champion horseshoe pitcher.
iis was long before television, but this man pitched horseshoes in front of
ery voter who would stand still long enough to watch him. The people
cted him and re-elected him and re-elected him because they were im-
essed by his superior ability. The fact that they were not hiring him to pitch
rseshoes on the public payroll made little difference.

Good television spots require the same imaginative approach demanded
the 30-minute segments. Usually it is more difficult to make a real impact in
or 30 seconds. But the professionals in this field can take any single idea and
l it within the limitations of the spot time segment.

In a 30-minute period the candidate's appearance and personality and
rds can enlist the support of the viewers without any real hard-sell vote-for-
approach. The spots require a different treatment. *Ask* the viewer to vote for
ur candidate and *name him.* Tell the viewer to vote for your candidate and
me him. Imply that everyone else is going to vote for your candidate and
me him. Then show or tell the reasons. But keep your candidate in character.
he is a homely man, let the camera record that fact. If he is an intellectual,
ep the pitch in that vein. If he is an activist, show him in an active situation.
on't remake the candidate to conform with someone's concept of what a
ccessful television image might require.

The hard-sell spots are usually more effective if the plea and the instruc-
on is given by someone other than the candidate. But show your candidate's
cture; show his name; show him in the background that will qualify him as
expert.

To date we have discussed only those television appearances which are
onsored and paid for by the campaign committee. Any candidate for a major

office will find numerous opportunities to appear on interview-type shows a
other sustaining or commercially sponsored station productions. These appea
ances must be carefully planned. On interview shows or televised press confe
ences the candidate must be prepared. Here the manager functions as to
mentor and devil's advocate. The full talents of the staff should be utilized
formulate the kind of embarrassing questions which can be expected fro
newspapermen in the usual no-holds-barred-we'll-get-the-truth-for-you foru
show.

If the candidate enters this arena adequately prepared, he can make I
greatest gains when responding to unfair questions. Tolerance, not temper,
the key note. The candidate must respond to his tormentors by mentionii
their names. If he has spoken on a subject, refer to the full text of this discu
sion. If the question is a truly sticky one, advise your candidate to quote one
two authorities on the subject. And above all, remind your candidate that
must be in command of the presentation. Some questions deserve a "yes"
"no" answer. In some instances a truthful "I don't know" is much better than
obvious equivocation. What the audience needs is assistance in recognizii
your candidate as a product quite different from his opponent. And the sho
authoritative friendly response helps to define those differences.

Candidate coffees have become extremely popular and very effective. Th
are arranged in homes by supporters and permit the candidate a chance
speak and to shake hands with 40 or 50 voters. Obviously, a man running in
large constituency can't find the time to attend enough coffees to make much
an impact. But the TV coffee can extend the area of influence.

Morning television time is relatively inexpensive. The coffee can be a
ranged with 30 or 40 people in the studio asking questions. The candida
should answer the questions without any reference to notes and should try fo
completely informal, off-the-cuff presentation.

A candidate who is gifted on television can do a coffee all by himself. T
format of the program is to have someone at a telephone receiving questio
from the viewers. Of course it will be necessary to have some of the questio
prepared in advance, but these can be solicited in advance and the name
the questioner should be read on the air. The candidate has a cup of coffee b
no time to drink it. The atmosphere to create is that of the candidate being
the home of the viewer at a private coffee session.

This type of program has been used in two campaigns of my experien
with great effect. By identifying the person who supplied the question, t
program becomes an exchange between the candidate and the voter. And
selecting the proper questions, the candidate can address himself to tho
major issues which have been previously identified by his research group.

Informal, inexpensive and extremely effective—such presentations can
expected to create comment and attract considerable audience.

In the great frenzy to embrace the new medium of television, there was a riod when radio was almost totally neglected. This is no longer true. The perts who buy time on radio and TV and space in the newspapers to move erchandise have rediscovered the truth: there is always somebody, some-1ere, listening to radio.

There are more radio sets in automobiles than there are television sets in mes. The household with one TV set usually has three or four radios. Radio companionable. It doesn't demand your full attention in the same way televi-»n claims its audience. Radio is far more flexible than present day television.

Here again the campaign manager must employ the services of an expert. 1e notion that anyone can write selling radio copy has long since been proven fallacy. Radio can be compelling, dramatic, informative. The medium of rsuasion is the voice or the sound which must cloak the words with attention-tting conviction. Because radio is more mature than its younger sister, televi-n, the art in this field has reached a higher stage of development. And the st of radio is extremely modest when compared to the prices charged for TV 1e.

Someone will say that nobody listens to a 15-minute speech on radio. The dience will hang on your words for 30 minutes if the content deserves their ention.

In those early days when I was managing my first political campaigns, lio was our only electronic medium. We always presented the candidate on lio as the campaign came to a climax, but we never let him sit down in a ιdio and read a speech. We created a function, clothed it with the trappings a special event, used a well known radio voice to describe the color of the remonies or proceedings, never introduced the candidate until the program d been in progress for at least two or three minutes. That required clearance, his is a paid political broadcast," loses some of its effect when the candidate s a two or three minute separation from the disclaimer. Any performer does tter when supported by an audience. The applause adds to the credibility for »se who hear the proceedings. In one minute on radio a competent an-uncer can make a very effective pitch for a political candidate.

One effective method of impressing a radio audience is to irritate. In one mpaign where we had very little money we used two voices, two housewives ssiping over the back fence, talking about the candidate. The script was itten purposely with incomplete sentences. One of the gals with a deep Irish ogue emphasized all the candidate's strong points or assets. The other par-ipant in this dialogue quietly and without rancor compared the good things out our candidate with the inadequacies of the opposition. Four and one-half nutes of two women talking over the back fence. In three days we exposed s so many times it would have been impossible for anyone who owned a lio set not to have heard the dialogue at least twice.

By various devices well known to the radio profession, we constantly

sampled the audience reaction. When the irritating repetition had produced
real impact, we pulled all the recordings off the air. We had hoped to do th
on Monday before election Tuesday but the effect actually peaked on Frid
before the election Tuesday. I felt sure that if we continued the broadcas
some of the voters would vote against my candidate to express their irritatic
It may be that some of them did anyway, but we won that contest and o
sampling the day after election revealed that more voters had heard the rad
dialogue or, at least, remembered hearing it than were affected by any oth
single advertisement on any of the media.

When planning a radio program, remember to insert some distinctive ide
tifying format—sound, voice, something—which will instantly inform the l
tener he is hearing about *your* candidate. In one campaign we used a whistl
another, a trumpet; in a third the roll of a drum; and once I used the Sherif
siren.

## NEWSPAPERS

Political advertising in newspapers can be divided into four general cat
gories . . . message ads, reminder ads, testimonial ads and black-type ads.

The message advertisement in a newspaper carries a short positive stat
ment from your candidate. In order to heighten the public understanding
the conflict, this type of appeal should carry a positive and a negative. Yo
candidate believes certain things; the opposition does not believe these thin;
Your candidate is committed to a particular course of action; the opposition
opposed to this course of action. Or, the opposition is committed to a course
action; your candidate is opposed to this course of action.

Message ads will have greater impact if they carry identification, a form
distinctively different permits the reader to make instant recognition.

Reminder ads are usually smaller in size, oftentimes not more than t
columns by two inches, and usually carry nothing more than the picture, d
tinctive identification, and either a plea for votes or an instruction to vote f
the candidate. Some readers respond better to a command which says "Vote f
Congressman Jones" than they do to a request stating "Please vote for Co
gressman Jones."

In my experience the candidate can maintain his impact in the newspap
by alternating between the message-type ad and the reminder-type ad, but t
layout or pattern must promote instant recognition.

Many candidates favor the testimonial-type ad. These are usually o
column by six or eight inches. They feature the picture of a prominent citiz
and carry his statement as to why he or she will vote for the candidat
Minority and special interest groups are frequently persuaded to follow th
group leaders to the polling place.

The fourth type ad which I call "black type" is probably more familiar
"the political ad." It carries considerable copy, the type is large and it literal
screams the virtues of the candidate or the vices of the opposition. A black ty

is indicated whenever your research has developed a serious defect in the
position.

In one campaign our research department came up with the information
at the opponent, speaking before a community group, had made a flat state-
ent which was offensive to all PTA members. This was material for a black
pe ad. Another time, an opponent had a police record which he had carefully
ncealed from the voters. This prompted a black type ad. Facts can be stated
antly. But where your opponent in the past has been guilty of bad or unwise
sociation, understate the issue.

In one campaign we had incontrovertible evidence that the opponent had
one time been a member of the Communist Party. A number of people on
r campaign staff wanted to do a black type ad and make the charge that our
ponent had been a communist.

The nation had just gone through the McCarthy hearings and the liberal
ess was ready to do battle for anyone accused of being "pink." I decided we
uld get more mileage out of the information by understating our case. We
l a black type ad, but the copy merely suggested that our opponent had at
e time been associated with the Communist Party.

The liberal press reacted beautifully. We were accused of attempting to
ablish guilt by association and almost every newspaper in the state carried
story of our charge and the defense which was offered against it.

In our second blast we said "yes, we had suggested that the opponent
ght be a communist, but we weren't practicing guilt by association" and we
inted proof of the charge.

In almost every political contest understatement of facts which you believe
be real blockbusters will open the door for offering the proof of the implied
arge to an eager, and usually skeptical, audience.

Every manager of a political campaign must learn to differentiate between
e legitimate advertising media and what I call "the blackmail papers." In the
ason of politics, numerous publications appear. They are sponsored by
lges, by associations, by minority interests. They all demand a share of your
vertising.

Almost invariably the candidate will suggest propitiating these people by
serting some small ads in every paper. In a number of campaigns I have
structed our agency to deny advertising placement to any publication of this
pe. My refusal has brought some rather warm and colorful language my way,
.t it never cost a candidate an election.

Legitimate news publications with verified circulation and a history of
gular publication should rightfully receive that portion of the candidate's
wspaper advertising budget which corresponds to the circulation guaranteed.

Weekly newspapers, even in areas served by metropolitan dailies, should
given special consideration. The weekly newspaper is usually read because
hometown or community loyalty. The big daily is busy exposing the evils of
ciety and saying unkind things about people. The weekly is filled with home-
wn gossip and complimentary comments. The readers of the weeklies invari-

ably have greater affection for the editorial opinion and the editorial content of these smaller newspapers than is held by the subscribers to the metropolitan daily press.

Dividing the political budget between television, radio, newspaper, billboard, direct mail and pamphlet printing is an individual problem which does not respond to generalization. Advertising agencies can usually be extremely helpful with advice on the allocation of budgets, but this warning is worth repeating: Political candidates are not like shoes or soap and the advertising budget should be divided after deciding where your candidate is a star. Is he excellent on television? Then this medium should receive major emphasis. Is he better when the voters hear him but do not see him? Use radio. If your candidate has difficulty selling himself on radio and TV, then pour your money into the newspapers. The manager's major responsibility in this area is to be sure that the advertising budget buys enough of the voters' attention to warrant the cost.

### PAMPHLETS, CARDS AND POSTERS

Millions of political pamphlets are printed every year. Some of them are very effective. Every candidate wants a brochure. The mistake here is that too many candidates are content with a single printed piece.

If your candidate is a one-dimensional personality, with a one-track mind with a single asset, then you can do him justice with a single printed piece. But if your candidate combines a number of competencies, if he is knowledgeable in a number of fields, if there are many sides to his personality, then you need separate pamphlet to reflect each major asset.

I was once called into a gubernatorial campaign very late in the political season. I discovered there had been no printing done for the candidate, but was assured by his managers that the copy was almost ready and we would have "the brochure" in a couple of weeks. Finally, by being obnoxiously insistent, I secured the copy which had been prepared. It was beautiful. Nine thousand words. Anyone reading the copy would have been convinced that our candidate had somehow combined in one person all the virtues of Washington, Jefferson, Lincoln, Wilson and Daniel Boone. I had a little trouble with Daniel Boone. I didn't see why the fact that our man had been born in Kentucky made him necessarily the voters' choice to be governor of a Western state.

I cut the copy as much as I could and the campaign staff finally accomplished the printing. Then they ran a full-page ad duplicating the pamphlet (About $1800 worth of newspaper space filled with 10-point type.) When the candidate showed it to me, my comment was: "Your mother may read it, but no one else will."

There is a drab, stereo-typed, repulsive similarity to most political pamphlets. The candidate was born. This is an accomplishment he has in common with every other breathing human being. Sometimes there is a glowing descrion of the candidate's mother and father. This is usually followed by a lengthy ecital of accomplishments and the piece ends with a photograph of the candi- ate's family group.

Effective political campaign pieces translate the assets of the candidate to a desirable qualification which will permit the candidate, if elected, to atisfy a major desire of the constituency. If your candidate has been a suc- essful businessman and one of the issues is governmental fiscal policy, by all leans relate this business experience as proof that your man has the compe- ence to discharge the fiscal responsibility he is seeking.

If your candidate is a lawyer and has written desirable legislation, trans- te this into a promise of future beneficial legislation. What your candidate has one for the voters, if substantial, will argue what he will do in the future. The amphlet will be particularly effective if it demonstrates the measurable differ- nces between your candidate and the opposition. A pamphlet which outlines our candidate's views on unions and unionism will not interest the rural popu- tion. A pamphlet which demonstrates your candidate's competency to deal 'ith problems of the farmer will not make any votes in the big city.

The list of available advertising specialties designed for sale to political indidates has no end—jewelry, buttons, pot holders, balloons, matches. At est, such items can only serve a single function: to make the candidate's name miliar. But what is printed on the matchbook you have in your pocket right ow? If you even noticed the printing, you are unusual. If you can remember hat it says, you are remarkable. This does not mean that printed book atches are a total waste of money. The policy to adopt with specialties is aution. If the specialty will serve a specific purpose, use it. Don't be seduced to believing that cost should be the deciding factor.

### ILLBOARDS AND OUTDOOR ADVERTISING

In the seasons of politics, thousands of eager candidates smile invitingly at le passing parade from the surface of billboards. I have yet to encounter a indidate who has been able to win a contested office without using outdoor dvertising.

In 1959 and 1960 when I was attemping to advise active managers of so any campaigns for the United States Senate, my first suggestion was—buy our billboard space now. This advice was offered in May of 1959. It took some dditional urging, but by December of 1959 the billboard space for most of ese candidates had been bought and paid for.

What's the hurry? There are only so many choice billboard locations in very constituency. When the season of politics rolls around, most of the out- oor advertising companies try to allocate 100 per cent or 200 per cent show- gs to each party. But, with few exceptions, they simply don't have the avail- ble space to give a candidate 100 per cent or 200 per cent showing.*

---

* 100 per cent showing—sufficient boards to assure that everyone in a given area will have seen the essage at least one time.

200 per cent showing—sufficient boards to assure that everyone in a given area will have seen the essage two or more times.

In the Massachusetts campaign of 1960, Chuck Colson contracted for th Saltonstall boards 10 months in advance of the scheduled showing. When th campaign was over, he told me that Saltonstall's opponent, Thomas J. O'Con nor, didn't have a single billboard in Massachusetts—there weren't any avai able.

Political billboards are normally displayed about 60 days. If the campaig fund is particularly flush, the posting might be extended to 90 days.

The normal two-month period has one inherent drawback. After 30 day the message, having been seen once or twice, no longer attracts attention. Th symmetry of the design, the location of the picture, the colors, no long challenge the eye.

If your billboard poster is to be up more than 30 days, plan to change it i some significant manner at the end of the first month. The billboard posting done on a 30-day schedule and you can have additional paper pasted in plac for a very nominal charge.

I have learned that a competent designer can plan in advance for a chang —for an addition of a splash of color or a change in wording—and this can b effected by pasting a small streamer over the original sign.

In one campaign for an incumbent United States Senator we added a re streamer with white letters carrying the words "Re-elect." The streamer wa pasted across one corner of the original billboard paper. It changed the geome try, it changed the color effect, it changed the wording. It made a brand nev poster and the additional printing for all of the billboards we bought tha season cost less than $25.00.

In one campaign the artist designed a spot to be superimposed, a square c bright orange paper changed the design and the impact of the poster.

In some states the use of small placards is discouraged. But every cand date must have something of this sort, if only to satisfy the demands of friend and supporters. The outdoor billboards, posters, small display cards should a carry a distinctive identifying pattern—something to promote instant recogn tion. Transit cards for display either inside or outside a public vehicle shoul carry the poster theme of the campaign.

The Burma-Shave jingle signs have produced extremely good results in number of my campaigns. Variations of this type of display will suggest them selves. Somewhere in every campaign there is room for a light touch.

Bucky O'Neill charged up San Juan Hill with Teddy Roosevelt and died hero's death. There is a great equestrian statue in the courthouse square c Yavapai County, Arizona. But Bucky is remembered not as a hero but as th most delightful candidate who ever campaigned for the office of sheriff back i the days when Arizona was still a territory.

Cowboy, miner, writer, newspaper editor—Bucky brought a sense c humor to his efforts to win political office. His first announcement bluntl admitted there were probably other men better qualified to serve in that po than Bucky O'Neill, but he wanted the job and needed it.

All of the other candidates were deadly serious. Bucky conducted a whim-
ical race. Who was elected? Bucky O'Neill, because he made it easy for the
oters to recognize the difference between his candidacy and that of his oppo-
ents. This is the ultimate goal of all political advertising. The voters who will
p the scales for victory must find the difference before they make the decision.

# 14 · *Don't Let Them*
# *Steal It From You*

WE WAS ROBBED" is a familiar cry. When applied to the outcome of an athletic
ontest or a business deal, the protest is often recognized as an alibi. The sordid
istory of vote fraud and stolen elections, which is a part of the American
olitical record, has made politics a dirty word. This being an imperfect world,
opulated by imperfect men, it would be naive to expect that man's sinful
reed which prompts him to steal, lie, cheat and wage war would be sub-
erged or held in check when the contest is for a political prize.

Every political campaign is an intensely partisan effort. Candidates, man-
gers and contributors combine to win a personal victory for the candidate and
he party. The prevention of election fraud is a public service. The democratic
rocess by which we attempt to govern ourselves is seriously threatened when
he integrity of the ballot can be questioned.

All politicians piously proclaim their devotion to public service. The best
vidence of that devotion can be found when candidates and managers support
vigorous enforcement of the election law. The police and the courts need the
elp of effective political organization to achieve this objective. Enforcement
gencies do not have the manpower or the training adequately to supervise the
olling places on Election Day. This work must be performed by conscientious
olunteers who have been given adequate training for the task.

Once a fraudulent vote has been cast and counted, it is difficult if not
npossible to correct the error. The secrecy of the ballot in this country gives
he dishonest as well as the honest vote equal standing once the tally has been
ade. It is relatively simple to prevent an unqualified voter from voting. It is
lmost impossible to change the outcome or even to detect the fraud after the

ballot has been placed in the box or the voter has been permitted to use th
machine.

All elections are supervised by officials of political subdivisions of th
states. State law establishes the qualifications for voting, designates the pollir
places and provides the necessary personnel. Paper ballots, which were on
universally employed, are gradually being replaced by voting machines.

To insure an honest vote and an honest count, observers, supported by a
contending factions, should police the activities in the polling place from th
moment the doors open until the last ballot is counted. Every qualified persc
must be permitted to cast his or her ballot. Every unqualified person must l
prevented from casting a ballot.

Most states require the voters to be registered in the precinct of the
residence several months prior to election day. Some states permit a citizen t
vote after making an affidavit of residence which certifies that the individual
a bonafide resident of the precinct, has been a resident for the required lengt
of time and is therefore entitled to vote. Anyone who files a false affidavit
subject to severe penalty.

This promised punishment does not always protect the ballot. In one cit
in North Dakota in 1960, more than 500 people voted on affidavits of residenc
Following the election, these people could not be found at the residence give
In many cases the street address on the affidavit proved to be fictitious. Gre
emphasis is placed upon making the privilege of the franchise available t
every qualified citizen. The North Dakota law makes it easy to vote but virtu
ally impossible to protect the integrity of the outcome.

Elections are properly policed by poll watchers and challengers. Thes
volunteer citizens, if they are to accomplish their assignment, must be give
adequate advance preparation.

In many areas the official charged with conducting the election operates
training session to instruct the officials employed at the polls—judges, inspe
tors, clerks, etc. Poll watchers, recruited on a volunteer basis, should be i
structed to attend these training sessions wherever possible. But, at best, suc
instruction is usually perfunctory.

The campaign manager or the party chairman should enlist the voluntee
poll watchers well in advance of election day. These individuals should b
assembled in convenient public meeting places and given a thorough instru
tion. The applicable election law should be explained, the valid reasons f
challenging must be covered and the poll watcher should become part of
carefully organized election day procedure.

It is vital to prevent fraudulent votes being cast. It is equally essential t
the process of democracy to bring all eligible voters to the polls. These tw
objectives must not be confused.

Challengers are in attendance on election day to prevent fraudulen
voting. Poll watchers are frequently used to enable the party to bring out th
votes.

The poll watching process has been described in many publications. It elatively simple and will operate effectively wherever the party or the candidate has sufficient volunteer manpower.

The poll watcher is given a copy of the great register for his precinct. As he citizens come in to vote, he checks off their names. By eleven or twelve o'clock on election day the party machinery should begin a concentrated effort to get qualified residents who have not voted to come out during the afternoon hours.

In my experience a card system has been useful. As a citizen votes, his card is placed in the "voted box" by the poll watcher. At eleven o'clock the "voted box" is sent to the party's precinct headquarters. By a process of elimination workers in the precinct can determine those who have not voted and either by telephone or personal calls, the work of getting slow voters to the polls commences.

The AFL-CIO COPE organization, which has been very effective in many elections, has done an excellent documentary on this subject called *The Wisconsin Story*. This begins with volunteers determining who are the friendly voters in a precinct. Then on election day these same volunteers make it their business to take all of the friendly voters to the polls.

The duties of poll watcher and challenger cannot be combined. Unfortunately, this had been attempted in many elections with the result that neither function is adequately served. The challenge operation begins with the precinct records which were compiled by the research department early in the campaign. These must be brought up to date after the registration lists are closed. Challengers must be provided with an accurate list of every citizen who is qualified by registration to vote in the precincts under watch. If this number has fluctuated widely in the past several elections, an attempt should be made to spot check the neighborhood. The fraudulent vote usually begins with a fraudulent registration.

Election officials are required by law to give a ballot to every individual whose name appears on the registration list. They have no way of determining whether or not the registration is valid. This is the job for the volunteer challenger.

Following the 1960 presidential election, evidence was developed to indicate that a number of unqualified voters were permitted to vote in certain precincts in Chicago. Some 30-odd votes were cast by people who claimed to reside in a building which had been demolished prior to election day.

There is a simple, effective and relatively inexpensive way to check the validity of the registration lists. About two weeks before election a first class letter should be mailed to every registered voter in a suspected precinct. The face of the envelope should bear the instruction: "Please do not forward," and a return address must be printed on the envelope.

The mailing need not be identified as coming from a political organization. If the campaign manager believes the opposition will attempt to cast some fraudulent votes in a particular precinct, he will probably want to adopt some harmless and innocent identity. The letter ostensibly could be authored by a civic betterment society or a charitable organization.

If the addressee is not available to receive mail at the address on the outside of the envelope, the cover will be returned to the sender. The courts have held that when the post office is unable to deliver first class mail to an individual at a specific address, this can be accepted as evidence that the individual does not in fact reside at that address.

The returned undeliverable letters should be given to the challengers. If any individual whose letter has been returned attempts to vote, that individual should be challenged on the ground that he or she is not a bonafide resident of the precinct.

The challengers will frequently encounter hostility. The challenged voter will protest and in some cases the election officials will protest. If there is a genuine conspiracy to encourage the casting of fraudulent ballots, the election officials may attempt to permit the questioned voter to cast a ballot despite the protest.

To protect your challenger, particularly in those precincts where your party is in the minority, it is essential to provide support. Long before election day the manager should enlist a special task force. Young lawyers are particularly suited to this job. But the supply of young lawyers is usually limited and it will be necessary to augment the force with intelligent, determined citizen volunteers.

The task force should be carefully schooled in the election laws of the constituency. Each member should be equipped with a digest of the pertinent sections of the law and should also have a full copy of the state election laws.

In a large city it is desirable to establish several neighborhood headquarters so this special task force will be available during the hours the polls are open. When the challenger encounters difficulty, he can send for reinforcements.

In one city of 500,000 population we had more than 300 trained workers prepared to answer calls for assistance on election day. The first call for help came about 20 minutes after the polls opened. We sent eight men, four lawyers and four prominent businessmen, to the polling place where the challenger had questioned a voter on the basis of a returned first class letter.

The men on this flying squad recited the law to the election officials. They secured an admission from the challenged voter that he had recently moved from the precinct but had come back to vote, thinking it would be all right. The leader of the task force promised he would make it his personal obligation to see to it that the election officials spent that night in jail if they permitted any violation of the election law.

Our particularly worrisome precincts in that election consisted of voters who were predominantly registered in the opposite party. We received a number of calls for help between six o'clock in the morning and nine-thirty a.m. Then the calls tapered off. The word had been spread through the neighborhood that if you were not qualified to vote, you better not try it. In that

lection some 5,000 fewer ballots were cast in these precincts than had been
ast just two years earlier.

Most polling places maintain accurate and duplicate records of the num-
er of qualified voters who have been given a ballot or admitted to the voting
nachines. The poll watcher should keep an independent tally. In a suspected
recinct this effort should be carried on openly in order to inform the election
fficials of the fact that their records will be checked at the end of the day.
uch an obvious check-off will discourage any attempt to stuff the ballot box.

In machine precincts the poll watcher should insist upon witnessing an
nspection of the machine tallies before the polls open. Voting machines are
sually delivered to the polling place sealed and certified by the Commissioner
f Elections. Sometimes voting machines are subject to mysterious failures.
They may arrive with a substantial total for one candidate on the machine at
he time it is installed. In one election our challenger discovered that two of the
our machines being used failed to register a vote for the Republican candidate
or governor. These machines were disqualified until a mechanic corrected the
nalfunction.

When voting machines are used, the matter of verifying the total is usually
 simple procedure. The challenger, who is permitted by law to witness the
ally when the polls are closed, should keep his own record of the totals on each
nachine. Most election officials are honest but sometimes numbers are trans-
osed on reports. In those precincts where past action warrants suspicion, an
ttempt should be made to have the machines impounded under supervision
mmediately after the polls are closed.

Paper ballot precincts ordinarily produce more error than machine pre-
incts. The tedious task of counting the paper ballot votes sometimes occupies
he election board until sunup the day after election. Human beings, weary
rom a day's service on an election board, frequently make honest mistakes. It
s in these long, drawn-out periods of counting that dishonest election officials
ind an opportunity to influence the outcome of the election.

Most states authorize the political parties to send official watchers to check
he count. These watchers must be trained by someone familiar with local
ractice. In a hotly contested race it is wise to give the official checker an
utomatic counter. When the tally clerk calls out a vote for a candidate, the
vatcher can automatically record this.

If there is more than one hotly contested race, additional checkers should
e sent to observe the counting. In addition to the number of ballots marked
or your candidate vis-a-vis the number marked for his opponent, an attempt
hould be made to keep track of the total number of ballots. Remember that
ot all voters mark their ballots for every candidate. Little automatic tally
levices, such as those used by door keepers to count attendance, can be very
elpful. Your watcher, with both hands in his pockets, can score the opponent's
votes with his left hand while counting your candidate's votes with his right.

Most election officials are scrupulously honest. Be wary of those who want
o postpone the counting, who suggest that time be taken out for dinner or for

coffee breaks. If this occurs, stay with the ballots even though they may ostensibly be locked away in a safe place.

When all the results are in it is wise to review the figures. If the normal turnout has been 80 per cent, you should be suspicious of the precinct which votes 95 per cent.

Poll watchers can frequently detect other improper actions on election day. If the voter comes into the polls bearing an instruction card, it is time to call for help. In most states the law prohibits the bringing of any political literature inside the polling place.

In the 1960 West Virginia primaries hundreds of voters were observed bringing to the polls a card bearing the slate of recommended candidates put out by one of the political organizations. These voters were not challenged but they should have been.

If your election day task force includes volunteers assigned to help get out the vote, it will pay to keep a constant check on the percentage voting in every precinct. If the vote is running extremely heavy in certain areas, you can accept this as an indication that someone is working those precincts skillfully and persistently.

Volunteer challengers sometimes get the notion they are not really contributing a great deal when they spend hour after hour in the polling place on election day without having to make a single challenge. It *is* a tedious assignment but the presence of challengers has a salutary effect upon those who may be planning any illegal action.

Many elections have been won or lost by just one vote in each precinct. Remind your volunteers of this. If their day of duty results in preventing just one illegal ballot, they may have made a major contribution to the integrity of that election. The days and weeks of the campaign effort, the labor of thousands of volunteers, plus all the money you spend, hangs in the balance on election day. If the polls are not policed, the victory you have earned may be stolen.

The day the campaign starts is the time to start planning your security measures for election day. Then, when all the ballots are counted, win or lose, you and all those who have worked with you will find satisfaction in the knowledge that you did everything you could do to advance your candidate, your philosophy, and to contribute to the effectiveness of representative government.

# 15 · *Election Timetables*

CANDIDATES and campaign managers will find this chapter interesting. The casual reader will perhaps be disappointed because there is little glamour in the hard work required to win elections.

The campaign commences when the candidate decides to run for public office. The odds will always favor the candidate who knows what he is going to do eighteen months or two years in advance of the day when the decision must be made public. But since most campaigns lack this advantage, the information presented here is applicable to a nine- or ten-month period.

*Step 1:* Select a campaign manager. It is not necessary to make any public announcement. In fact it will be wise to withhold any public statement about a campaign organization until the candidate makes his formal declaration to the press and other media.

*Step 2:* Authorize the campaign manager to enlist the group of specialists who will actually be conducting the campaign efforts.

*Step 3:* Read the election law. Ask a competent lawyer to give you a digest of his opinion of the requirements. Be sure that you know the filing date, the required filing fees if any, petition requirements if nomination is done by petition, restrictions against spending, and requirements for identification on campaign literature. Remember it is a federal offense to put out literature in an election for a federal office which is not clearly identified as to authorship. This doesn't mean that all of your literature has to come from your official campaign sources. You can have numerous committees with innocent identities, but the literature must be identified.

*Step 4:* Create the research department and put it to work on the possible opponent or opponents, on the history of recent elections, on the development of resource material, on the probable issues.

*Step 5:* Commence enlisting the Cell Group.

*Step 6:* Recruit the advisory board or resource team who will help brainstorm the strategy and analyze the opposition.

*Step 7:* Have the campaign photographs taken. Candidates become very weary—this reflects in their appearance. A photo made eight or nine months in advance of the day of decision will be an honest representation of the candidate. Don't use a picture made three or five or ten years ago. Instruct the photographer to capture the qualities in the candidate which will be emphasized during the campaign.

*Step 8:* Appoint a treasurer and a finance chairman. Make sure that both of these important assistants clearly understand the election laws. If the treasurer has available an expert bookkeeper, so much the better. There are many campaign expenses which need not be reported. But accurate books, reflecting contributions and expenditures, must be kept. The pitfalls here are too many to be enumerated. They vary from state to state. Improper records or inadequate reporting can disqualify a victor. The finance chairman's primary job is to raise money. The treasurer's job is to make sure that money is accounted for and expended at the direction of the campaign manager.

*Step 9:* Assemble the full team and start them thinking about the candidate, about his opponent and about the issues.

*Step 10:* Order the billboards. If your candidate has not made a public announcement, buy the space in the name of some commercial firm whose ownership is friendly to your candidate. (In Oregon I once bought 300 billboards, ostensibly for the Volkswagen automobile. In Arizona we placed our orders in the name of an ice company.) Do whatever is necessary to have the billboards committed at least eight months in advance.

*Step 11:* Buy your television time. As election day approaches, the available TV time will be in great demand. By placing your order seven or eight months in advance, you can probably secure good segments for the week before election. And if there is to be an effort to secure simulcast scheduling, it must be done well in advance. The five-minute daytime and spots can all be ordered at a much later period, but the good 30-minute availabilities are limited, and unless a request is put in well in advance, the chances are your candidate will not be on TV under the most favorable circumstances during the final two weeks of the campaign.

*Step 12:* Move your candidate through the constituency. If he is not presently holding public office, schedule him as a speaker at some civic or community project. But start to build the exposure which will be necessary.

*Step 13:* Develop a campaign budget. At this point the manager should have a fair understanding of what is required. Money can be committed in lump sums to various media, the operation of the campaign group, rent for headquarters, telephones, etc.

*Step 14:* Pick the day to open the campaign—remember the public memory is short. The days between Labor Day and election day are adequate for the full-scale public campaign, provided adequate preparation has been made in the preceding months.

*Step 15:* Plan your campaign literature. It may be you will need two or three short pamphlets. Remember that no one really wants to read campaign literature. It must be attractive, adequately illustrated and to the point. If the constituency varies in its economic, political, social and educational attitudes, you will probably need more than one leaflet. Every written piece should have time to cool before it goes into print. If preparations are made well in advance, the campaign manager will not find himself stealing time from some important current necessity to review the proofs of the campaign printed matter.

*Step 16:* Order your window stickers or bumper strips. If you give the printer adequate time, he will do a better job and you will avoid the possibility of a delay, an improperly printed strip or stickers that won't stay stuck. Give yourself sufficient time to do the whole job over again if necessary.

*Step 17:* Develop your candidate's campaign itinerary and stay with it. Don't overload him. Don't let travel time requirements consume those hours when he should be appearing before the people.

*Step 18:* Now establish the time schedule for the public campaign. Plan the activities of the first four weeks and make sure they accelerate every day. Now ask this question: can we maintain acceleration?

*Step 19:* Start all over again and plan the activities for the final week. Fill every hour of each day. Now work backwards. Reduce the number of actvities or appearances in that period two weeks before election day. By scheduling backwards it will become apparent that in the first few days of the campaign one major appearance and one or two visits to small communities will be sufficient.

*Step 20:* Sit down with the advertising people and allocate the media money. Instruct your agency to produce every possible television film and radio transcription in advance of the opening date of the campaign. If you do this, you will have a relaxed, confident, refreshed candidate. If you postpone making video tapes or the films until the middle of the active season, you are likely to have a tired and lackluster candidate.

Put a deadline on all these plans—August 1. By this time you should have the results of the issue response from the Cell Group, the image surveys, and you should know where the ducks are. You should have an intimate understanding of your opponent and you can plan the real strategy—the series of important home run balls your candidate is going to hit.

If you plan to use the telephone, organize your task force now. Assign volunteers to putting telephone numbers beside the names of those who are registered in your party. This is a tedious, time-consuming task, but the volunteers will do it cheerfully provided you give them ample time to accomplish the work. Remember it takes four weeks for the telephone company to put in the extra lines you will need for a Foot Soldier campaign or for a Get-Out-The-Vote campaign.

When all this preliminary work is done—the charts have been made, the tapes and the films all cut—commence looking for blind-alley issues . . . any questions that can be raised which may possibly divert your opponent from what should be the mainstream of his strategy.

Prepare instructions for the volunteers who will ask eagerly: "What can I do to help?" Remember to assign a specific chore within the competency of all volunteers and put an element of accountability into your request. Volunteers truly want to work but they need direction to be effective. And unless a report is required, some of them will postpone their efforts and you will have gaping holes in your planned coverage.

The campaign group should be meeting at least once a week by August 1. The feedback from the Cell Group should be reviewed with the Advisory Board. The transcribed radio and pre-filmed television should be reviewed by the Advisory Board. Listen attentively to everyone's opinion. When all the reports are in and all the opinions have been registered, the candidate and the campaign manager must sit down and make their decisions. Once the active campaigning starts, there is very little room for improvisation.

I have made up dozens of calendars for campaign managers. In almost every instance they have departed from the calendar under the pressure of local circumstances. But without the calendar, it is doubtful that very many of the necessary chores would have been performed. There are a number of aspects to campaigns which can be planned in advance and need not ever be changed.

Media purchased before the campaign opens and adequately scheduled will hold up through any campaign. The message may be substituted to meet some new threat or to take advantage of some new opportunity, but the exposure, as planned, should remain constant.

The campaign itinerary should never be changed except for the most urgent of reasons. A great deal of effort is required to prepare a coffee or a public meeting and it will take twice as much effort to make explanations and soothe ruffled feathers if a planned appearance is cancelled.

The issues developed in the early portion of the campaign will rarely change and by sticking by those which are truly germane, the planned campaign contributes to a growing confidence on the part of the candidate as he deals with these issues.

One final word about money: get it early, get as much as you can and never commit a dollar which is not in the campaign till.

With a little bit of luck, a great deal of hard work and a sincere dedication to the task, the planned campaign with an adequate candidate will produce a victory. In some cases, victory is not possible. Here defeat can be accepted, but the candidate and manager who lose a campaign because they failed to plan, to assess the opposition correctly, to make provision for contingencies, to enlist the support of a knowledgeable advisory group, will never be able to forgive themselves for their failure.

# 16 · *For Men of Good Conscience*

In this small volume on *How To Win An Election* we have moved from the world of casual citizenship into the harsh domain of practical politics. Those who have never before considered the preparation and labor required to win a political contest may be inclined to question the wisdom of political judgments. The best man does not always win. Scoundrels and saints have served this nation in positions of public trust. But for all its imperfections, the system has worked and worked successfully.

The great virtue in representative government is to be found in those provisions which call for a constant reassessment of the validity of the public choice. Our institutions and our elected officials are constantly on trial. Our system still allocates sovereignty to the individual citizen. Victory at the polling place is tentative and temporary. On both the day before and the day after election the world of the victor and the vanquished is filled with uncertainty.

The successful candidate must face an entirely new and frequently frightening responsibility. The excitement and the elation over victory is fleeting. In return for his certificate of successful election, the candidate must forever surrender his right to privacy. Now he belongs to the public—to those who voted against him as well as to those who voted for him.

The loser in a political contest, stinging from defeat, suffers an immediate pain which is not inflicted upon the victor. There is a loss of self-confidence, an inevitable feeling that his friends were not loyal, the bitter reflection over what might have been, the frequent late-blooming knowledge that his defeat was produced not because his opponent was superior, but because of his own blunders in strategy or planning.

Then there is the perplexing, perpetual question: Shall he try again? Should he bind up the financial wounds, the shattered ego and the broken promises and do it all over again?

Losing an election contest—with all its pain—is a profitable experience. For the loser, more surely than the winner, has identified his true friends.

Abraham Lincoln lost several elections before he won the Presidency. Richard Nixon won every election until he lost for the Presidency.

There is no infallible balance upon which the eternal values of victory or defeat may be weighed. We must confess there is bitterness and pain in victory and sweetness and consolation in defeat.

The price of political decision is that some must lose and some must win. Measured against the eternal problems of all mankind, the cost in human disappointment is small. For what all men must seek is a just and ordered society where the instrumentalities of government are used not to enrich or to punish but to advance the relationship of each man to his neighbor in a manner which contributes to the ultimate dignity and responsibility of all men.

If political victory brings responsibility, political defeat should engender charity. No political candidate, no political party has a monopoly on virtue or patriotism. Our task is to support the democratic decisions of this Republic. Where we believe those decisions to be in error, we should labor to reform them. Where we believe them to be right, we should support them. Where they are weak, we should strengthen them.

For many candidates success requires a change of residence from their home to the State Capitol or from their home state to the National Capitol. Old friends are left behind, familiar supports of prior years are withdrawn. New loyalties intrude . . . the public business and the public interest must come ahead of family, hobbies, business or profession.

The corporate jungle where ambitious men are constantly striving to climb the ladders of success by stepping on the shoulders of the less agile or the unwary has been adequately pictured in many novels.

In the political world where men compete for the voters' favor, the clawing and the scratching is persistent. Jealousy and contention within the candidate's party structure will require him to reach decisions in a cold, friendless vacuum.

The successful politician, whatever the new role he has won, will immediately be confronted with a disturbing, hitherto unfamiliar temptation. Theodore Roosevelt once said: "The patriot's first duty is to get himself re-elected." But how far should a man go? George Washington, at the Constitutional Convention, said: "If to please the people we offer what we ourselves disapprove, how can we afterward defend our work?"

A man in the Congress of the United States must constantly find that thin dividing line between pork-barrel, vote-getting legislation and genuine national interest. Friends will impose upon him, and friendship is not something to be dismissed lightly. There will inevitably be long periods of separation from family. His critics will seize upon every mistake as an opportunity to question his veracity, his wisdom and his patriotism.

Men elected to the Congress enjoy the power and perquisites but they must also make a sacrifice. The world of Washington, D.C., is indeed cruel for this is a city of judgment incapable of rendering judgment. The successful candidate who imagined the campaign was bitter and merciless will discover the antagonisms, the petty conniving and the constant undercutting is now a regular part of the pattern of his life.

We require that our governmental servants divorce themselves from the practical world of commerce. We insist that, like Caesar's wife, they must be above suspicion. Yet, the structure of our government places these newly elected servants in a situation where their integrity is constantly under pressure. Some men have made themselves rich through governmental service. Many honest men have been unjustly criticized for accepting small gifts or services. When betrayals of public trust are revealed, we invariably hear an outcry for new legislation to make men good or honest. This is often urged by men who apparently believe in a double standard of morality—one for public service, another for private endeavor.

The winner in a political contest pays a high price for victory. Friends who once dealt with him frankly now fall into that insidious pattern of hero worship. He will find it difficult to hear the truth and almost impossible to separate honest criticism from partisan detraction.

No matter what the victory, the winner will become an immediate target for the opposition press. His personal imperfections will be spread in headlines before his constituents. If he is tired and says the wrong thing, no one will make excuses. Some of his friends and supporters will demand favors in return for the support they gave him at election time. He will be embarrassed in a thousand ways by individuals who truly wish him well. From the moment the first returns are in, he is compelled to worry about the results of the next election.

Most men elected to public office are not independently wealthy. After two, four or six years away from their businesses or their professions, they recognize the difficulties involved in starting over again in private life. Re-election becomes almost a necessity. There is a certain amount of fame to victory. The ego is supported by the knowledge that "I won," but fame is fleeting. Voters are very apt to adopt the attitude expressed in that question: "What have you done for me lately?"

Abraham Lincoln, on the occasion of his departure from Illinois to become President, spoke on behalf of all men who win elections and enter public service when he said:

My Friends:

No one, not in my situation, can appreciate my feeling of sadness at this parting. To this place, and the kindness of these people, I owe everything. Here I have lived a quarter of a century, and have passed from a young to an old man. Here my children have been born, and one is buried. I now leave, not knowing when or whether ever I may return, with a task before me greater than that which rested upon Washington. Without the assistance of that Divine Being who ever attended him, I cannot succeed. With that assistance, I cannot fail. Trusting in Him who can go with me, and remain with you, and be everywhere for good, let us confidently hope that all will yet be well. To His care commending you, as I hope in your prayers you will commend me, I bid you an affectionate farewell.

# SCREWTAPE
# PROPOSES A TOAST

# SCREWTAPE PROPOSES A TOAST

*by C. S. Lewis*

# Screwtape Proposes a Toast

*(The scene is in Hell at the annual dinner of the Tempters' Training College for young devils. The principal, Dr. Slubgob, has just proposed the health of the guests. Screwtape, a very experienced devil, who is the guest of honour, rises to reply:)*

MR. PRINCIPAL, your Imminence, your Disgraces, my Thorns, Shadies, and Gentle-devils:

It is customary on these occasions for the speaker to address himself chiefly to those among you who have just graduated and who will very soon be posted to official Tempterships on Earth. It is a custom I willingly obey. I well remember with what trepidation I awaited my own first appointment. I hope, and believe, that each one of you has the same uneasiness tonight. Your career is before you. Hell expects and demands that it should be—as mine was—one of unbroken success. If it is not, you know what awaits you.

I have no wish to reduce the wholesome and realistic element of terror, the unremitting anxiety, which must act as the lash and spur to your endeavours. How often you will envy the humans their faculty of sleep! Yet at the same time I would wish to put before you a moderately encouraging view of the strategical situation as a whole.

Your dreaded Principal has included in a speech full of points something like an apology for the banquet which he has set before us. Well, gentle-devils, no one blames *him*. But it would be vain to deny that the human souls on whose anguish we have been feasting tonight were of pretty poor quality. Not all the most skillful cookery of our tormentors could make them better than insipid.

Oh, to get one's teeth again into a Farinata, a Henry VIII or even a Hitler! There was real crackling there; something to crunch; a rage, an egotism, a cruelty only just less robust than our own. It put up a delicious resistance to being devoured. It warmed your inwards when you'd got it down.

Instead of this, what have we had tonight? There was a municipal authority with Graft sauce. But personally I could not detect in him the flavour of a really passionate and brutal avarice such as delighted one in the great tycoons of the last century. Was he not unmistakably a Little Man—a creature of the petty rake-off pocketed with a petty joke in private and denied with the stalest platitudes in his public utterances—a grubby little nonentity who had drifted into corruption, only just realizing that he was corrupt, and chiefly because everyone else did it? Then there was the lukewarm Casserole of Adulterers. Could you find in it any trace of a fully inflamed, defiant, rebellious, insatiable lust? I couldn't. They all tasted to me like undersexed morons who had blundered or trickled into the wrong beds in automatic response to sexy advertisements, or to make themselves feel modern and emancipated, or to reassure themselves about their virility or their "normalcy," or even because they had nothing else to do. Frankly, to me who have tasted Messalina and Casanova, they were nauseating. The Trade Unionist stuffed with sedition was perhaps a shade better. He had done some real harm. He had, not quite unknowingly, worked for bloodshed, famine, and the extinction of liberty. Yes, in a way. But what a way! He thought of those ultimate objectives so little. Toeing the party line, self-importance, and above all mere routine, were what really dominated his life.

But now comes the point. Gastronomically, all this is deplorable. But I hope none of us puts gastronomy first. Is it not, in another and far more serious way, full of hope and promise?

Consider, first, the mere quantity. The quality may be wretched; but we never had souls (of a sort) in more abundance.

And then the triumph. We are tempted to say that such souls—or such residual puddles of what once was soul—are hardly worth damning. Yes, but the Enemy (for whatever inscrutable and perverse reason) thought them worth trying to save. Believe me, He did. You youngsters who have not yet been on active service have no idea with what labour, with what delicate skill, each of these miserable creatures was finally captured.

The difficulty lay in their very smallness and flabbiness. Here were vermin so muddled in mind, so passively responsive to environment, that it was very hard to raise them to that level of clarity and deliberateness at which mortal sin becomes possible. To raise them just enough; but not that fatal millimetre of "too much." For then, of course, all would possibly have been lost. They might have seen; they might have repented. On the other hand, if they had been raised too little, they would very possibly have qualified for Limbo, as creatures suitable neither for Heaven nor for Hell; things that, having failed to make the grade, are allowed to sink into a more or less contented subhumanity forever.

In each individual choice of what the Enemy would call the "wrong" turning, such creatures are at first hardly, if at all, in a state of full spiritual responsibility. They do not understand either the source or the real character of the prohibitions they are breaking. Their consciousness hardly exists apart from the social atmosphere that surrounds them. And of course we have contrived that their very language should be all smudge and blur; what would be a *bribe* in someone else's profession is a *tip* or a *present* in theirs. The job of their Tempters was first, of course, to harden these choices of the Hellward roads into a habit by steady repetition. But then (and this was all-important) to turn the habit into a principle—a principle the creature is prepared to defend. After that, all will go well. Conformity to the social environment, at first merely instinctive or even mechanical—how should a *jelly* not conform?—now becomes an unacknowledged creed or ideal of Togetherness or Being Like Folks. Mere ignorance of the law they break now turns into a vague theory about it—remember, they know no history—a theory expressed by calling it *conventional* or *Puritan* or *bourgeois* "morality." Thus gradually there comes to exist at the centre of the creature a hard, tight, settled core of resolution to go on being what it is, and even to resist moods that might tend to alter it. It is a very small core; not at all reflective (they are too ignorant) nor defiant (their emotional and imaginative poverty excludes that); almost, in its own way, prim and demure; like a pebble, or a very young cancer. But it will serve our turn. Here at last is a real and deliberate, though not fully articulate, rejection of what the Enemy calls Grace.

These, then, are two welcome phenomena. First, the abundance of our captures: however tasteless our fare, we are in no danger of famine. And secondly, the triumph: the skill of our Tempters has never stood higher. But the third moral, which I have not yet drawn, is the most important of all.

The sort of souls on whose despair and ruin we have—well, I won't say feasted, but at any rate subsisted—tonight are increasing in numbers and will continue to increase. Our advices from Lower Command assure us that this is so; our directives warn us to orient all our tactics in view of this situation. The "great" sinners, those in whom vivid and genial passions have been pushed beyond the bounds and in whom an immense concentration of will has been devoted to objects which the Enemy abhors, will not disappear. But they will grow rarer. Our catches will be ever more numerous; but they will consist increasingly of trash—trash which we should once have thrown to Cerberus and the hellhounds as unfit for diabolical consumption. And there are two things I want you to understand about this: First, that however depressing it may seem, it is really a change for the better. And secondly, I would draw your attention to the means by which it has been brought about.

It is a change for the better. The great (and toothsome) sinners are made out of the very same material as those horrible phenomena the great Saints. The virtual disappearance of such material may mean insipid meals for us. But is it not utter frustration and famine for the Enemy? He did not create the humans —He did not become one of them and die among them by torture—in order to produce candidates for Limbo, "failed" humans. He wanted to make Saints;

gods; things like Himself. Is the dullness of your present fare not a very small price to pay for the delicious knowledge that His whole great experiment is petering out? But not only that. As the great sinners grow fewer, and the majority lose all individuality, the great sinners become far more effective agents for us. Every dictator or even demagogue—almost every film star or crooner—can now draw tens of thousands of the human sheep with him. They give themselves (what there is of them) to him; in him, to us. There may come a time when we shall have no need to bother about *individual* temptation at all, except for the few. Catch the bellwether, and his whole flock comes after him.

But do you realize how we have succeeded in reducing so many of the human race to the level of ciphers? This has not come about by accident. It has been our answer—and a magnificent answer it is—to one of the most serious challenges we ever had to face.

Let me recall to your minds what the human situation was in the latter half of the nineteenth century—the period at which I ceased to be a practising Tempter and was rewarded with an administrative post. The great movement towards liberty and equality among men had by then borne solid fruits and grown mature. Slavery had been abolished. The American War of Independence had been won. The French Revolution had succeeded. Religious toleration was almost everywhere on the increase. In that movement there had originally been many elements which were in our favour. Much Atheism, much Anticlericalism, much envy and thirst for revenge, even some (rather absurd) attempts to revive Paganism, were mixed in it. It was not easy to determine what our own attitude should be. On the one hand it was a bitter blow to us—it still is—that any sort of men who had been hungry should be fed or any who had long worn chains should have them struck off. But on the other hand, there was in the movement so much rejection of faith, so much materialism, secularism, and hatred, that we felt we were bound to encourage it.

But by the latter part of the century the situation was much simpler, and also much more ominous. In the English sector (where I saw most of my frontline service) a horrible thing had happened. The Enemy, with His usual sleight of hand, had largely appropriated this progressive or liberalizing movement and perverted it to His own ends. Very little of its old anti-Christianity remained. The dangerous phenomenon called Christian Socialism was rampant. Factory owners of the good old type who grew rich on sweated labour, instead of being assassinated by their workpeople—we could have used that—were being frowned upon by their own class. The rich were increasingly giving up their powers, not in the face of revolution and compulsion, but in obedience to their own consciences. As for the poor who benefited by this, they were behaving in a most disappointing fashion. Instead of using their new liberties—as we reasonably hoped and expected—for massacre, rape, and looting, or even for perpetual intoxication, they were perversely engaged in becoming cleaner, more orderly, more thrifty, better educated, and even more virtuous. Believe me, gentle-devils, the threat of something like a really healthy state of society seemed then perfectly serious.

Thanks to Our Father Below, the threat was averted. Our counterattack was on two levels. On the deepest level our leaders contrived to call into full life an element which had been implicit in the movement from its earliest days. Hidden in the heart of this striving for Liberty there was also a deep hatred of personal freedom. That invaluable man Rousseau first revealed it. In his perfect democracy, you remember, only the state religion is permitted, slavery is restored, and the individual is told that he has really willed (though he didn't know it) whatever the Government tells him to do. From that starting point, via Hegel (another indispensable propagandist on our side), we easily contrived both the Nazi and the Communist state. Even in England we were pretty successful. I heard the other day that in that country a man could not, without a permit, cut down his own tree with his own axe, make it into planks with his own saw, and use the planks to build a tool-shed in his own garden.

Such was our counterattack on one level. You, who are mere beginners, will not be entrusted with work of that kind. You will be attached as Tempters to private persons. Against them, or through them, our counterattack takes a different form.

*Democracy* is the word with which you must lead them by the nose. The good work which our philological experts have already done in the corruption of human language makes it unnecessary to warn you that they should never be allowed to give this word a clear and definable meaning. They won't. It will never occur to them that *Democracy* is properly the name of a political system, even a system of voting, and that this has only the most remote and tenuous connection with what you are trying to sell them. Nor of course must they ever be allowed to raise Aristotle's question: whether "democratic behaviour" means the behaviour that democracies like or the behaviour that will preserve a democracy. For if they did, it could hardly fail to occur to them that these need not be the same.

You are to use the word purely as an incantation; if you like, purely for its selling power. It is a name they venerate. And of course it is connected with the political ideal that men should be equally treated. You then make a stealthy transition in their minds from this political ideal to a factual belief that all men are equal. Especially the man you are working on. As a result you can use the word *Democracy* to sanction in his thought the most degrading (and also the least enjoyable) of all human feelings. You can get him to practise, not only without shame but with a positive glow of self-approval, conduct which, if undefended by the magic word, would be universally derided.

The feeling I mean is of course that which prompts a man to say *I'm as good as you.*

The first and most obvious advantage is that you thus induce him to enthrone at the centre of his life a good solid, resounding lie. I don't mean merely that his statement is false in fact, that he is no more equal to everyone he meets in kindness, honesty, and good sense than in height or waist measurement. I mean that he does not believe it himself. No man who says *I'm as good as you* believes it. He would not say it if he did. The St. Bernard never says it to the toy dog, nor the scholar to the dunce, nor the employable to the bum, nor the pretty woman to the plain. The claim to equality, outside the strictly political field, is made only by those who feel themselves to be in some way inferior. What it expresses is precisely the itching, smarting, writhing awareness of an inferiority which the patient refuses to accept.

And therefore resents. Yes, and therefore resents every kind of superiority in others; denigrates it; wishes its annihilation. Presently he suspects every mere difference of being a claim to superiority. No one must be different from himself in voice, clothes, manners, recreations, choice of food: "Here is some-one who speaks English rather more clearly and euphoniously than I—it must be a vile, upstage, la-di-da affectation. Here's a fellow who says he doesn't like hot dogs—thinks himself too good for them, no doubt. Here's a man who hasn't turned on the jukebox—he's one of those goddam highbrows and is doing it to show off. If they were honest-to-God all-right Joes they'd be like me. They've no business to be different. It's undemocratic."

Now, this useful phenomenon is in itself by no means new. Under the name of Envy it has been known to the humans for thousands of years. But hitherto they always regarded it as the most odious, and also the most comical, of vices. Those who were aware of feeling it felt it with shame; those who were not gave it no quarter in others. The delightful novelty of the present situation is that you can sanction it—make it respectable and even laudable—by the incantatory use of the word *democratic*.

Under the influence of this incantation those who are in any or every way inferior can labour more wholeheartedly and successfully than ever before to pull down everyone else to their own level. But that is not all. Under the same influence, those who come, or could come, nearer to a full humanity, actually draw back from it for fear of being *undemocratic*. I am credibly informed that young humans now sometimes suppress an incipient taste for classical music or good literature because it might prevent their Being Like Folks; that people who would really wish to be—and are offered the Grace which would enable them to be—honest, chaste, or temperate refuse it. To accept might make them Different, might offend against the Way of Life, take them out of Togetherness, impair their Integration with the Group. They might (horror of horrors!) become individuals.

All is summed up in the prayer which a young female human is said to have uttered recently: "O God, make me a normal twentieth century girl!" Thanks to our labours, this will mean increasingly, "Make me a minx, a moron and a parasite."

Meanwhile, as a delightful by-product, the few (fewer every day) who will not be made Normal and Regular and Like Folks and Integrated increasingly tend to become in reality the prigs and cranks which the rabble would in any case have believed them to be. For suspicion often creates what it suspects ("Since, whatever I do, the neighbours are going to think me a witch, or a Communist agent, I might as well be hanged for a sheep as a lamb, and become one in reality.") As a result we now have an intelligentsia which though very small, is very useful to the cause of Hell.

But that is a mere by-product. What I want to fix your attention on is the vast, overall movement towards the discrediting, and finally the elimination, of every kind of human excellence—moral, cultural, social, or intellectual. And is it not pretty to notice how *Democracy* (in the incantatory sense) is now doing for us the work that was once done by the most ancient Dictatorships, and by the same methods? You remember how one of the Greek Dictators (they called them "tyrants" then) sent an envoy to another Dictator to ask his advice about the principles of government. The second Dictator led the envoy into a field of grain, and there he snicked off with his cane the top of every stalk that rose an inch or so above the general level. The moral was plain. Allow no preeminence among your subjects. Let no man live who is wiser or better or more famous or even handsomer than the mass. Cut them all down to a level: all slaves, all ciphers, all nobodies. All equals. Thus Tyrants could practise, in a sense, "democracy." But now "democracy" can do the same work without any tyranny other than her own. No one need now go through the field with a cane. The little stalks will now of themselves bite the tops off the big ones. The big ones are beginning to bite off their own in their desire to Be Like Stalks.

I have said that to secure the damnation of these little souls, these creatures that have almost ceased to be individual, is a laborious and tricky work. But if proper pains and skill are expended, you can be fairly confident of the result. The great sinners *seem* easier to catch. But then they are incalculable. After you have played them for seventy years, the Enemy may snatch them from your claws in the seventy-first. They are capable, you see, of real repentance. They are conscious of real guilt. They are, if things take the wrong turn, as ready to defy the social pressures around them for the Enemy's sake as they were to defy them for ours. It is in some ways more troublesome to track and swat an evasive wasp than to shoot, at close range, a wild elephant. But the elephant is more troublesome if you miss.

My own experience, as I have said, was mainly on the English sector, and I still get more news from it than from any other. It may be that what I am now going to say will not apply so fully to the sectors in which some of you may be operating. But you can make the necessary adjustments when you get there. Some application it will almost certainly have. If it has too little, you must labour to make the country you are dealing with more like what England already is.

In that promising land the spirit of *I'm as good as you* has already become something more than a generally social influence. It begins to work itself into their educational system. How far its operations there have gone at the present moment, I should not like to say with certainty. Nor does it matter. Once you have grasped the tendency, you can easily predict its future developments; especially as we ourselves will play our part in the developing. The basic principle of the new education is to be that dunces and idlers must not be made to feel inferior to intelligent and industrious pupils. That would be "undemocratic." These differences between the pupils—for they are obviously and nakedly *individual* differences—must be disguised. This can be done on various levels. At universities, examinations must be framed so that nearly all the students get good marks. Entrance examinations must be framed so that all, or nearly all, citizens can go to universities, whether they have any power (or wish) to profit by higher education or not. At schools, the children who are too stupid or lazy to learn languages and mathematics and elementary science can be set to doing the things that children used to do in their spare time. Let them, for example, make mud pies and call it modelling. But all the time there must be no faintest hint that they are inferior to the children who are at work. Whatever nonsense they are engaged in must have—I believe the English already use the phrase—"parity of esteem." An even more drastic scheme is not impossible. Children who are fit to proceed to a higher class may be artificially kept back, because the others would get a *trauma*—Beelzebub, what a useful word!—by being left behind. The bright pupil thus remains democratically fettered to his own age group throughout his school career, and a boy who would be capable of tackling Aeschylus or Dante sits listening to his coeval's attempts to spell out A CAT SAT ON A MAT.

In a word, we may reasonably hope for the virtual abolition of education when *I'm as good as you* has fully had its way. All incentives to learn and all penalties for not learning will vanish. The few who might want to learn will be prevented; who are they to overtop their fellows? And anyway the teachers—or should I say, nurses?—will be far too busy reassuring the dunces and patting them on the back to waste any time on real teaching. We shall no longer have to plan and toil to spread imperturbable conceit and incurable ignorance among men. The little vermin themselves will do it for us.

Of course, this would not follow unless all education became state education. But it will. That is part of the same movement. Penal taxes, designed for that purpose, are liquidating the Middle Class, the class who were prepared to save and spend and make sacrifices in order to have their children privately educated. The removal of this class, besides linking up with the abolition of education, is, fortunately, an inevitable effect of the spirit that says *I'm as good as you*. This was, after all, the social group which gave to the humans the overwhelming majority of their scientists, physicians, philosophers, theologians, poets, artists, composers, architects, jurists, and administrators. If ever there was a bunch of tall stalks that needed their tops knocked off, it was surely they. As an English politician remarked not long ago, "A democracy does not want great men."

It would be idle to ask of such a creature whether by *want* it meant "need" or "like." But you had better be clear. For here Aristotle's question comes up again.

We, in Hell, would welcome the disappearance of democracy in the strict sense of that word, the political arrangement so called. Like all forms of government, it often works to our advantage, but on the whole less often than other forms. And what we must realize is that "democracy" in the diabolical sense (*I'm as good as you*, Being like Folks, Togetherness) is the finest instru ment we could possibly have for extirpating political democracies from the face of the earth.

For "democracy" or the "democratic spirit" (diabolical sense) leads to a nation without great men, a nation mainly of subliterates, full of the cocksureness which flattery breeds on ignorance, and quick to snarl or whimper at the first hint of criticism. And that is what Hell wishes every democratic people to be. For when such a nation meets in conflict a nation where children have been made to work at school, where talent is placed in high posts, and where the ignorant mass are allowed no say at all in public affairs, only one result is possible.

The democracies were surprised lately when they found that Russia had got ahead of them in science. What a delicious specimen of human blindness! If the whole tendency of their society is opposed to every sort of excellence, why did they expect their scientists to excel?

It is our function to encourage the behaviour, the manners, the whole attitude of mind, which democracies naturally like and enjoy, because these are the very things which, if unchecked, will destroy democracy. You would almost wonder that even humans don't see it themselves. Even if they don't read Aristotle (that would be undemocratic) you would have thought the French Revolution would have taught them that the behaviour aristocrats naturally like is not the behaviour that preserves aristocracy. They might then have applied the same principle to all forms of government.

But I would not end on that note. I would not—Hell forbid! encourage in your own minds that delusion which you must carefully foster in the minds of your human victims. I mean the delusion that the fate of nations is *in itself* more important than that of individual souls. The overthrow of free peoples and the multiplication of slave states are for us a means (besides, of course, being fun); but the real end is the destruction of individuals. For only individuals can be saved or damned, can become sons of the Enemy or food for us. The ultimate value, for us, of any revolution, war, or famine lies in the individual anguish, treachery, hatred, rage, and despair which it may produce. *I'm as good as you* is a useful means for the destruction of democratic societies. But it has a far deeper value as an end in itself, as a state of mind which, necessarily excluding humility, charity, contentment, and all the pleasures of gratitude or admiration, turns a human being away from almost every road which might finally lead him to Heaven.

But now for the pleasantest part of my duty. It falls to my lot to propose on behalf of the guest the health of Principal Slubgob and the Tempters' Training College. Fill your glasses. What is this I see? What is this delicious bouquet I inhale? Can't it be? Mr. Principal, I unsay all my hard words about the dinner. I see, and smell, that even under wartime conditions the College cellar still has a few dozen of sound old vintage *Pharisee*. Well, well, well. This is like old times. Hold it beneath your nostrils for a moment, gentle-devils. Hold it up to the light. Look at those fiery streaks that writhe and tangle in its dark heart, as if they were contending. And so they are. You know how this wine is blended? Different types of Pharisee have been harvested, trodden, and fermented together to produce its subtle flavour. Types that were most antagonistic to one another on Earth. Some were all rules and relics and rosaries; others were all drab clothes, long faces, and petty traditional abstinences from wine or cards or the theatre. Both had in common their self-righteousness and the almost infinite distance between their actual outlook and anything the Enemy really is or commands. The wickedness of other religions was the really live doctrine in the religion of each; slander was its gospel and denigration its litany. How they hated each other up there where the sun shone! How much more they hate each other now that they are forever conjoined but not reconciled. Their astonishment, their resentment, at the combination, the festering of their eternally impenitent spite, passing into our spiritual digestion, will work like fire. Dark fire. All said and done, my friends, it will be an ill day for us if what most humans mean by "religion" ever vanishes from the Earth. It can still send us the truly delicious sins. The fine flower of unholiness can grow only in the close neighbourhood of the Holy. Nowhere do we tempt so successfully as on the very steps of the altar.

Your Imminence, your Disgraces, my Thorns, Shadies, and Gentle-devils: I give you the toast of—Principal Slubgob and the College!

# THE
# CONVENIENT STATE

# THE
# CONVENIENT STATE

*by Garry Wills*

# The Convenient State

THE LIBERAL AND THE CONSERVATIVE who would sort out their differences, for some constructive purpose, encounter from the outset an unusual problem: the very things that seem to unite them are a cause of confusion and deeper cleavage. Even when we of the West fall out, we select our weapons from the same armory; and, as (in the stock jibe) the same medieval God heard the prayers of opposed armies, so Plato and Aristotle seem to hover over the ranks of every possible faction in the civilization they helped to create. Even when men undermine our citadel, they do it with our engines; and, in greatest part, unconsciously. This brings the bitterness of fratricide into the dispute over our inheritance. The conservative claims guardianship over the storehouse of Western wisdom. The Liberal contends that the genius of the West lies in its capacity for innovation, in a daring reliance on reason and a resiliency towards change.

Because these two forces share a vocabulary and, to some extent, a vision, the discovery that they are saying different things in the same words leads, on either side, to suspicion of betrayal; and the variations in meaning that the common vocabulary suffers seem to open an unbridgeable chasm. In no case is this so clear as in the allegiance of both sides to the principles of freedom and order; for neither party denies the necessity of some polarity and balance between the two. The Liberal is traditionally considered the spokesman of freedom, the conservative of order. But, even aside from the shifting maneuvers these terms have lately performed, no one ever claimed that such a simplistic division was absolute. The most partisan Liberal cannot, if he claims to speak responsibly, deny that conservatives are concerned with guaranteeing freedom. And the archest reactionary this side of insanity cannot claim that the Liberal is not trying to construct a social order. In fact, as time wears on, the stress on principles ancillary to their professed ones makes Liberals and conservatives seem to change places, so that Liberals now champion a strong central government, and conservatives speak for economic and political individualism. Is the difference between these two, then, merely accidental at any moment because it is, in the long run, only a matter of degree, the conservative laying heavy emphasis on the prescriptive, the Liberal on the spontaneous, elements in political life? Given the same set of ingredients, do the cooks simply vary their recipes? No; the shared language disguises, and so perpetuates, fundamental differences.

Freedom and order, justice and settled interests, progress and tradition . . . the words are used of different things in the different camps; and when these concepts cluster to form more complex groupings of ideas—republic, democracy, self-determination, aristocracy—the differences undergo a staggering multiplication. It is true that freedom and order will be correlates in any of the systems advanced. But this, again, impedes communication, since the varieties of meaning in the one word will exact an answering variation in the other. It is useless, therefore, to debate whether the emphasis should be on freedom or order, or to adjudicate between major political systems by discussing the *degree* of freedom desired, or the *extent* of order, as if these were constant substances varying only in quantity. The question should be *what kind* of order, *what kind* of freedom, is at issue. Our history is littered with defeated varieties of each virtue. To take an obvious case, there is the theocratic definition of freedom and order—principles which become, under this rubric, Providence and Virtue. In such a scheme, freedom is freedom to be virtuous, and order is the right to exact virtue from man as his proper attribute. At another extreme of our experience is anarchism, which (read the paradox how you will) is a system for avoiding system. It, too, has a principle of order—the removal and continued negation of political coercion—corresponding to its untrammeled freedom.

These systems are both unworkable, since virtue that is enforced is not virtue, and anarchy that is guaranteed against control is to that extent controlled. But their *ignis fatuus* has drawn men down tragic paths, and they will continue to beckon. The important thing is to see that there is no use distinguishing such schemes by *degree*, as having a different internal disposition of freedom and order. The anarchist does not err in exalting freedom over order, but in exalting the wrong kind of freedom and the wrong kind of order. It is his whole philosophical framework that is incorrectly established. He is right about the machinery of these correlates; he is only wrong about the world. To put it another way, the relation of freedom to order is a dynamic one that can manifest itself in any number of consistent programs; and a political system is therefore to be judged by its substance, not by its dynamics.

Thus Mill cripples his discourse from the start when he calls the treatise on liberty an attempt to adjudicate the ancient "struggle between Liberty and Authority,"—as if these were two things of perduring and permanent meaning, but with shifting relations, towards each other, of supremacy or subjection. The real difference, for instance, between the historically normative polities of ancient Greece and the "barbarians" was not simply one of liberty as opposed to tyranny. The ancient empires had a mystical sanction. Their art and customs show no awareness of the individualism that emerged in Hellas' statues of man.

Liberty, in such a society, has another meaning than it was to take on in the debates of the Hellenes. And in the primitive societies so thoroughly scrutinized by modern anthropologists, the instruments for educating and preserving the individual, under severe disadvantages, are the very disciplines for initiation into the political order on which all life depends. In such a world, the relation of freedom to order continues to exist, but as a drastically reduced version of the religious maxim, *cui servire regnare*. A similar paradox is worked out in the Marxist dialectic, and summarized, satirically, in Orwell's "Freedom is slavery." Far from being a game of the mind, this slogan expresses the only possible approach to freedom in the Marxist world; the Communist paradox has the same consistency as the Christian language used to describe a freedom heightened to indefectible obedience in the beatific vision. The only error is trying to acclimatize heaven to the intemperate regions of practical politics. Again, men are right about the relation of freedom to order, and only wrong about the world.

Since freedom and order are correlates, an absolutism at one pole leads to an absolutism at the other. The Marxist starts from order and asserts that "freedom is slavery." The absolutists of individualism start at the other pole but end in the same contradiction. Even the most extreme libertarian must justify his position by an appeal to order. Mill, for instance, advocates a free market of ideas as the most infallible guide to certitude—enough talk automatically producing truth, triumphant over all pretenders and "self-evident." Thus freedom becomes authority and arms itself with all the instruments the Liberal state has taken to itself in order to advance man's "self-evident" rights.

But if freedom always implies order in any consistent system, why has Western civilization made freedom a separate aim and motto, so that the boast of Greece was to have invented freedom, and a war of national liberation like America's could float the banner "liberty or death?" The reason is that the Western tradition—as opposed to all others, even the most sophisticated Oriental disciplines—has exalted the individual person. This civilization, centered in the primacy of the private soul, brought a whole new ordering of society into human history. The difference is immediately apparent when Greek thought and art enter the world. Impersonal pattern, hieratic system, absorption in the eternity of the Ideal give way to the naked splendor and particularity of man; even the gods assumed those anthropomorphic forms still vital in Western imaginations. The Greek "idea" was first detached and delineated in the cult statues given various gods' names, but in reality sharing one title: Man. No longer did man achieve his man-hood by religio-political initiation into secrets of order. The individual reason became the test of reality with the Greeks, and this reason asserted itself by defying the order of magic and mystery. The state religion was secularized; it sloughed off its theric elements, boasting of this liberation under the symbol of battle with centaurs and other half-human powers. The individual reason, thus exalted, ventured on the distinctive Western achievements—systematic logic and science, a philosophy freed of superstition.

The discovery of the individual's unique resources, the testing of the world against the private reason, forced the state into a new role. Formerly, man's hard-won achievements had been stored up in the authority of the community, kept under sacred leadership and symbols. But the Greek mind freed itself of this total dependence on tradition, and man's sights were set on the uncharted areas where no collective approach to mystery could lead him. The state took on a humbler function, keeping order among the individuals whose free quest gave Greek cities their divided, spontaneous, almost anarchic individuality.

Thus freedom became an assertion of the individual's right to pursue his own vision; and liberty became a prior demand for all human speculation or education. This demand did not lessen as the Hellenic world spread and was transmuted by Christianity. In fact, the Christian emphasis on the individual soul's worth, and its other-worldly goal, deepened the cleavage between man and the religious state. The Christian recognizes a divided loyalty, giving to Caesar what is Caesar's, but to God the inestimably vaster reaches of the soul that belong to God.

But if the state's order is no longer, in the Greek world, co-extensive with man's attempt to order his private world, what role is government to play? Where does the supremacy of the private person find its frontier, or verge on other claims? How do the sacred areas of each man's individuality meet and adjust to each other? It is this question that has put the problem of freedom at the center of Western political dispute. And, in a kind of slovenly philosophical shorthand, this problem has been cast as a search for the *amount* of freedom man is to enjoy. But the problem is that the Greek world introduced an entirely new conception of human life, one still novel today; a conception that runs into contradiction if pushed by a ruthless logic. The autonomy of the individual, the fight against tradition, seem to make government at worst a causeless evil, at best a necessary evil. But experience has taught that a "freedom" which travels down the road of anarchy is never seen again. Thus the problem of the Western world has been to find a new kind of order to act as foundation for its fugitive new kind of freedom. Many attempts at the solution of this problem have been short-lived, because they did not come to grips with the particular kind of freedom—with its almost impossible demands—that the West has chosen to pursue. The attempts which remain in the central line of Western experiment cluster into two main groups. These continuing schools of thought, or lines of approach, correspond in some degree with the popular division of political thinkers into Liberal and conservative. In some degree, but not exactly; and the popular terms are no longer precise. It will be better, then, to give unequivocal if unfamiliar names to the two, calling them the Order of Justice and the Order of Convenience.

## I  THE ORDER OF JUSTICE

If the state is not meant to initiate man into his place in the world, what is its function? The earliest and most arresting answer is Plato's: the end of the state is justice. The liberated intellect of man discerns, behind all disciplines of mystery, an order whose sole force is its claim upon the reason. This is the order of each thing's due, of justice as an Idea. But some intellects are not capable of grasping this ideal form; and so it is the task of human society to find and put in office the intellects fitted for communion with the Idea of justice. The rest of men will have to take what these rulers dispense, as they mediate the light of justice to men bewildered by shadows.

Plato wrote when the Greek adventure into individuality seemed to be reaching a suicidal point of fission. He wrote to meet the practical demand for order, and to forestall the resurgence of sheer mystery—in this case, the mystery of force—as a claim on man's obedience. He makes the claims of the state meet the challenge of reason; but the Platonic state answers this challenge so successfully that it again becomes the entire area of man's endeavor. The state brings justice into the flux of history. Theocracy has returned, and absolutism; but reason is the new deity and absolute. The assertion of the individual intellect leads to an equal assertion of the state's power as the seat of truth. Men throw off mystery, only to be ruled by Idea.

Aristotle, though he introduced emperical elements of observation and psychological realism into political theory, nonetheless based the state on metaphysical principles as two-edged as Plato's. The Greeks had advanced the boast of the individual's self-sufficiency against the hieratic absolutism of less rational civilizations. Aristotle considered the reason's own claim to autonomy with rigor and found that man, isolated, cannot meet the test of self-sufficiency, or *autarkeia,* either economically or psychologically. The smallest unit that can make a pretense at *autarkeia* is the state that is armed against foreign aggression and able to supply internal economic needs. Then, translating human dependence into logical dependence, Aristotle argues: "By the very order of things, the state is prior in right to the family, and to each of us singly, since the whole is of necessity prior to the part" (1253a19-20). Man, without the *polis* to complete him, is not even a man: perhaps an animal, perhaps a god (1253a29). Like "an isolated piece at draughts," such a man has no function aside from the action of the total set of markers. The entire business of being man, which is to be just (1253a16-18), is only fulfilled in the state, the guardian of justice: "The virtue of justice has, as its sphere, the *polis.* For the virtue of justice (*dikaiosunē*) establishes what is just (*to dikaion*), and this order of justice (*dikē*) gives men's relations their political pattern (*politikēs koinōnias taxis*)" (1253a37-39). Therefore the state alone is equipped to achieve the highest good (1252a4-6).

In his own way, Aristotle repeats the Platonic recoil of a complete individuality into a new state absolutism. Both systems tried to achieve freedom of the will through the free exercise of reason. But the reason is not free. It is an instrument for reaching an outside and objective reality, which is single under single aspects. Man can refuse to think, or think confusedly; but once the evidences of reality are received within the intellect, it is not free to think anything it pleases. Thus any attempt to base political freedom on the claims of man's intellect makes the state the center of truth—in Plato, truth as moral enlightenment; in Aristotle, truth as a set of logical imperatives—and nothing is more absolute than the claim of truth upon man.

The empirical observations of Aristotle gave origin to a certain political realism, but the authoritarian principle hidden in his definition of the state haunts us. The Christian Aristotelian could no longer take *autarkeia* as the test of man's achievement. For the Christian, man's nobility comes from the fact that he is out of place in the world, meant for another City, with a higher and lasting citizenship. There is a further problem. Aristotle wrote that the state is prior to man "by nature," or in the order of things. The Christian doctrines of Creation, the Fall, and Heaven give a range of meanings to the word "nature" that Aristotle could never have imagined. In the new scheme, "nature" can mean the proper ordination of things as intended in the pristine state of man. Or nature is *fallen* nature—the human conditon weighted by tendencies towards sin; the rest of creation scarred, and subject to catastrophe, as a result of man's rebellion. Or nature can mean the evidences of original order still asserting themselves in, and adapting themselves to, the present state of man. Nature can mean the good product of God's hand or the twisted remains of man's work. It can be contrasted with "unnatural" acts, as the model of ordination; or it can be contrasted with grace, as the frustrated thing unable to rise to its goal without redemption from a supernatural source.

For the Christian, the state can no longer fill up man's failings or aim at self-sufficiency and ideal justice. The earthly order must be identified as temporal, an area of trial and transition. As Augustine posed the problem, citizens of the two eternal Cities, the heavenly and the diabolic, must live together and mix in earthly polities, the wheat and chaff growing together before the final sifting. The earthly political community must concentrate on a limited agreement to ensure tranquillity, a state of truce in which citizens of both eternal Cities work out the mystery of their salvation or damnation.

But Aquinas, after putting Aristotle's politics in a context which transmutes it entirely, in a metaphysical realism and a theological history, let the Aristotelian terms and transitions stand as a model analysis in the order of intellect. To be uesful as a practical science, this analysis must be applied, in concrete instances and by the use of prudence, to a real world radically altered in the light of revelation. The trouble is that the followers of Aquinas could not or would not follow the alterations that must be made when an Aristotelian politics is put in the existential framework of Christian theology. By the same process that dehydrated the entire Thomist metaphysics, the logical terms of Aristotle were once more applied to reality without the mediation of metaphysical realism and the moral act of prudence. *Autarkeia* clashed too obviously with the Christian mentality; but "the common good" took over the content of that key term, as an ideal order perfecting the "individual good." And justice is treated as the aim of the state, almost as simply as in Aristotle's time, by many modern Thomists.[1]

As the Thomist politics was denatured, "natural law" became the sanction of "divine right" theories of government. Here, the Christian religion replaced reason in the Hellenic scheme, making the ruler the source of justice for other men.[2] Then the "laws of nature" were totally emptied of realistic content to become the ideal "Nature" of the eighteenth century. The rebellion against a

monarch's "natural" legitimacy turned political union into a free contract, arising from the insufficiencies of the "natural" condition. But Rousseau treads the
same perilous circle that Plato first traced—out from the state as mystery and
back to supreme political authority in the form of reason. In the eighteenth-
century myth of a "state of nature," reason, in a vacuum, constructs a "case" for
government, draws up a contract, insists on its terms as if they were points in
logic, then consents to this invention of the mind.

Those things which have been criticized as inconsistencies in Rousseau—
his union of extreme individualism with collective tyranny—are actually the
result of his penetrating logic. He saw that Locke's doctrine of natural rights
surrendered by agreement leads to a state that is either absolutely just, or—
when the state fails in some particular, and tries to prevent dissolution of the
agreement by force—absolutely unjust. Society and the state are coextensive
terms. Prior to the social contract, each man is a world apart; and the absolute
autonomy of this condition can only be surrendered to a custodian that discerns
and demands absolute right. That is why the eighteenth-century reformers had
to believe that Nature's intent was clear, everywhere "self-evident," in order to
embark on their experiments. It is fascinating to watch this antinomy at work,
individualism reaching an extreme where it is automatically transmuted into
governmental absolutism:

> no more perfect union is possible, and no associate has any subse-
> quent demand to make. For if the individual retained any rights whatever,
> this is what would happen: there being no common superior able to say
> the last word on any issue between him and the public, he would be his
> own judge on this or that point, and so would try before long to be his
> own judge on all points. . . . Each gives himself to everybody so that he
> gives himself to nobody.[3]

Because man's reason is not of itself free, the state based on "pure reason" only
recognizes the freedom to be right; the state must, in Rousseau's famous
phrase, "force men to be free":

> In and of itself, a people always wills, but does not always see, what
> is good; while the general will is always well-intentioned, the judgment
> that directs it is not always an instructed judgment. It must be brought to
> see things as they are. It must be brought, sometimes, to see things as they
> ought to appear. It must be shown the right road, which it is seeking.[4]

Since, in the purely rational world of Socrates and Rousseau, men only do
wrong through some mistake in judgment or information, putting them on the
right way is not forcing the will but "freeing the mind of error." Once again,
the fallacy of extreme individualism, or simple democracy—society's attempt to
make its circumference, or whole area, its own center—results in a reverse
reading of the riddle: the center, source of truth, becomes the circumference,
enclosing all human activities in a rigid rule.

The enduring attractiveness of the Order of Justice arises from its total reliance on reason. Rationalism flatters the individual; it is particularly seductive in the Western tradition, where the unfettered reason has accomplished so much; and it always produced spokesmen of the highest logical dexterity. Men of this school can invoke the great political theoreticians—Plato, Aristotle, Rousseau—though they find little support in the great political institutions of the past, in the achievements of the real order, usually wrought by slow accumulation of constitutional safeguards, or by a system of compromise and enlightened expedience.

Perhaps an even deeper source of inspiration for this view of the state is the fact that it taps moral, religious, and humanitarian enthusiasms. When a man argues that the state should not be an oracle of justice, a teacher of morals, or a dispenser of human comfort, the defenders of the Order of Justice frequently represent such a man's stand as an attack on justice itself, or a lack of moral principle, or an insensitivity to the demands of the human heart. Of course, it is precisely the state's usurpation of a religious and moral role that leads to its betrayal of freedom. Proponents of such a state always demand a hard orthodoxy of its subjects. Plato makes a grasp of ideal justice the qualification for political office. The "divine right" theories of government rest on a common profession of faith. The Enlightenment theories are based on the certitude that the "laws of Nature" are easily discernible and universally recognized. The beginnings of a Paine-Jefferson orthodoxy in America, based on these "self-evident" laws, were aborted by the religious fundamentalism of Americans and the system of compromise that effected the federalist union.[5] But the modern Liberals have reintroduced an orthodoxy of self-evident rights by their positivist insistence on the universal validity and viability of certain concepts, like "democracy," "equality," and "self-determination."

It will be seen that the Order of Justice I have described corresponds, accidental usages aside, to what is generally termed the Liberal strand in Western political discourse.[6] The title arises from the initial stress, in all these systems, on reason and the free individual. But the turning of a rationalist freedom into a tyranny of intellect is not, as has so often been supposed, a mere accident or relapse of human weakness under the demands of a great ideal. The seeds of tyranny were in the ideal from the beginning. Robespierre and the Terror are the logical consequence of Rousseau and the Social Contract. When men realize this, they will cease wondering at the "inconsistencies" in Plato's or Rousseau's authoritarian state, or at the conversion of "divine right" into sheer might under a simplistic reading of the natural law. The Order of Justice is like the statue of Justice; its attributes are a blindfold, and the sword.

## II   THE ORDER OF CONVENIENCE

The title I have given this second form of order will strike some as frivolous; and "convenience" is, I admit, susceptible to misunderstanding. But other words that suggest themselves are even more misleading—rule by the expedient or the opportune (which now connote a lack of moral probity), government by concurrence (which gets mixed up, now, with dogmas of democratic procedure, though I would use the word in Calhoun's sense), or the principle of community (a word now dessicated by abstract definitions of the "common good"). So there is nothing for it but to choose a comparatively neutral word, at first glance trivial, and give it a specific function for this discussion.[7]

The problem of finding a single word is not accidental, or a quibble on method. The lack of an accepted term indicates a chronic failure in political discourse, the chasm between theory and practice; for the order I am considering is not nameless because unimportant, or absent from our history. In fact, each highest form of political community succeeded because this order informed and stiffened it invisibly. The Greek democracy was not doctrinaire. There is no theorist of Athenian democracy, no proponent of a doctrine. All the major political theorists of Hellas formed their ideal systems as alternatives to the real order, admittedly fallible, that was stimulating their investigations. Thucydides, Plato, Aristotle—"oligarchs" all. It is true that there are some democratic speeches put in the mouths of Herodotean and Euripidean characters. But the speculative recommendations of democracy are very few; perhaps the most famous is the speech Thucydides invented for Pericles, a boast ironically voiced under the shadow of defeat. The Roman Empire actually professed a spurious theory, maintaining the façade of a republic. Medieval theory tried to redeem feudal and merchant practice but acted merely as a component force working for balance.[8] England is notoriously the producer and product of a kind of unconscious constitution. And America, after the *furor ideologicus* had passed that lifted the colonies on the wings of war, based its Constitution on an unashamed profession of compromise. The political ideal of *The Federalist* elevates compromise to a principle of harmony. It is one of the major attempts to articulate an Order of Convenience.

Do these preliminary remarks mean that politics must simply be opposed to theory; in the foolish modern word, "anti-intellectual"?[9] No. But the Order of Convenience must be built on a basic truth that is even more scandalous to modern ears: the particular aim of the state is not to achieve justice, and certainly not to dispense it. In the words of Newman, "satisfaction, peace, liberty, conservative interests [are] the supreme end of the law, not mere raw justice as such."[10] This, of course, does not mean that the state is to be unjust, or free of the imperatives of the moral law. The state, like the family, like the corporation, like the labor union, is bound by the laws of morality that are incumbent on all human endeavor, corporate as well as individual. In carrying out its function, the state must act with justice. But its specific aim is not to enforce justice as such. The family, too, must observe right order—the child obeying, the parent avoiding undue laxity or severity; husband and wife helping each other, yet observing measure in their demands upon each other. This due measure, this order of right, is achieved by the observance of justice; yet the formal aim of the family is not sheer justice as such. Its aim is to give birth and education to new members of our race, to recruit partners in the human adventure. Only when this purpose is clearly understood can the order of claims and the areas of just activity be discerned in the life of the family.

In the same way, the state must observe justice in its activities; but its aim is more limited, more concretely specified. And unless that aim is made clear, there is no way of knowing what justice is for the state; politics becomes an instrument for seeking every kind of good thing, for bringing ideal justice itself down to earth. We have seen the theocratic consequences of such an undertaking goal is the marshaling of force in the state. All tyrannies give legitimacy to the source of every tyranny that is not sheer outlawry, and the permanent temptation of every state. The nineteenth-century liberals found something evil in power itself, as if tyranny customarily advanced by some brutal and naked appeal of its own nature. But every truly powerful system of oppression was shaped by an ideal that can recruit talent, can use other energies than the thirst of a few for the acme of human rule. When ideal justice is set before the community as its political end, the only efficient path towards that ever receding goal is the marshaling of force in the state. All tyrannies give legitimacy to oppression by making it a transitional period through which men must pass on their way to Utopia, a kind of induced labor that is to bring forth the new order. So it was with the despots who had to "establish divine right," so with the Terror, so with the Utilitarian acceptance of the "growing pains" of industrialism, so with the dictatorship of the proletariat.

I do not mean to minimize, no conservative can, the effects of original sin in the life of society; but the most heartbreaking, and politically far-reaching, of these effects is not the drive of sheer evil, but the misguided and desperate grasping after good—the enthusiasms, heresies, crusades that can mobilize human generosity. The optimistic Liberal does not recognize that society is ultimately hurt less by individuals who catch at instant advantage than by the messiahs who undertake great missions with long-range planning, ingenuity, patient endurance, and conviction of ultimate triumph. We are witnessing the scale of this menace in the fiery spread and intensity of the Communist vision.[11]

The talk of "power" as a constant factor everywhere to be minimized is as self-defeating as the quantitative approach to freedom (something everywhere to be increased). The two views are, in fact, reverse sides of a single coin. Power arms itself for the long pull, invades the mind, and gives structure to human effort, not when it is a spasm leading to dissolution, but when it is summoned up by a false god, with rights over the whole man and all men. Nero is personally more despicable, but politically less destructive, than Robespierre or Lenin.[12]

But if the state is not to be founded on an ideal order of justice, what is its basis? Obviously, the real order—the order of man's needs. The individual only finds his natural fulfillment in society. As Aristotle pointed out, even language is a convention, a "coming together." Language is itself society. And all man's other achievements involve a similar social opportunity for the individual's self-expression. But if there is a society, there must be a state. As a necessary physical regimen keeps the individual alive, so there must be a regime, an order, a discipline in society. That regime is the state.

The fallacy of the rationalists is that they begin the construction of their political models with the isolated reason of the individual. They make the pure autonomy of the individual clash and, finally, merge with the autonomy of a just order. But man does not start with a formed and pure freedom. Man "free" of society is man free of air; free, that is, to suffocate. The rationalist pits the individual against an abstract order of justice in the state, instead of tracing the spontaneous growth and grouping of social forms that give the individual a field for expression and activity. The state appears, apocalyptically, in such theories, bringing justice "new-born" into prior chaos. But in the real order, the state arises from a hierarchy of social organizations, of groups formed to fill particular needs. The state stabilizes this spontaneous social expression. It answers a natural demand for unity. It cannot initiate such unity, or carve countries out of the map by legislative fiat.

Although it is a commonplace that man is a "social animal," the rationalist theories contradict this commonplace. For if the state arises out of man's social instinct, then the state destroys its own roots when it denies free scope to the other forms of social life. The state, when it is made the source of justice, must be equally and instantly available to all citizens; and, in achieving this, in sweeping away the confusion of claims raised by families, economic orders, educational conventions, codes of conduct, natural gradations of privilege, the Liberal leaves society atomized, each man isolated, with all the weight of political power coming unintercepted upon him.[18] The higher forms of organization do not grow out of and strengthen the lower, but counter and erase them. This is what has happened under the Order of Justice from the time when Plato pitted the state against the family to the modern breakdown of divided jurisdiction in the centralized state. As usual, Rousseau follows the logic of this position to its fated end:

> Where, however, blocs are formed, lesser associations at the expense of the broader one, the will of each of these associations comes to be general with respect to its members and particular with respect to the state. ... If, then, we are to have a clear declaration of the general will, we must see to it that there are no partial societies within the state, so that each citizen forms his own opinions.[14]

By this route, the Liberal state arrives, everywhere, at contradiction: though the state is instituted to assure the development of personality, societies that embrace the rationalist ideal are marked by a cult of impersonality. Plato attempted to erase the distinction between the sexes. The French and Russian revolutions came up with titles meant to attack titles: "Citizen" in one case, "Tovarich" in the other. Since political justice conditions all of a man's life in such societies, men rejoice in the reduction of persons to a minimal legal status and equality. In such communities, loyalty to the state is expressed as duty towards abstract justice, not as patriotism.

For the realist, on the other hand, the state, by disciplining a particular society, expresses the character of that society, protects its spontaneity and symbolic self-confrontation at all levels of life, draws on the society's specific resources, and commands a loyalty that is personalized as patriotism. How does the state accomplish this? How complement the multiple, spontaneous, or consanguineous forms of social coherence? As all things complement: by supplying what is lacking. Other social groups than the political have a positive bond of mutual affection or defined and positive interest. This is their strength, but it circumscribes their appeal. Only those qualify to take part who share the interests of a family or a class, of a school of thought or a creed. But conflicts of interest arise in the common area of life in which these activities take place. The task of adjudicating these conflicts by a shared code, and of including all the strata of society in a single frame of minimal order, must be entrusted to an agent of order with force at its disposal. This agency circumscribes a larger community than the partial groupings; it is not voluntary from moment to moment; it can enforce its judgments in the name of the very social forces that become obstreperous. The state is necessary because the other, overlapping social forms extend across a field of human activity that no one of them can circumscribe. Thus the end of the state is the orderly advancement and discipline of society as the necessary ground of human activity. And the necessary, basic condition for the formation of a state is a shared good that must be protected if all social and individual effort is to thrive. That is why Newman calls a common possession the basis of the state.[15]

The state, as extending throughout all other levels of social solidarity, must have a certain neutrality towards them all, and as the order-enforcing agent, it must take upon itself a certain negative, punitive function. This neutral and negative aspect of the state will be perverted, and become a positive push—as life-giving, rather than life-preserving—if the other forms of spontaneous activity wither; or if the state officials try to use their power to call up a positive vision of their own; or of politics is considered the all-inclusive area of man's achievement of excellence. To continue the comparison of individual regimen to social regime, such a society is like the health crank, who expends all his energy on the achievement of an ideal physical equilibrium, not using the body's forces for the essentially human tasks.

To prevent this usurpation on the part of the state, every society that is long-lived or successful finds ways of limiting the action of political force. The disciplinary agent of society is itself disciplined by society; the rulers are ruled. This system of checks is worked out by each community, but it is based on the general truth that the state's role is to enforce equity and order, rather than justice and charity. The free agencies of society must preserve their function by circumscribing the state's role in the totality of social activity. This fact has been instinctively recognized by all those theorists who, after talking about ideal forms of government, recommend a mixture of forms, striking a balance between all possible ruling forces in the state. This roundabout descent from the ideal to the real is clumsy. The true form of society is not to be found in a mixture of pure components, but in the particular aim and energy of each real community.

Each society must form a unique *constitution*, an "agreed station" of components, growing out of the resources it can command. The ideal state—of a justice or a freedom defined outside any particular human context—is as meaningless as some uniform ideal of individual fulfillment. Is monarchy, aristocracy, or democracy the best form of government? Such a question simply breeds further questions: Best for what society? And what kind of monarchy, or democracy? These questions are as hopeless as similar ones would be in the case of an ideal life for individuals. Is it better that man be an artist or philosopher, monk or martyr, doctor or teacher, worker or statesman? And if he is a doctor, should he engage in research, psychology, or compassionate work among the poor? If an artist, should he write or paint in an austere or demonstrative style? To attempt an abstract answer to these questions is to deny the mystery of individuality, the secret springs of motive, that make up the human fact of freedom. As ever, rationalism leads to sterile paradox, to an ideal freedom that is a denial of freedom. Calhoun rightly says:

> the great and broad distinction between governments is,—not that of the one, the few, or the many,—but of the constitutional and the absolute.[16]

And what is meant by a constitutional government? According to Calhoun, it is that government in which all the free forms and forces of society—or as many as possible—retain their life and "concur" in a political area of peaceful co-operation and compromise. According to Newman, it is that society in which the character of those "concurring" is best allowed for and given scope for development:

> As individuals have characters of their own, so do races. . . . Moreover, growing out of these varieties or idiosyncrasies, and corresponding to them, will be found in these several races, and proper to each, a certain assemblage of beliefs, convictions, rules, usages, traditions, proverbs, and principles . . . tending to some definite form of government. . . . It is something more than law; it is the embodiment of special ideas, ideas perhaps which have been held by a race for ages, which are of immemorial usage, which have fixed themselves in its innermost heart, which are in its eyes sacred. . . . They are the creative and conservative influences of Society; they erect nations into States, and invest States with Constitutions.[17]

Absolutism, or despotism, is a sheer thrust of force across the grain of these free and preservative influences, a defiance of the spontaneous life that checks government even as it impels it forward. A constitutional regime gives both *life* and *limit* to government; it maintains a system that rules even society's rulers. The force exercised by despots may be, and often is, the assertion of an ideal, but of an ideal unrooted, unembodied in the flesh and substance of society. It is, literally, a ghostly thing seeking to haunt or possess the body politic by unnatural forces. For this reason, the answer to Lincoln's question must be that no nation *can* long endure if it is only "dedicated to a proposition." It must be dedicated to a people, to its particular human possibilities, since

> that must be pronounced no State, but a mere fortuitous collection of individuals, which has no unity stronger than despotism, or deeper than law.[18]

One cannot simply ask whether a thing is just (as abolition of slavery is just, whether in fifth-century Athens, first-century Rome, or nineteenth-century Richmond); whether it is desirable (as better education of the young is desirable); whether it is moral (as sexual continence is moral). In politics one must ask at the same time, always, whether it is constitutional. Should the state act, and if so to what extent, with what precautions, and following what precedents; in conjunction with what tempering and expanding activity on the part of spontaneous organizations? If these questions are not asked, if the state enters the private area of morals, then censorship and orthodoxy give the political guardian a divine character. There is no limitation of the state but by the single test of constitutionality.

The constitution is not always, and is never merely, a written document.[19] It is the "shared situation" of society, that continuous arrangement whereby men preserve their common stake in a political regime. It is composed of all the influences that make a state continue to express the character of its people; that recruit and give room for the development of talent; that develop the resources of personality through society. Newman even wrote that "bribery" (*i.e.*, the buying of titles and offices), after it had been systematized as a recognized and efficient part of the British government's balanced operation, was part of the English constitution; and therefore to be used as a tool of the community, provided no specific act of immorality is committed, like the breaking of an oath.[20] In the same way, a society that is basically tribal in organization must have a state that is based on the tribes. Otherwise, the society has no way of meshing with its political order, of making its character felt, of maintaining identity while it grows towards a different mode of articulating itself, politically. Such a society proves the

> inexpediency of suffering the tradition of Law to flow separate from that of popular feeling . . . there ought to be a continual influx of the national mind into the judicial conscience; and, unless there was this careful adjustment between law and politics, the standards of right and wrong set up at Westminster would diverge from those received by the community at large, and the Nation might some day find itself condemned and baffled by its own supreme oracle. . . .[21]

As an instance, the "democratic" regimes being established in Africa, over inchoate areas arbitrarily defined as nations, perfectly exemplify Calhoun's maxim that the only realistic division of governments is into constitutional and absolute. These "democracies," imported from a Hellenic-Christian tradition of many centuries' growth, and imposed on stray parts of the tribal labyrinth of Africa, are not based on any real consensus. So-called popular support and "nationalism" do not express the genius of Africa itself, of any real nation. The native groups who "express their will" so simply with the marking of a ballot have merely expressed a hope that Western material comforts will magically be made theirs by this method. The result is an absolutism—an enlightened one, it may be claimed, but surely an absolutism. The term "democracy" means little or nothing in such a context; whereas other forms of government, today condemned out of hand as "dictatorships," may have a very effective constitutional system.

Does this mean that society must settle, always, for what it has, never push out towards higher achievement; must it forswear leadership in order to avoid loss of "constitution," treat all hope of better things as a temptation to visionary absolutism?

On the contrary, a constitution fosters not only liberty but leadership. In an integral community, the leaders really lead; they are followed. There is no chasm between the masses and the intelligentsia. One of the principal ironies of modern democracy is that egalitarian doctrine has driven a greater wedge between thinkers and the populace than most systems of privilege ever did, so that it seems almost necessary that "clerks" be traitors. The interplay of various groups within accepted tradition makes talent serve the community, not seek a false elevation by institutionalizing rebellion. When a nation has no tradition to appeal to but a "tradition of revolution," it has confessed bankruptcy; it can no longer marshal the potentials of the populace to serve the common stake, the constitution. When artists and philosophers and churchmen cannot find a meaningful area of mutual enrichment, then politicians must supply the social cohesion *ex nihilo,* and enforce it by militant centralization of power. In this situation, the boasts of broad franchise or democratic ritual do not give substance to man's liberty. For liberty is not the product of mechanical instruments like the electoral process.[22]

In modern democratic myth, man's freedom is given him entire at birth, a thing solid and circular in its perfection, but shattered and dispersed as time goes on. To prevent the final dissolution of all freedom, men form polities by chipping off a piece of liberty and surrendering it to the state, which is thus constructed out of the surrendered quantities of individual rights. The art of constructing a just state consists in finding how to sacrifice the thinnest possible slices of individual "sovereignty," and the most uniform, so that all these contribute to the central storehouse of national sovereignty. But man's freedom is not whole nor homogeneous. It is as complex as man himself, since it makes him man.

First, there is the basic freedom which consists in possession of a will. This will can never be taken away, or tampered with at its source. It can be killed, but only by killing the man, or reducing him to a subhuman level. Even in prison, the will is free so long as it exists.

Second, there is the last fulfillment of liberty, the state of continual choice that uses and never abuses freedom. This, according to Christian teaching, is the freedom of man at rest in his eternal reward. But according to authoritarian state systems, it is also a political ideal. All such systems imply, or, if pushed to logic, assert that man's freedom is freedom to do good. As Rousseau put it, the state forces man to be free.

In a third sense, freedom means the condition that encourages and allows for the active exercise of the will. This condition is achieved by education, by surroundings that stimulate and nurture free choice, by social discipline that gives man a peaceful area of movement. This is the freedom to which political discipline makes essential contributions. It is the freedom of a nation; not given by the state, but protected by it. Those who isolate a particular "political freedom" from the rest of man's self-extension into social institutions are usually reduced to the worship of various absolutes—the franchise, a widespread press, a public education—without regard to the genius of the groups and individuals finding common ground and seeking expression in the particular society. These absolutes can be as imprisoning as the authoritarian systems.[23] Plato says that freedom for "lead men" consists in obedience to the "gold men," the modern Liberal insists that freedom for the Congolese consists in an electoral and parliamentary system not geared to mesh with regional, tribal, emotional and intellectual differences or difficulties. The result in both cases is a union of chaos and compulsion, both impinging on the real exercise of freedom.

There is a fourth definition of freedom—this one spurious—as a mere lack of outside compulsion. But freedom is a spontaneity towards several alternatives, a principle of action. To define it as a lack is absurd. This leads to the ideal of the "open society," in which definite intellectual and cultural molds are avoided or broken, throwing the individual back on his own resources and responsibility at each step of his life. The ideal society, it is suggested, would be a kind of Great Books Club in which each person chooses his favorite historical and intellectual milieu, or browses among them all with an ultimate choice in mind. Such a society is impossible. There would be no agreed language, no common terms for contracts, no shared understanding of the way to get work done, no possibility of educational discipline. That is, there would be no society.[24] *Identity* would disappear, first in the society, then in the individual.

Freedom is not a mere lack; it is an urge to extend one's self by the exercise of choice, and unless there is a defined and delimited self, no extension is possible. There is no range of choice or reach of possibilities unless man operates from an established base of some sort. Unless a society can retain and enrich its identity, it does not admit the possibility of human fulfillment within its continuity, or even the luxury of revolt. All rebels would hate a genuinely open society; there would be nothing to rebel against. Tradition, what Burke calls "prejudice," is necessary to give freedom range in the real order, just as an individual, with all his limitations, is the necessary vehicle for the free will itself. And so, by another route, we find that freedom and order are correlates; and that rationally limited freedom is the partner of a humanly limited order, the limits being set by man's effort to achieve a fully human life under each society's historical conditions. The attempts at an absolute freedom recoil, logically and in experience, towards a political absolutism. Freedom must be concrete because man is; freedom is man.

Only the Order of Convenience, of enlightened expedience, of prejudice mobilized towards improvement, can give the practical art of politics a combination of flexibility and stability. The Order of Convenience can take the findings of the great political theorists and use them, without incurring the results of mistaken metaphysics. It can learn from Plato the importance, to society, of education and morality, without making the state a New Jerusalem of the intellect. It can take from Aristotle a realistic grasp of social psychology, of the uses of property, of moderation in reform, without making the state prior in right to the individual. It can learn from Rousseau the need for constant adjustment of political forms to the structure of society, without basing all forms on an explicit and rational "contract." Perhaps most significant of all, this kind of politics can return to the real genius of natural-law theory. It will recognize the laws of nature, not as dictates for an ideal life, but as the structure of reality calling, at each moment, for a real response, individual and social. It will seek "the common good," not as some ideal scheme of order, or quantitative accumulation of individual goods, but as the real life of the "commonalty," of community in all its mutually enriching forms. This true politics of the natural law is, as a modern exponent of that obscured system reminds us, rooted in a metaphysics vastly different from the eighteenth-century definition of Nature. Taking the American Republic as a concrete example, John Courtney Murray writes:

> Its basis was not the philosophic rationalism that called itself Enlightenment, but only a political pragmatism more enlightened than the Enlightenment ever was, because it looked to the light of experience to illuminate the prudential norms necessary to guide it in handling a concrete social reality that is vastly complicated.[25]

The political realist also preserves the virtue of justice, by assigning it its true place in the life of the state. This justice is primarily a matter of equity and procedure, of the fair enforcement of the constitution. This is not a role as inspiring or ambitious as justice plays in the states aiming at an ideal order. It is primarily a matter of fair rules for the free development of a society's particular impulses, the virtues of an umpire or a policeman; and, under threat of foreign aggression, the virtues of a watchdog. In fact, the disappointment of idealists, when faced with this system, is violent. Even Lord Acton, the moralist of liberty, considered Newman's politics "immoral"; and Augustine's attack on the *just* state of Plato has largely been ignored, or dismissed as a "deplorable lapse" in an otherwise great thinker.[26] But this recognition of the state's limited function is the means for freeing man in his extra-political and supra-political roles.

The Greeks sundered man from the hieratic order of politics, secularizing the state by an exercise of reason. But the order of reason, in the final theorsits of Hellas, became as strict a political regimen as the religious state had been. Christianity completed the secularization of the state by placing man's goal on the other side of time, distinguishing, finally, the things of God from the things of Caesar. This duality, approached variously under the understandings and misunderstandings of the Two Cities or the Two Swords, led Christian wisdom to define and defy political absolutism. "Two there are," wrote Gelasius I to Anastasius I, "by which this world is ruled on title of sovereign right"—the area of priestly ministration, that is, of the individual soul and its divine freedom; and the order of kingly authority, that is, of temporal peace, establishing the condition in which men can discern and exercise their ultimate freedom.[27]

The effects of this new, and final, secularization were farther-reaching than the establishment of religious freedom. Once the state lost its primacy as an interpreter of the eternal order, it lost the claim by which it cowed all interme-diate societies—the family, the free organizations of groups in which man seeks the answer to his own mysteries. As John Courtney Murray says, in a chapter called "Are There Two Or One?", "this comprehensive right [of the Church] asserted within the political community requires as its complement that all the intrapolitical sacrednesses (*res sacra in temporalibus*) be assured of their proper immunity from politicization."[28]

Although the medieval limitation on the state arose out of the state's recognition of the Church's mission, the Christian ordination of man has left a sacredness about the individual soul that has survived the breakup of a single center for Christendom. The modern state, in its best manifestations (like the American Constitution), retains the secularization paradoxically created by Christianity's other worldliness. The state must be agnostic, if nothing else, about the possibilities and final goal of the individual; and allow the human adventure to proceed, not pre-empting the place of that unknown City that may be calling man. Thus the apparently mincing ideal of the state that shocks Liberals is the charter of freedom for the spirit of man. By foregoing the inspirational political theories, man taps other and more enduring sources of inspiration. Such are the virtues of convenience. For "convenience," in its older English usage, meant consonance, especially the correspondence of things with thought. The convenient state has constant reference to man, and is adjusted to his real endeavors. It is the meeting of political institutions with the mystery and activity of man, a standing-together (constitution) of political discipline and the individual discipline of exercised freedom.

It would be useless to claim that the term "conservative" always means, or should mean, the advocacy of such a convenient state. As we have seen, the "divine right" and providential branch of conservatism belongs rather with the proponents of an Order of Justice. But I think it is true that the really great conservatives were not believers in the sacredness of the *status quo*. What